YOUR GUIDE TO
THE SOIL

THE SCIENCE FOR EVERYMAN SERIES

Your Guide to the Soil is one of a series of up-to-date and authoritative books on modern science, written for the non-specialist reader by Dr. J. Gordon Cook.

The Science for Everyman series forms a fascinating and easy-to-read reference library of information on important scientific topics. A General Index, obtainable from the publishers, enables the reader to refer quickly and easily to the thousands of subjects covered by the books.

The Science for Everyman series includes the following titles :

1. The Fight for Food
2. Our Astonishing Atmosphere
3. The World of Water
4. We Live by the Sun
5. Electrons go to Work
6. Virus in the Cell
7. Your Guide to Plastics
8. Your Guide to the Soil
   and
The Science for Everyman Encyclopaedia.

Other titles are in preparation.

Information about the books of the Science for Everyman series may be obtained from Merrow Publishing Co. Ltd., 276 Hempstead Road, Watford, Herts., England.

YOUR GUIDE TO
THE SOIL

by

J. Gordon Cook
B.Sc., Ph.D., F.R.I.C.

MERROW PUBLISHING CO. LTD
276, HEMPSTEAD ROAD, WATFORD
HERTS., ENGLAND

© *J. Gordon Cook 1960, 1965*

First published 1960

Second Edition (Revised and Enlarged) 1965

Made in Great Britain. Printed and bound at the
St Ann's Press, Park Road, Altrincham

PREFACE

We human beings are gardeners all! Whether we live in the centre of a city or in a farmhouse far from the nearest town, we find a source of deep satisfaction in the cultivation of the soil.

For thousands of years, we have relied upon the soil as our source of food. Our interest in the soil has become instinctive; we know that life goes on only because the soil continues to produce the food we need.

In recent years, scientists have built up an immense background of information about the soil. The traditional skills and experience of the gardener and farmer are now being reinforced by scientific knowledge and understanding.

This book outlines the more important aspects of our present knowledge of the soil. It describes how the chemical foods needed by plants are produced in the soil by weathering of parent rocks, and by the decay of organic matter. It shows how we can add these chemical nutrients directly in the form of fertilizers, and sustain the structure of the soil by proper cultivation and the use of humus. It deals with the microbes that live in thousands of millions in every handful of soil, and describes how these tiny creatures help with the chemical transformations that enable the soil to serve as food store of the world.

The text has been divided into four parts in order to separate different aspects of the information dealing with soil.

Part 1, "Our Living Soil", outlines the story of soil as it affects the lives of everyone.

Part 2, "You and Your Soil" describes how an understanding of the soil can be applied in practice by gardeners, horticulturalists and farmers in their cultivation techniques.

Part 3, "Science and the Soil", explains in greater detail some of the more important characteristics of soil. Information from earlier sections is re-stressed in places to avoid undue cross-referencing and to preserve continuity.

Part 4, the Reference Section, provides condensed information on many aspects of soils and their relationships with plants.

The information and illustrations have come from many sources. I would like to thank all who have kindly helped me and I am especially grateful to the following firms and organizations in this respect:

Du Pont de Nemours International S.A.
F.A.O.
Fisons Fertilizers Ltd.
National Plant Food Institute.
Pan Britannica Industries Ltd.
Soil Conservation Society of America.
Soil Science Society of America.
U.S. Dept. of Agriculture.
Vitax Fertilizers Ltd.

I would like to acknowledge with thanks the help given to me by Dr. E. W. Russell of East African Agriculture and Forestry Research Organization, and B. Clayden Esq., of Soil Survey of England and Wales, who made many valuable comments on the manuscript.

J.G.C.

CONTENTS

PART 1

OUR LIVING SOIL

1

The Soil is Born

In the beginning, there was rock. Bare rock, hard and inhospitable. There was no life; there was nothing to support life.

Then the vapours condensed and the rains came. Water swept across the earth's surface, filling the hollows in the folded crust. The winds blew and the hot sun shone. Summer passed into winter, and winter back into summer. Slowly, inexorably, with a thousand years an instant in the march of time, the surface of the rocks gave way before the onslaught of the elements. In the heat of the sun, the rocks expanded; and under the bitter lash of winter they cooled and shrank. The surface cracked, and into the tiny fissures flowed the rainwater. The frosts came, and the water froze to ice, prizing the rocks apart with incredible force. Little particles of rock broke off, and the hard bare surface underneath was, in its turn, subjected to the ceaseless gnawing of the weather.

For millions of years the attack went on. Slowly, the surface of the earth covered itself with a layer of powdered rock. Some remained where it had been formed, above its parent rock. Some was ground and crushed and pushed about by huge glaciers that flowed over the surface of the earth. Some was swept along by water or blown from afar by winds.

Then life appeared. From the formless slimes of the sea, simple plants emerged and established themselves on the land. They found shelter in the crevices and between the particles of powdered rock. They evolved roots to anchor themselves against the wind and rain, and the roots wriggled down in search of food. This they found in the form of minerals dissolved by water from the rocks. So the plants grew in the fissures and amongst the particles, pushing and pressing and intensifying the break-up of the rock.

On the surface of the earth, a myriad forms of life evolved. The animals came. All lived and multiplied, depending for their food on the plants that grew on the surface of the land. They died, and their remains were mixed up with the powdered rock. As they decayed, the dead materials gave up their substance to be used again as food by new generations of living plants. The unending cycle of life and death had begun.

So, as time went on, the surface of the earth covered itself over with a complex mixture of materials. Where once there had been powdered rock, there was now a blanket of mineral particles mixed with the residues of once-living matter. Amongst it all were bacteria, moulds and micro-organisms living on the dead material and on each other. There were insects and little animals, living and dying and adding their bodies to the teeming mass. In place of the powdered rock, there was now a layer that had become the home of thousands of different forms of life. Plants grew profusely on this living layer, and animals roamed its surface, feeding on the plants and leaving the materials of their bodies to be incorporated into it.

Larder of Life

When the human race was young, the earth was already covered with this surface layer, pulsating with life. Like other animals, human beings depended for their food upon the plants that grew on the land. They ate the plant foods themselves, or preyed on other animals which had relied upon plants as food. The plants in their turn drew food supplies from the air and from the substances absorbed through the roots that probed down into the living layer.

This layer, upon which the entire plant and animal worlds still depend for food to sustain life, is what we now call the soil. To regard it as nothing more than a lifeless mass of rock particles is to think of a town as a lot of buildings. The soil is teeming with life, as busy and exciting as the life that changes a town from a structure of bricks and mortar into a bustling community.

The soil has become the larder of all living things. In it are the simple chemical foods needed by plants; from these chemicals, and from water and air, the growing plant can build the complex substances which form its living structure. These substances are then used as food by the animal world.

The value of the soil in any region of the earth is measured by its ability to grow the plants we need as raw materials and as food. Some soils can support vegetation in abundance. Others, through some shortcoming in their chemical, physical or biological make-up, are able to grow only a sparse covering of useful plants. A few soils are entirely barren.

The human race is now approaching 3000 million people, and it is increasing at an alarming rate. Every human being depends for food upon plants grown in the soil. At the present time, there is insufficient food to go round, and millions of people live on a semi-starvation diet. As the population increases, the problem is becoming more difficult to solve. It is a problem whose immediate solution must lie in the soil itself. By adequate understanding and treatment of the soil we can increase its wealth of crops until it gives us the food we need.

The human race has no greater responsibility to carry than that which lies in proper care of the soil. Our soil is the most valuable of all the possessions that have been handed on to us by our ancestors. It is a heritage we must cherish and, in our turn, hand over in good heart to our children.

A Neglected Science

It is strange that with life itself depending directly upon the health and fertility of the soil, we still know comparatively little about it. The study of soil is a science that has been neglected. It has a background of little more than a hundred years, and it is only during the last half century that real progress has been made.

To the scientist, soil is a difficult subject for study. There is an infinite variety of soils in the world; no two soils are ever identical. Like human beings, individual soils have personalities which defy any rigid classification.

The processes which created the original soils from powdered rock and decaying materials are still going on. Soil particles are still being weathered and worn, and modified by plants and animals, micro-organisms and insects. Minerals are released by chemical changes in the rock particles and by the decay of once-living matter. Plants grow, and their roots stir up the soil; animals and plants continue to die and return their body substances to the soil from which they came. Nothing ever stands still in the soil. Something is always happening to change its character even when nature is left to do the job alone; where man has come with his agriculture he has added his own disturbance to the surface of the soil. Sometimes, where he has used his powers skilfully, man has added to the richness of the soil. Often, he has plundered and stolen the stores of plant food that the soil has held, until it could produce no more.

This ever-busy, living soil is the laboratory in which science is now seeking to learn the secrets of modern agriculture. In it, innumerable experiments are going on at the same time; each is complicated and influenced by changes that are happening beside it. All are interde-

Cultivator used in ancient Egypt was inefficient and back-breaking.

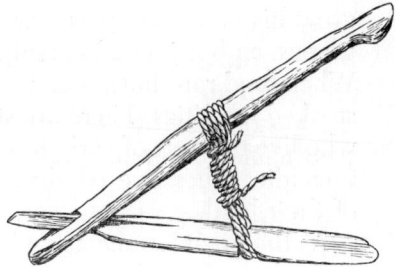

pendent and interrelated; together, they make up the larder that supplies all forms of life on earth. The living soil.

CULTIVATION BEGINS

A peasant scratches at the earth of China with a wooden hoe; in the Middle West of the United States a tractor chugs across the prairie dragging a plough with twenty blades; in an English allotment, a sturdy miner turns the soil of his onion bed with a well-worn spade. In every country of the world, men are at work on the soil, stirring it and turning it, digging and ploughing, harrowing and raking. All to one purpose. They are preparing it to do its job of growing the plants on which all human life depends.

Cultivation of the soil is the basic occupation of the human race. From the soil comes almost all our food. Cultivation encourages the soil to produce sufficient food to satisfy our needs.

Cultivation marks a boundary between two phases of human life. On one side are the wandering nomads, the savages who were our early ancestors; on the other side is civilized man, settling down to the ordered existence that has enabled him to increase the richness of his life.

Measured in terms of human evolution, soil cultivation is a recently discovered art. Ten thousand years ago, or even less, man had not yet learned to till the soil and grow his crops. He was a wanderer, living on apples and grapes, on berries and parsnips that grew wild on the land. When food ran short, man wandered off to new and better-stocked localities. There are still people in the world today who live this sort of early Stone Age life. In Central Africa, nomadic tribes live off the natural vegetation and fauna of their land.

As the great ice sheets melted and drew back during the early days of man's existence, the land which he inhabited became more arid. In the regions of the eastern Mediterranean and south-west Asia, primitive hunters and nomads moved gradually toward the rivers. Here, vegetation was lush and food more plentiful.

In time, fruit- and berry-collecting began to take precedence over hunting. Food plants were recognized and selected, and man encouraged the growth of the plants that he preferred. Using a pointed stick, he cleared other plants from around his food plants, breaking up the surrounding soil.

He watched as seeds fell to the ground and grew into new plants. He discovered that he could collect the seeds and sow them for himself. Some of the seeds he could use as food, and some he could carry with him as he moved from place to place. Scattered on the ground, his seeds would grow and provide him with his future needs of food. Man was becoming independent of his environment. He was learning to control his sources of food supply.

Assartage

To grow his food plants, primitive man cleared patches in the forest. Trees and bushes were grubbed up after the rains. As the wood dried in the summer sun, it was burned. In the half-cleared land the seeds were planted.

As the young plants sprouted they were tended and their fruits, in due course, harvested. In the clearing, another crop would be grown—and another—until the soil became exhausted and the plants would grow no more. Then the clearing was abandoned to the jungle once again, and a fresh patch cleared and the process repeated.

This system of cultivation, called assartage, is still practised by primitive peoples today. It is adequate so long as there is plenty of virgin land available and the needs of the people are few. But assartage cannot provide for a growing population with a tendency toward settled existence.

In the hot, dry lands of the Middle East, where civilization took early root, people found that they could grow one crop after another in the fertile valley soils. The Euphrates, the Tigris and the Nile, flooding their banks every year, deposited a layer of rich new soil over the surrounding land. In this soil, plants grew abundantly during the periods between the floods. The people scattered seeds upon the soil, and gathered the harvest before the next flood swept across the valley. Agriculture became an ordered business to these flourishing river communities. Plants had to be grown within the seasonal conditions laid down by nature.

When the floods receded, the mud baked hard in the summer sun. To sow their seeds, the people had to dig and pound at the hard surface with their digging sticks. They tended their plants carefully to ensure that they matured in proper season.

Along the banks of these historic rivers, civilizations flourished. Towns were built and community life developed. All were dependent on the food that grew in the fields beside the river.

In these early days of civilization, agriculture acquired some of the techniques that have served it to the present time. As they worked on the rich soil, people improved their simple implements. The digging stick with a flattened end was found more suitable for turning the soil; so came the spade. Two sticks bound at an angle to each other became a simple hoe.

The Plough Arrives

Though the flood plains were blessed with a fertile soil, the farmer had to till the soil assiduously to break it down to the fine tilth needed for planting his seeds. At an unknown point in history, someone eased his burden by mounting a hoe or spade behind a draft animal. The power of the animal was harnessed to the primitive hand implement, and the plough had been invented.

With the coming of the plough, the farmer was able to stir his soil quickly and effectively. The plough made possible the cultivation of larger areas of land by fewer people. It increased the output of food and left more time for other pursuits.

As century followed century, the people of these Middle East civilizations learned how to care for their soil and to encourage it to grow the food they needed. Husbandry became an art founded on inherited experience and skill. Trial and error was the technique through which the farmer learned the elements of his trade.

Irrigation

From the earliest times, man understood the essential part played by water in cultivating plants. Civilizations grew in hot regions where rainfall was low during the greater part of the year. In Babylon and Nineveh, in Crete and Carthage, water in the form of rain was scarce; the water needed for the land was brought through ducts and channels from the rivers. This method of watering cultivated plants by irrigation has survived to the present time in many countries.

Irrigation works discovered by archaeologists have

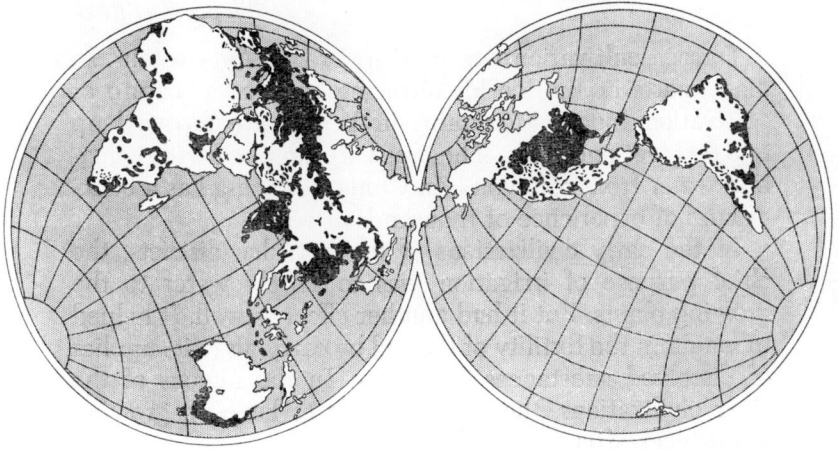

Cultivated Areas. Only a very small part of the earth's land surface is cultivated, amounting to about 8 per cent of the available land. This represents less than 2 per cent of the total surface of the earth. The cultivated regions are shown in black on the map.

shown that early civilizations had developed a high degree of engineering skill. Great aqueducts were built to carry water; pipes were made from the trunks of trees, and water was distributed through the fields in complex networks of irrigation ditches.

Terrace Cultivation

To early man, the hills were often a refuge in which he could shelter from marauding bands that swept across the plains. To sustain him in the hills, he carried his agriculture with him to the mountain slopes. Here, he built terraces of soil supported on walls of wood or rubble. In these flat ridges of soil that followed the contours of the mountainside, he grew his crops. Where rainfall was low, terracing and irrigation were used together, the terraced ridges conserving moisture and holding the precious soil onto the slopes.

Terrace cultivation was used in Bronze Age Britain. In many parts of the world, terracing remains a feature of cultivation today. Mountains in Yemen are terraced up to 5,000 feet and more. The crops are supplied with irrigation water from reservoirs. In China, terracing has a background of experience of thousands of years.

In the early civilizations of the hot, dry districts, the chief purpose of irrigation was to supply water to the growing plants. But it had another effect as well. It helped to maintain the fertility of the soil by carrying to it supplies of dissolved substances from afar. In the regions of the river civilizations, the soil was able to keep on growing crops, year after year.

The spread of civilization brought with it an increasing pressure on the land. People had to find new areas in which to live; they left the rich valleys and deltas, taking their skills and experience with them. They settled in colder lands, where rain took the place of irrigation water. And they had to learn how to make their soil feed them, without the enrichment brought to the soil by irrigation and river flood.

Soil feeds the Plant

Man soon learned that the plant-growing capacity of any soil was limited. Something in the soil was apparently used by the plant, enabling it to grow. The soil fed the plant, and when its food supplies were exhausted, the plant would wither and die.

This idea of the soil providing food for the plant has been at the back of men's minds for thousands of years. But the nature of these plant foods has remained a mystery until comparatively recent times.

Experience and observation showed that animal and vegetable remains were able to maintain the fertility of the soil. Anything that had lived, or been concerned with life, could revitalize the soil into which it was dug. These things could do for the soil what irrigation did for the river farmers.

So manure and compost, seaweed, leaves and other once-living things became accepted as "fertilizers" for the soil. They returned to the soil that which they had taken from it when they lived.

Slowly, as civilization spread out to different parts of the world, these fundamental ideas on cultivation were carried with it. In Europe, progress was slow compared with that in Egypt and south-west Asia. The soils lacked the richness of the flood plains, and the climate tended to be harsh.

From Egypt, the plough cut its furrow over the surface of the earth. By 3000 B.C. it had reached the fertile valleys of China, and up into Central Europe. In China, the plough stimulated the civilizations that flourished in the days when Britons lived a life of primitive savagery. The Black Earth regions of Russia were being ploughed nearly five thousand years ago. Parts of Germany and Czechoslovakia were under cultivation by 2500 B.C. Much of Europe, though, was covered with swamp and forest. The deep roots of the trees were too strong to yield to the primitive ploughs that preceded the Iron Age. Development of these cold inhospitable lands had to await the coming of the iron plough.

By the time the Roman legions penetrated through Europe and into Britain, farming had reached all stages of development in different parts of the world. Rome did much to stabilize and rationalize the argicultural knowledge within her empire. By the beginning of the Christian era, hundreds of years of experience lay behind the iron plough. A vast background of information was at the disposal of the farmer.

It had been known for a thousand years that soil could recuperate if left for a season without a crop. The rest would enable it to regenerate some of its lost fertility.

When they entered the Promised Land, the Israelites laid down by law that the land must lie fallow for one year out of seven.

The value of dead and decomposing matter as a soil fertilizer had been appreciated since before the days of recorded history. Xenophon, the Greek historian, was proclaiming by 400 B.C. the virtues of digging weeds and other growing crops into the soil. The body material of these things could restore fertility to the soil in the same way as manure.

Rotation of Crops

The Romans understood the value of growing different crops in succession on cultivated ground. Roman writers laid down rules of cultivation and crop rotation that would maintain the fertility of the soil. Certain crops – leguminous crops like clover and beans – were recognized as being able to improve the soil fertility, and systems of rotation were worked out to keep the soil in good heart. Using dung and manure as fertilizers, the Romans operated a three-year rotation in which a year of fallow was followed by a season of wheat and then of beans.

With the beginning of the Christian era, the foundations of systematic agriculture had been laid. Centuries of experience and skill had been accumulated. Tools and implements were primitive, but man had learned the essentials needed by the soil if it was to function as his food provider. He realized that bad management of his cultivation could exhaust the soil. He knew instinctively that from the soil came something that was needed by the growing plant as food. He did not understand just what this plant food was; inevitably, it was associated with the remains of living things, for these were able to maintain the fertility of the soil. He knew that the soil, left in peace for a season or two, could often revitalize itself in some mysterious way.

When Rome fell, this fabric of experience in husbandry

was torn down. Europe under the barbarian made little progress in agriculture for a thousand years or more. But the skills which had been built up in the thousands of years since man began scratching at the earth, remained. In a few isolated places, the traditions of agriculture survived to provide nuclei for the growth of modern understanding of the land.

After the fall of Rome, the three-field system of cultivation became established in the humid climate of Europe, adjusting itself to the primitive conditions that prevailed. One field lay fallow every year, while the other two produced the crops. Throughout most of Europe, this pattern of soil cultivation remained the same, extending even into Russia and parts of India.

Three-field Farming

Over this slowly developing Western world, the land was settled by self-contained village communities. Each village grew its own food and provided for itself in almost every way, the nucleus of the community life being its agriculture.

Low-lying land near the village became the meadows. This land was fenced off in strips, each strip being allocated by ballot to a tenent every year. From Annunciation Day (March 25) to hay harvest, the tenant looked after his "allotment" of meadowland. And after the hay had been collected, the meadow reverted to common pasture.

Beyond the meadows lay the three great tillage fields that supplied the bulk of the food for the village. In these fields, the three-year system of crop rotation went on year after year, along the lines laid down in the days of the Roman Empire. Each tillage field was divided into strips which became the responsibility of individual serfs. Each serf held a strip in every one of the three fields, amounting to as much as an acre a strip.

In one of the fields, a winter grain was sown – wheat or

WEATHERING OF ROCK

The mineral particles in soil are formed from parent rocks of the earth's crust. These are attacked and broken down by a number of natural processes which are described generally as erosion and "weathering". Some weathering processes are physical; they break the rock into smaller and smaller particles, but leave the material of the rock unchanged. Other weathering processes are chemical; they convert the rock materials into new substances which are released into the soil.

1. *Temperature Changes*

Unequal expansion and contraction of rocks under the effect of changing temperatures result in fracture of the rock surface (see page 71). The effect is greatest in tropical regions, where the daily temperature changes are at their highest.

2. *Glacial Action*

Huge sheets of ice moved over the rocks of the earth's crust during past Ice Ages, rubbing off tremendous quantities of rock particles of all shapes and sizes. These particles have become parent materials of many soils, such as boulder clay and till.

3. *Freezing and Thawing*

Water trapped in cracks and fissures will break up rocks as it freezes and expands (see page 69). This is a most important factor in weathering in the colder regions of the earth. The more porous rocks are affected to a greater extent than the hard, impervious rocks.

Freezing and thawing is an effective way of breaking down clayey clods. Water held in the pores between the particles freezes and expands; when it thaws, the clods are broken down into smaller pieces.

4. *Moving Water*

As rocks and stones are swept along by moving water, they bump against each other. Particles are broken away and the pieces of rock become gradually smaller. Rock is also broken down in this way by waves beating against a coast.

5. *Wind*

Small particles are carried along by winds, and bump against each other and against larger particles of rock. In wind-swept regions, this can result in considerable wearing-away of rock surfaces.

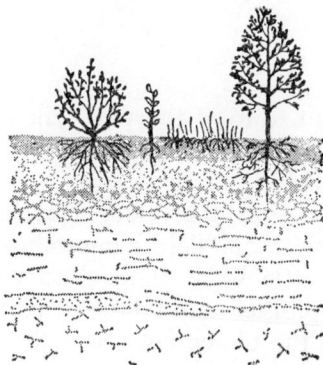

6. *Chemical Changes*

Rocks are attacked by water, carbon dioxide and oxygen from the air, which cause chemical changes. New materials produced in confined spaces can break away particles of rock, which fall to the ground (see page 74). The new substances produced become a part of the soil material.

Many rocks, such as basalt, contain iron in a form which is capable of combining with further amounts of oxygen. When these rocks are exposed to air and moisture, they are oxidised in this way, forming the reddish coloured iron compounds which are a feature of soils from many igneous rocks.

The chemical attack on rock materials continues within the soil itself. Carbon dioxide formed by the decay of organic matter, and by the roots of plants, dissolves in the soil water to form carbonic acid. This attacks many rock minerals, undergoing chemical reaction with some constituents and releasing other constituents unchanged. Igneous rocks, for example, form carbonates from some constituents; these may dissolve in the soil water, releasing hydrated aluminium silicate particles as clay. Particles of quartz which were present in the rock are not attacked by the carbonic acid, and these are released as sand.

7. *Animals*

The soil is teeming with insects and other animals in great variety, and these may contribute to the breakdown of mineral particles. Earthworms, for example, pass soil material through their bodies, grinding up small particles on the way.

8. *Plants*

Plants contribute to the chemical changes of the soil by releasing carbon dioxide from their roots, and from their remains when they die. The roots also help to open up cracks and fissures in the rocks and soil, making the mineral surfaces accessible to air and water.

rye, or a mixture of the two called "maslin." The second
field carried spring corn – barley, oats, beans or peas; and
the third field lay fallow.

Year by year, the crop carried by each field was
changed, with one field lying fallow every year. After the
harvest, cattle were allowed to wander over the three
fields, nipping off any follow-crops that grew.

Beyond the tillage fields was the rough land, providing
the community with its wood and rushes and reeds for
building, its grazing for sheep, and acorns for the swine.

In this old system of three-field farming applied to self-
supporting village life, the essentials of Roman agriculture
were preserved for centuries. Two years out of every three,
the soil of the tillage fields produced its crops. During the
third year, the soil rested and restored its fertility sufficiently to carry its crops again.

This system adequately served its simple community.
But it was inefficient and wasteful. The amount of food
produced was governed by the ability of the soil to restore
its own fertility as it rested. The level of production was
not high.

The strips of field allotted to the tenants were too small
to be cultivated properly. Adequate drainage was impossible. The value of manure was largely lost by allowing
the cattle to wander over too great an area.

So long as community life remained in little isolated vil-
lages, change was inevitably slow. But during late
mediaeval times, the government of Western nations grew
up on a broader plan. Property became more secure, and
people emerged from the traditions of serfdom. Communi-
cations improved; ideas could spread. Gradually, the old
three-field system of agriculture broke up; it could not
meet the needs of people who were learning to abandon
feudal life.

As communities grew, the demands on the soil increased. No longer could it be left to produce at its own

slow rate. Something had to be done to make the soil support more crops and to provide the food that was needed by the increasing populations of the world.

Agricultural Revolution

During the seventeenth century, agriculture was caught up in the great sweep forward toward a more scientific and productive way of life. The old traditions of agriculture, based on the three-field system of rotation, began to fade away. The growing development of scientific thought was reflected in agriculture; in particular, the science of chemistry made possible a coherent study of plant nutrition. Western Europe, particularly Britain, became the focal point of agricultural progress.

The seventeenth century saw new techniques of agriculture being introduced into Britain. Flemish farmers had by that time abandoned the bare fallow which left the land unproductive for one year out of every three. They grew clover and turnips during the year which had been previously allocated as fallow. They had a food crop every year.

This was a century of quickening progress in the world of agriculture. Crops were improved with the help of better seed and deeper cultivation. But change did not come easily. The three-field system was strongly entrenched in the traditions of British farming, and so long as this system remained, there was little opportunity for progress. Improvement came only when the individual farmer could control his own land over long periods of time. As the open fields gave way to individually owned enclosures, progress became possible.

In agriculture, as in most other fields of art and science, history was marked out by the work of a few determined and enlightened men. They led, and others followed.

Jethro Tull

One of the greatest of these farming revolutionaries was

the famous Jethro Tull. During the early eighteenth century, Tull introduced new techniques which were to have a tremendous effect on British agriculture. Until that time, field crops had always been sown broadcast, the seeds being scattered as evenly as possible over the ground. In 1731, Jethro Tull began planting field crops in rows. By growing his wheat and barley in this way, he found that he could hoe between the rows, keeping down the weeds which grew apace when seed was broadcast and could not easily be hoed.

Even this simple and effective idea was a long time in taking root. Tull proved that it increased his crop yields, and to make the technique a practical proposition he invented the drill, which enabled him to sow his seed easily in rows.

Intertillage, as this hoeing of weeds came to be called, had a remarkable effect on farming practice. It allowed the farmer to come to the aid of crops which had previously fought a desperate lone battle against the weeds. Yet Jethro Tull, with his drills and intertillage, was regarded by many farmers as a crank; although he practised what he preached for years, with great success, his ideas were slow to be accepted.

Norfolk Rotation

Meanwhile, another famous farmer was introducing a new system of crop rotation. In Norfolk, Lord Townshend was working out a four-year rotation of wheat, turnips, barley, and clover or beans. These crops, with the help of manure ploughed into the ground, improved returns of food from the soil.

With the gradual acceptance of the Norfolk rotation and the intertillage of Jethro Tull, agriculture began to make real progress in Britain. England, during the eighteenth and nineteenth centuries, led the world in farming practice, and the soil repaid the careful treatment that it was receiving. With the improvement in cultivation techniques came progress in other branches of agriculture. Better livestock was being bred; new varieties of plants were selected and developed.

Arthur Young – the Prophet

In 1770, the great prophet of modern agriculture, Arthur Young, wrote his book, *Rural Economy.* In it, he crystallized the trends of the new agriculture that was sweeping over the land. Young proclaimed that good husbandry was possible only when plenty of manure was available. He reaffirmed the idea of plant foods in the soil; without them no plant could flourish and grow. Unless the supply of these materials in the soil was maintained, plants would wither away and die of starvation like an animal deprived of food. Some day, Young predicted, "compound" manures would be found which would give the earth a vastly increased fertility.

Throughout the eighteenth and nineteenth centuries, this resurgence of agricultural improvement continued. The soil and its relationships with plants became a subject of logical study. Agriculture was becoming a science.

With this understanding came practical results that were to bring the world an abundance of food. In mediaeval times, English soil was producing eight bushels of wheat to the acre; by 1840, the yield had risen to twenty bushels. But more was yet to come.

2

Soil Feeds the Plant

Until little more than a century ago, ideas about the foods needed by plants were vague and uncoordinated. It was easy to see how animals got their food, and there was an obvious relationship between such food and the animal which ate it. Meat and fats, for example, form part of the human body, and meat and fats are normal constituents of animal and human foods.

But plants were different. The seed was planted in the soil, and gradually it grew. Above the ground the living plant spread its branches and leaves, and below the soil the roots thrust down into the earth. The plant grew larger. But there was no mouth taking in supplies of food to provide for the needs of the growing plant. There was no food in any recognizable form being absorbed. How, then, did the plant grow?

Van Helmont's Experiment

In the early part of the seventeenth century, a Flemish scientist called Van Helmont carried out an experiment with a willow shoot to try and find out what it used as food. The willow was grown in a box of soil and watered with rain water. After five years the shoot, weighing initially 5 pounds, had grown into a young tree which weighed 169 pounds.

Van Helmont weighed his soil at the beginning and at the end of his experiment, and found that only 2 ounces of the original 200 pounds had been lost. This was so small a proportion of the total soil that Van Helmont decided that the loss must be due to experimental error. The whole of the 164 pounds in weight gained by the tree, he said, came from the water that had been given to it.

Many experiments of this sort were carried out during the next century or so, and people began to realize that water was not the plant's only need. A plant grew by taking something else from the soil. Van Helmont's lost 2 ounces had not been due to experimental error. They represented a loss due to substances absorbed into the plant from the soil. If these substances had not been available in the soil, the willow shoot could not have grown.

In 1804, a Swiss scientist, de Saussure, showed that nitrogen and mineral elements were taken by the plant from the soil. These elements, most of which were still unidentified, were raw materials involved in the growth processes of the plant. But still they did not account for

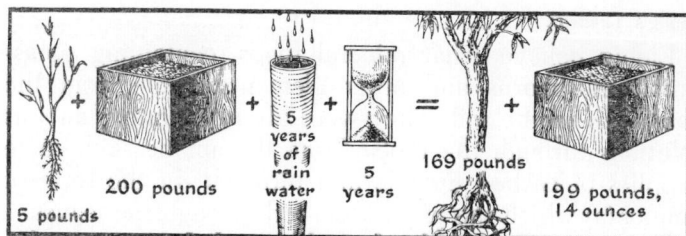

VAN HELMONT'S EXPERIMENT

In five years, the shoot weighing originally 5 pounds, had increased in weight to 169 pounds. Only 2 ounces of soil material had been used, from a total of 200 pounds. The rest of the tree's weight, Van Helmont believed, must have come from the rainwater — *From Principles of Plant Physiology by James Bonner and Arthur W. Galston. San Francisco: W. H. Freeman and Company, 1952.*

the tremendous increase in weight of a plant during growth.

In 1779, a Dutch physician, Jan Ingenhousz, had proved that plants give off oxygen gas during the day and absorb it at night. The gases of the air, as well as the minerals of the soil, were therefore involved in plant growth. And de Saussure showed that carbon dioxide gas was taken up as oxygen was lost during daylight, so indicating a source of supply of the bulk of the plant material. It came apparently from carbon dioxide in the air.

Although these scattered facts about plant nutrition had accumulated by the early nineteenth century, it still remained for someone to organize them into a coherent theory of how plants feed and grow. This was done by the great German scientist, Justus von Liebig, who took up the study of plant physiology in 1838. Liebig collected together the scattered facts of practical husbandry and plant nutrition and set out to establish agriculture on a sound scientific basis.

Liebig's Theories

Liebig believed that mineral foods, containing potassium, phosphorus and other elements, came from the chemicals in the soil. They were absorbed into plants as solutions through the roots. From the air, he said, came supplies of carbon dioxide and nitrogen (in the form of ammonia) which the plant absorbed through the leaves.

Trying to provide the facts he needed to sustain his theories, Liebig carried out experiments on his ten-acre farm. He used manures containing the mineral foods he believed were needed by the plant. But the results were discouraging. For Liebig was mistaken in his assumption that the plant took in its nitrogen supplies from the air. As we now know, nitrogen is absorbed through the plant roots, like the mineral elements, in the form of simple chemicals.

WHAT IS PLANT FOOD?

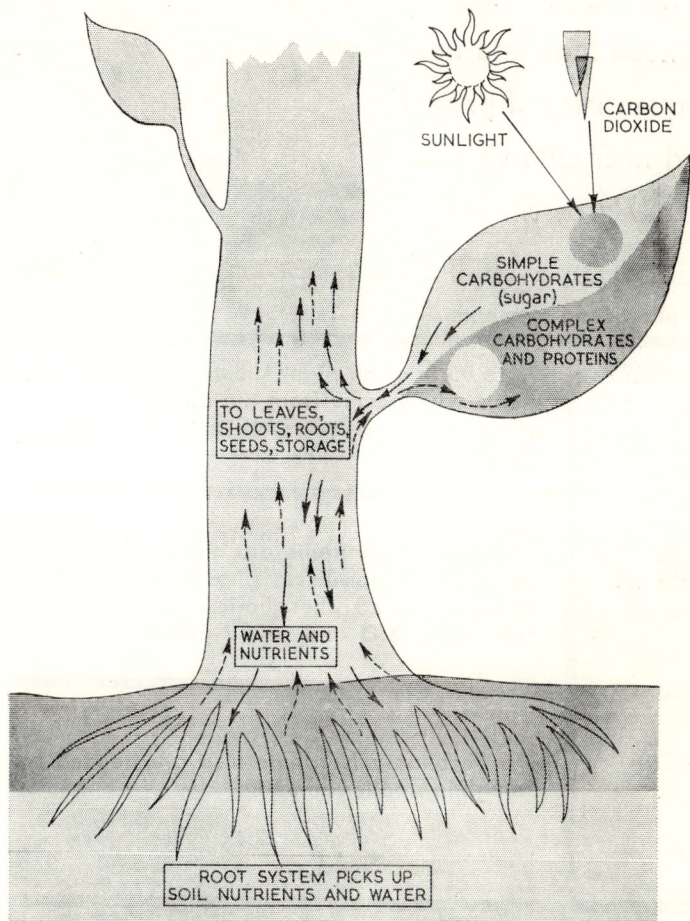

The living matter of the plant is constructed, like all forms of matter, from the elements which are the basic materials of our world. There are some 92 naturally-occurring elements, and it is probable that many of these play some sort of role in plant growth. A few of them are known to be essential, some of them in comparatively large amounts, and supplies of these elements reach the plants in substances entering via the roots and leaves.

Carbon and oxygen reach the plant as carbon dioxide gas, which is absorbed from the air through the leaves. Hydrogen and oxygen are supplied by water entering through the roots. Oxygen also enters the plant directly from the air. Using sunlight as a source of energy, the plant manufactures sugars from these raw materials. The sugars are combined with nitrogen, potassium, phosphorus and other elements absorbed as solutions of chemicals from the soil, forming proteins, complex carbohydrates, fats, oils, vitamins and hormones.

Plants, like all growing things, need food and must have liberal quantities of properly balanced nutrients to ensure satisfactory growth.

Essential plant food elements

Hydrogen (H) Oxygen (O) Carbon (C)	90 to 95% of all plant substance is due to these elements which come from the air and water.
Nitrogen N) Phosphorus (P) Potassium (K)	The *Primary Nutrients* are needed by crops in large amounts. In fertilizers phosphorus is expressed as P_2O_5 and called phosphoric oxide; potassium is expressed as K_2O and called potash.
Calcium (Ca) Magnesium (Mg) Sulphur (S)	The *Secondary Nutrients* also are needed by plants, though in smaller amounts.
Boron (B) Manganese (Mn) Copper (Cu) Zinc (Zn) Iron (Fe) Molybdenum (Mo) Chlorine (Cl)	Although the *Micro Nutrients* are required by plants in very small quantities, they may be deficient or unavailable in soils, and thus have to be added. *Additional Elements:* Research is being conducted by plant physiologists to determine whether additional elements are necessary for plant growth. Sodium, iodine, cobalt and possibly selenium, are required by animals, but have not been shown to be essential for plants. Boron and molybdenum have not been established as necessary for animals.

Although Liebig was unable to set the seal on his theories of plant nutrition by showing how they could be carried through in practice, he had made possible a real understanding of plant feeding. And the outlook of agriculture began to change. Growing food had, until then, been a skill established on a foundation of centuries of past experience. Farming was something that was learned by growing up with it. But now, agriculture was meeting up with applied science. Traditional methods of cultivation, manuring and crop rotation could be studied in relation to the amount of simple chemical foods they made available in the soil.

John Bennet Lawes of Rothamsted

It was in England that Liebig's theories were developed and brought into agricultural practice by one of the great agriculturalists of modern times, John Bennet Lawes of Rothamsted. As a young man, Lawes inherited his family estate at Rothamsted in Berkshire. He became interested in soil fertility, and began experimenting with crop plants. Hearing of Liebig's work, he carried out pot experiments in which different substances were added to the soil. Guano, bone dust, farmyard manure, potash, and ammonium salts were some of the materials he used. In 1839, Lawes extended the scale of his researches and carried out experiments on crops growing in his fields at Rothamsted. He tried, in particular, to improve the turnip crops he was growing by dressing the ground with bone meal. But results were disappointing.

Lawes knew, however, that the main chemical in bones was calcium phosphate. This substance did not dissolve readily in water, and could not make its way quickly into the plant as a solution absorbed through the roots. Lawes therefore treated bones with sulphuric acid, turning them into a new material which he called superphosphate. Applied to the soil, the superphosphate dissolved more easily in the rainwater percolating through the soil, providing plants with a solution containing the phosphorus chemicals they required. This solution they could absorb through their roots.

Lawes tried his superphosphates as a "fertilizer" in soil which was carrying the turnip crop on his estate. The results were striking; the plants were stronger and the yield improved. For the first time, an artificially-made chemical was being applied to the soil as an aid to farming. It was a historic moment in the history of agriculture.

After taking out a patent in May, 1842, Lawes began manufacturing superphosphates from mineral calcium phosphate instead of from the calcium phosphate of bones. On July 1, 1843, his first advertisement appeared in the *Gardener's Chronicle* :

J. B. Lawes' Plant Manures composed of Superphosphates of Lime, Phosphate of Ammonia, Silicate of Potass, etc. are now for sale at his factory, Deptford Creek, London, price 4/6 per bushel.

A Revolution Begins

To the farmers of a century ago, Lawes' announcement was revolutionary in its implications. It came as the herald of new techniques in farming, with an understanding of scientific principles being overlaid upon the traditions of a thousand years. From the barn that Lawes first used as his laboratory has grown the huge synthetic-fertilizer industry of today, with its output measured in millions of tons a year.

The discovery of superphosphates was only the beginning of Lawes' work for agriculture. He realized that what he had done had merely touched the fringe of the science of plant-feeding, and he set to work to study the subject of soil fertility as a whole. Lawes' fields at Rothamsted were laid out in strips and plots on which crops were given different feeding treatments. These experiments have now

SECONDARY PLANT NUTRIENTS

Until recent years, little attention was given to the importance of secondary and micro elements – calcium, magnesium, sulphur, boron, manganese, copper, zinc, iron, chlorine and molybdenum – in fertilizers. It was thought that most soils would contain sufficient natural supplies. Also, commercial fertilizers included considerable quantities of these elements as impurities and carriers of the primary nutrients.

The development of more highly refined materials carrying more nitrogen, phosphorus and potassium has reduced supplies of some secondary and micro elements in fertilizers. Also, with intensive cropping, greater emphasis on higher yields per acre, and with soils becoming older and more depleted, the need for all essential elements has become more pronounced.

It is now known that poor yields may be due to deficiencies of one or more of the secondary or micro elements, and for efficient crop production it is necessary to give more attention to these nutrients.

CALCIUM

A major constituent of various limestones, shells, slags, phosphate rock, superphosphate and gypsum.

* Promotes early root formation and growth.
* Improves general plant vigour and stiffness of straw.
* Influences the intake of other plant foods.
* Neutralizes poisons produced in the plant.
* Encourages grain and seed production.
* Increases calcium content of food and feed crops.

MAGNESIUM

A constituent of dolomitic limestone, magnesium sulphate, magnesium potassium sulphate, magnesium oxide, and seed meals.

* Is an essential constituent of chlorophyll, which gives green colour to the leaves.
* Is necessary for the formation of sugar from carbon dioxide and water with the help of sunlight.
* Regulates the uptake of other plant foods.
* Acts as carrier of phosphorus in the plant.
* Promotes the formation of oils and fats.
* Plays a part in the translocation of starch.

SULPHUR

Is present in many fertilizer materials, including gypsum, ordinary superphosphate, ammonium sulphate and potassium sulphate. Natural sulphur is also used, and sulphur is liberated into the atmosphere when coal is burned, much of it finding its way into the soil.

* Gives increased root growth.
* Helps maintain dark green colour.
* Promotes nodule formation on legumes.
* Stimulates seed production.
* Encourages more vigorous plant growth.

MICRO PLANT NUTRIENTS

The micro nutrients, also known as trace or minor elements, are boron, manganese, copper, zinc, iron, chlorine and molybdenum. Although only very small quantities are required, all are necessary for plant growth.

Unsatisfactory growth, especially on sandy and on muck soils, is sometimes traceable to the lack of one or more of these elements. Deficiencies are not so widespread, however, as to warrant their general addition to all fertilizers. When soil deficiencies do exist, they can usually be corrected by the addition of small amounts of these elements to commercial fertilizers, or by direct application to the soil or plant.

In many cases, micro nutrients are more effectively used as a spray applied to the growing crop. This is a practical means of application on tree fruits.

With some of these elements, the range between beneficial and detrimental amounts is very narrow, so they must be carefully used, for too much may cause injury.

BORON has improved the quality and increased the yields of alfalfa, fruit and vegetables in many districts.

COPPER is generally deficient in peat and muck soils. Deficiencies mainly involve onions, small grains, fruit trees, corn and grasses.

IRON deficiency occurs mainly in more arid regions, affecting especially fruit trees and ornamentals.

MANGANESE deficiency affects most crops in certain areas, and has been noted in soybeans, fruits, vegetables and oats in areas where general deficiency has not occurred.

SODIUM is not classed as an essential element, but under some conditions it promotes the growth of certain plants.

MOLYBDENUM has been recognised as an essential element only for a comparatively short time. Cauliflower, broccoli, clover and soybeans are mostly affected by molybdenum shortage. It is fixed in acid soils, and liming tends to make it available.

ZINC deficiencies occur in fruit trees, corn and other crops.

CHLORINE in large amounts adversely affects the quality of potatoes, tobacco and other crops. Chlorine deficiencies are rare.

been carried out continuously for over a century, and today Rothamsted is one of many similar agricultural experimental stations which have been established throughout the world.

In 1843, Lawes engaged a young chemist, Joseph Henry Gilbert, to help him with his scientific assessment of the chemical foods used by plants. This was the beginning of a partnership which was to last fifty-seven years, ending when Lawes died in 1900. Between them, these two agriculturalists carried out chemical analyses of crops and soil, rainwater, manures and fertilizers from the experimental field strips. They brought science to farming, and grafted chemistry on to agriculture.

The Living Factory

During the latter half of the nineteenth century, the study of plant nutrition established this chemical approach to plant feeding. It was realized that the raw materials taken by plants from the air and from the soil are simple chemicals. Farmyard manures and composts mixed into the soil are not, in themselves, the food of plants; they release supplies of chemicals into the soil as they decay, and these chemicals are absorbed through the roots of the plant. They are raw materials from which the plant rebuilds the complex chemical structures that it needs.

In this respect, the living plant is a chemical factory in which chemicals from the soil and air are turned into fats and proteins, carbohydrates and vitamins. These are the substances involved in the living processes of plant and animal alike. But the plant is a more competent machine than the animal. It can construct the substances it needs from simple chemicals. Animals rely on plants to provide them with these substances ready-made in their food.

The bulk of every green plant consists of three elements: carbon, hydrogen and oxygen. These elements have to be absorbed in great quantity to provide the raw material that is needed for making most of the substances forming the plant structure.

Carbon is brought into the plant through the leaves in the form of carbon dioxide gas, which is always present in the air. Hydrogen comes from the water, consisting of hydrogen and oxygen, which enters the plant through its roots. Oxygen is present in both carbon dioxide and water, and the gas itself is available as one of the main constituents of the air (see page 25).

More than nine-tenths of the normal green plant is built up from the three elements provided by the two raw materials, water and carbon dioxide.

Trace Elements

The remaining matter of the plant, consisting of a tenth or less of the total, is formed from a number of other elements; six of them—nitrogen, phosphorus, sulphur, calcium, potassium and magnesium—make up the greater part of this tenth, and the others, including iron, manganese, copper, zinc, boron and molybdenum, are present in the merest traces. The latter are often called, in fact, the trace elements (see pages 29, 30).

These elements, although making up such a small proportion of the plant, are vitally important to its proper growth. Without an adequate amount of any one of them, something will go wrong. They are like the tiny bearings in a watch; they form an insignificant part of the whole, but the mechanism cannot work without them.

The essential elements are taken by the plant from the soil. Given an adequate supply of all of them, the plant can flourish. It has everything it needs to build the cell materials that form its structure. Nitrogen, for example, is combined with carbon, hydrogen and oxygen in the proteins that are an essential part of every living thing. Magnesium is present in every molecule of chlorophyll,

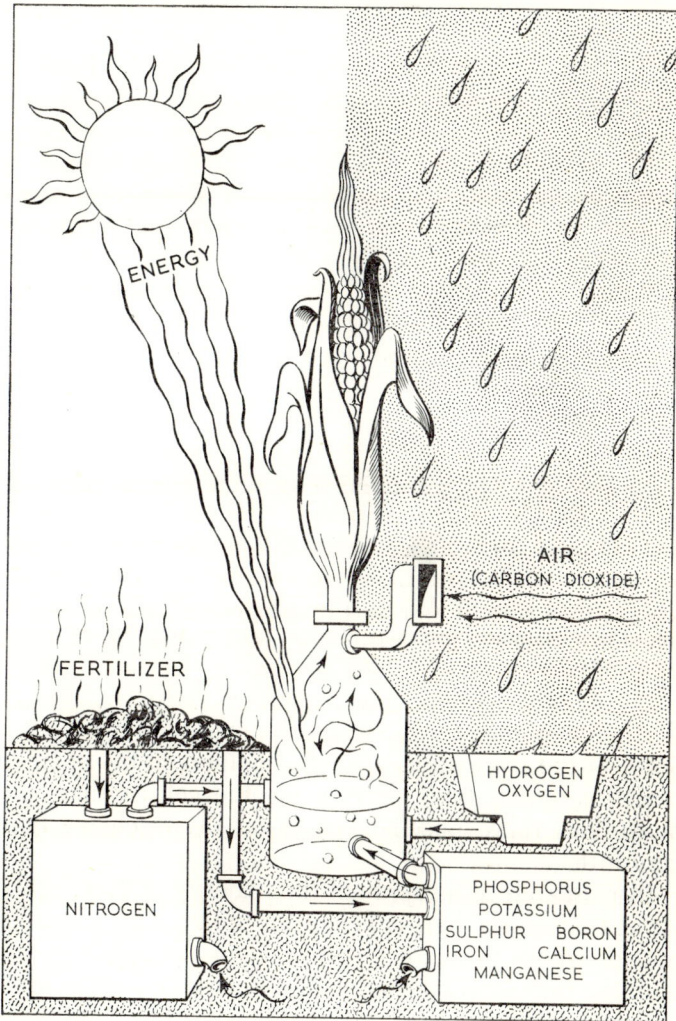

ENERGY

AIR
(CARBON DIOXIDE)

FERTILIZER

HYDROGEN
OXYGEN

NITROGEN

PHOSPHORUS
POTASSIUM
SULPHUR   BORON
IRON   CALCIUM
MANGANESE

This simplified diagram shows how crops grow by using raw materials which come from the soil and the air. Nitrogen is obtained from fertilizer applied to the soil, or sprayed onto the plant. Sunshine provides the energy that sustains the chemical processes of the plant.

B

THE NITROGEN CYCLE

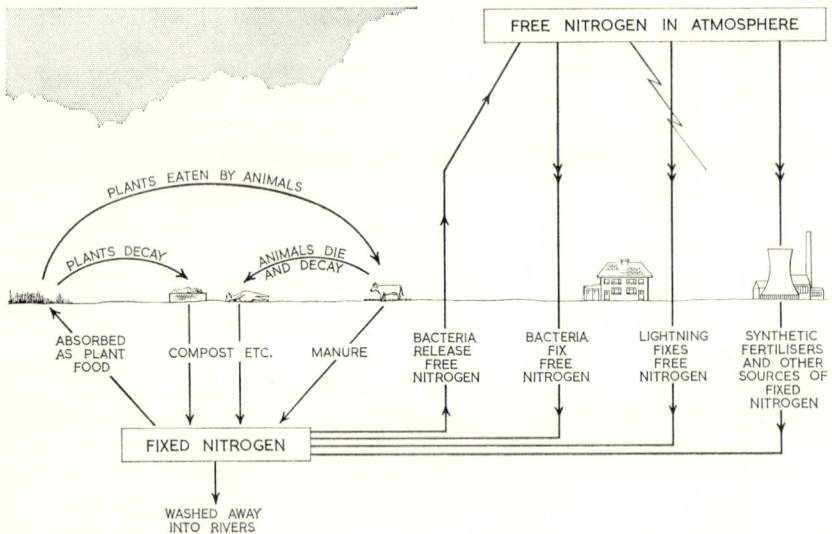

FREE NITROGEN IN ATMOSPHERE

PLANTS EATEN BY ANIMALS

PLANTS DECAY

ANIMALS DIE AND DECAY

| ABSORBED AS PLANT FOOD | COMPOST ETC. | MANURE | BACTERIA RELEASE FREE NITROGEN | BACTERIA FIX FREE NITROGEN | LIGHTNING FIXES FREE NITROGEN | SYNTHETIC FERTILISERS AND OTHER SOURCES OF FIXED NITROGEN |

FIXED NITROGEN

WASHED AWAY INTO RIVERS

Nitrogen is an essential constituent of living matter. The element is involved in a continuous exchange between living things, the soil and the atmosphere.

the green pigment which absorbs energy from the sun. Some of the trace elements act as helpers in the chemical reactions which take place inside the cells. Others play mysterious roles in cell mechanisms of which we know very little.

In most soils, the supply of the majority of the essential elements is more than sufficient for the growing crop. The rate at which they are replenished in the soil is greater than the rate at which the plant absorbs them. But chemicals containing the three elements, potassium, phosphorus and nitrogen, are needed in such quantities by the plant that the soil is often unable to meet the requirements of the growing crop.

Natural Balance

Under natural conditions, the soil maintains its supplies of all the elements it needs by weathering of the rocks and the decay of dead plant and animal matter. Two of the three elements that are liable to be in short supply—potassium and phosphorus—are released by the weathering of rocks and minerals in which they are locked away. Additional supplies come from plant and animal remains as they decay; they are returning the potassium and phosphorus they removed from the soil when they were alive.

The third of the "rationed" elements—nitrogen—is not found in the rocks of the earth's crust at all, and weathering does not release nitrogen chemicals into the soil. The primary source of nitrogen is the atmosphere, four-fifths of which is nitrogen gas. But plants cannot use nitrogen gas itself as a source of the nitrogen they need. It can be absorbed into the roots only after it has been turned into simple chemicals which can be dissolved in the soil water.

Where Nature is left to her own devices, nitrogen needed by the plants that cover the earth is provided largely by the remains of plants and animals that have died. The nitrogen takes part in a cycle between the soil and living plants and animals. When living things die, the nitrogen that they used is locked away inside complex body substances such as proteins. In the soil, the nitrogen from these substances is liberated once again, with the help of bacteria, as simple nitrogen chemicals which can be absorbed into the roots of a new generation of plants. To make good the wastage caused by rainwater that washes these chemicals from the soil, and by the breakdown of the chemicals to atmospheric nitrogen, Nature relies to a great extent on other bacteria in the soil. These bacteria are able to "fix" atmospheric nitrogen by combining it with other elements and making it available to plants in the form of simple chemicals (see page 34).

Where the land is covered by a layer of natural vegeta-

FOOD CROPS REMOVE PLANT NUTRIENTS

NUTRIENTS
RETURNED
TO THE SOIL

Under natural conditions, nutrients are taken from the soil by plants, and used in the construction of their living matter. Animals use the plants as food, the nutrient elements forming part of the animal body. When plants and animals die, their remains fall to the ground, and the nutrient elements are released into the soil again by the processes of decay.

A natural balance is established, the soil supporting a vegetation in accordance with the nutrient chemicals it can provide. Weathering and natural nitrogen fixation processes make good the loss of nutrients by leaching etc.

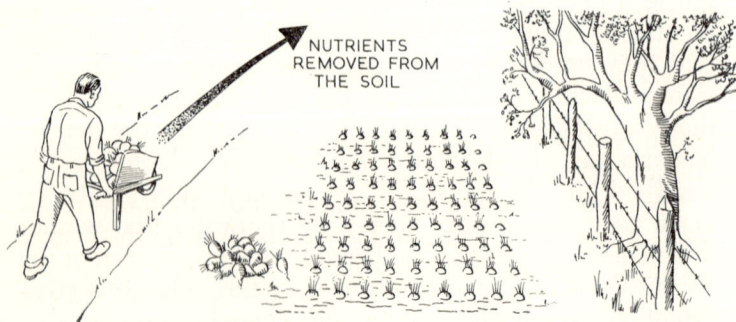

NUTRIENTS
REMOVED FROM
THE SOIL

When man cultivates the soil, he increases the demands made upon it. More nutrients are needed to provide raw material for the crops, and a large part of these nutrients is removed permanently from the soil to serve as human food. The nutrient elements used by the human body are not returned to the land – they find their way eventually to the sea in the form of sewage.

tion, the supplies of essential elements are maintained largely by these joint efforts of the weather and the bacteria in the soil. Slow decomposition of the rock provides supplies of all the elements except nitrogen. Bacterial activity releases nitrogen and other chemicals from decaying materials and brings in additional supplies from the nitrogen of the air. Lightning flashes also add their quota of nitrogen chemicals to the soil, by bringing about the chemical union of nitrogen and oxygen in the air.

Under these natural conditions, the richness of the vegetation is controlled by the supply of plant-food chemicals regenerated in the soil from year to year. As in the case of animals, the plant must have a properly balanced diet with enough of each essential element there. The growth of the plant is limited by the element which is in shortest supply.

Agriculture disturbs the Balance

Where man has come with his crops and agriculture, the natural balance worked out by nature is disturbed. The plants no longer return their substance to the soil when they die; much of the crop is eaten and the elements it contains are lost to the land from which they came. Every grain of corn we grind to flour, every potato we eat contains a store of essential elements that have been taken from the soil. An acre of corn takes the equivalent of a bushel of superphosphate from the soil. Twenty thousand gallons of milk will carry away a ton of superphosphate and a ton of lime (see page 39).

Under modern conditions of agriculture, the pressure on the land is intense, and the soil cannot provide the chemical foods that are needed year after year. The amount of dead material returned to it is too small; and even if plenty of manure and compost were available, the rate of decay is often too slow to provide the chemicals that are needed by crops under intensive cultivation.

In order to maintain the output of food essential to sustain the growing population of the world, we have to provide the soil with the plant food it needs in the form of the simple chemicals themselves.

This practical problem of plant feeding usually resolves itself into providing adequate amounts of potassium, phosphorus and nitrogen chemicals. These are the essential nutrients that tend to be used up faster than the soil itself can replace them.

So far as potassium and phosphorus are concerned, it is largely a question of finding minerals containing a rich supply of one or other of the elements, perhaps modifying them chemically to make them suitable for use by plants, and scattering them on soil that is in need of them.

In the case of nitrogen, the problem is more complex. We have had to learn how to turn the nitrogen of the air into simple chemicals similar to those that are released naturally by bacterial action in the soil.

What Is Required To Produce A 150-Bushel Crop Of Corn Including Roots, Stover and Grain

Substance	Symbol	Approximate Pounds Per Acre	Remarks
Water	H_2O	6,450,000 to 8,250,000	29 to 36 inches of rain
Oxygen	O_2	10,200	Air is about 20% oxygen
Carbon	C	7,800 Carbon or 28,500 Carbon Dioxide (CO_2)	Carbon contained in 6 tons of coal
Nitrogen	N	310	These are the three nutrients contained in most mixed fertilizers.
Phosphorus $P \times 2.29 = P_2O_5$	P	120 pounds P_2O_5 or 52 pounds P	
Potassium $K \times 1.20 = K_2O$	K	245 pounds K_2O or 205 pounds K	
Calcium	Ca	58	Approx. 150 lbs. of agricultural limestone, or equivalent
Sulphur	S	33	33 lbs. of sulphur, or equivalent
Magnesium	Mg	50	Approx. 275 lbs. of epsom salt, or 550 lbs. sulphate of potash-magnesia
Iron	Fe	3	15 lbs. of iron sulphate, or equivalent
Manganese	Mn	0.45	Approx. 1.3 lbs. of manganese sulphate, or equivalent
Boron	B	0.10	Approx. 1.0 lb. of borax, or equivalent
Zinc	Zn	trace	Small amount of zinc sulphate, or equivalent
Copper	Cu	trace	Small amount of copper sulphate or oxide
Molybdenum	Mo	trace	Very small amount of sodium or ammonium molybdate

3

Potassium, Phosphorus, Nitrogen—
The Big Three

POTASSIUM

There are ample supplies of potassium in the earth's crust, and it is evenly distributed about the world. Hard, igneous rocks such as granite contain potassium in their chemical structure. This potassium is shown up by chemical analysis of soil containing particles of igneous rock. But the potassium in this form is useless to the growing plant. The rock particles are insoluble in the soil water. It is only as the soil is weathered that the potassium is released in the form of soluble chemicals.

An average crop will take some 20 to 30 pounds of potassium from every acre of soil; in a bushel of wheat there is up to a pound of potassium, all of which has been taken in through the roots of the growing plants. This seems little enough, particularly when an acre of the soil in which it grew may have as much as four tons of potassium in the top foot-thick layer. But so slow is the weathering process that releases the potassium in the form of soluble chemicals that plants growing in a potassium-rich soil of this sort can yield a poor crop through insufficiency of potassium in their diet. It is the *available* rather than the *total* amount of any element that is important so far as plant feeding is concerned.

Stassfurt Deposits

In 1852, Lawes and Gilbert showed by their field experiments that potassium was an element essential to plant nutrition. Five years later, an immense underground deposit of soluble potassium salts was discovered at Stassfurt in Germany. These salts, like most of the simple potassium chemicals involved in plant feeding, are described as "potash." (In the early days of chemistry, potassium salts were extracted from the ash remaining in pots in which wood was burned. Wood and seaweed ashes have been mixed into cultivated soil from time immemorial; they supply the plants with "pot ash.")

The Stassfurt deposits were to become the main source of potash for the world, and an invaluable asset to Germany. But farmers were slow to apply Lawes' and Gilbert's discoveries, and it was not until after 1890 that potash was used to any great extent as a fertilizer.

Since then, the Stassfurt deposits have been supplying the world with most of its potash needs. By 1928, Germany was producing nearly two million tons of potash a year— some three-quarters of the world's supply.

Since the First World War, when farmers felt the pinch of Germany's potash monopoly, other sources have been developed. Potash is produced at Searle's Lake in California, in the eastern Carpathian Mountains in Austria, in the Urals of Russia, and from the Dead Sea in Palestine. France mines potash in Alsace.

In the sea, we have an almost limitless supply of potash —more than a million million tons of it altogether.

Clay contains Potash

Potash deficiency is usually most marked in sandy or chalky soils. Clay is a sign of a good supply of potash; it is formed by the weathering of older igneous rocks in which potassium is a constituent. But even in clay soils, the potassium may still not be in an available form, and additional

Potassium is a constituent of all living matter. It is required in large amounts by all plants, and is one of the three major fertilizer elements.

Potassium does not occur as the free metal in nature, but it is a constituent of many rocks and minerals. Concentrations of potassium salts are found in certain parts of the world, such as the Stassfurt deposits in Germany, and the brines of Searles Lake, California.

The term "potash" was used originally for potassium carbonate, left behind when plant material is burned. The name is commonly used for all potassium salts, such as potassium hydroxide (caustic potash), potassium chloride (muriate of potash), and potassium sulphate (sulphate of potash). In soil and fertilizer analyses, potash signifies the hypothetical potassium oxide, K_2O.

Most soils are richer in potash than in either nitrogen or phosphorus, but most of the potassium is locked up in a form that is unavailable for plant use. A soil may have as much as 40,000 lbs. of potash per acre within the plough layer, and yet only a few pounds will be made available during a cropping season.

Many potassium salts are applied to the soil as fertilizer. Potassium chloride (muriate of potash) (50% K_2O) is the most popular; potassium sulphate (48% K_2O) and potassium magnesium sulphate (22–26% K_2O) are also used.

POTASH FERTILIZERS

Potassium is needed in comparatively large amounts by plants. It makes its way to the seeds, fruit and nuts as these develop. Root crops also require large amounts of potassium.

Unlike nitrogen and phosphorus, potassium does not appear to become part of complex organic structures in the plant. It is released readily when the plant dies, and manures and composts usually provide available potassium without undergoing extensive decomposition.

Potassium is supplied to the soil in the form of soluble salts, commonly *muriate of potash* and *sulphate of potash*. Both are obtained from natural sources in various parts of the world.

* *Muriate of Potash* (Potassium chloride; KCl) contains 50% potash.

* *Sulphate of Potash* (Potassium sulphate; K_2SO_4) contains 48% potash.

* *Potash Salts* are a crude mixture, which may contain 20–30% of potash.

* *Kainit* is a mixture of crude potash salts containing common salt, which is commonly used on root crops.

* *Wood Ashes* contain potassium carbonate, K_2CO_3, when freshly made. The potash is soon washed out by rainwater unless the ashes are adequately protected.

WHAT POTASSIUM DOES

* Improves the flavour of fruit and vegetables.
* Imparts increased vigour and disease-resistance to plants.
* Produces strong, stiff stalks.
* Increases plumpness of grain and seed.
* Takes essential part in formation and transfer of starches, sugars and oils.
* Imparts winter hardiness to legumes and other crops.
* Improves the colour of fruit, flowers and vegetables.

POTASSIUM IN THE SOIL

Potassium is a constituent of many igneous rocks, and silt and sand particles will often contain potassium reserves. These are released very slowly by weathering, but the soluble potassium salts may be leached from the soil by rainwater in very humid regions.

Potassium ions are held by clay particles, and take part in ion-exchange processes. Potassium ions will often account for about 3% of all the exchangeable ions in the clay, and this is an important reserve of readily available potassium in the soil.

The soil water will carry only a relatively small amount of dissolved potassium – perhaps 1 to 5% of the exchangeable potassium – but this is in equilibrium with the exchangeable potassium. As dissolved potassium is removed from the soil solution, for example by plants, potassium ions will leave the clay particles to restore the concentration in water. Likewise, if extra soluble potassium is added in the form of fertilizer, more ions will crowd onto the clay particle, increasing the amount of exchangeable potassium that is held in reserve.

A further reserve of potassium is held by certain types of clay mineral, such as montmorillonite and illite. These clay particles have expandable structures, and the ions of potassium are able to make their way between the layers of alumina-silica from which the crystalline particle is built (see page 316). If large numbers of potassium ions make their way into an illite particle, for example, the structure is drawn together and the potassium ions cannot escape. Addition of lime to an illite soil can release potassium held in this way; calcium ions prise the layers apart, allowing potassium ions to move into and out of the particle.

In clay soils, there are usually ample basic reserves of potassium, and extra supplies are not required to the extent that they are on sandy soils. Chalky soils, and soils rich in organic matter, will often benefit greatly from potash fertilizers.

The nature of the crop is much more significant in the case of potash than for nitrogen or phosphorus. Root crops, fruits and leguminous crops will respond well to extra dressings of potash.

supplies of soluble potash will be needed if the ground is to produce a rich crop.

Potash helps the plant to make its sugars and starch. Root crops, for example, which store large quantities of starch, need plenty of potash if they are to flourish. Leguminous crops such as peas and beans, or clover, have bacteria living in the nodules on their roots. These bacteria provide the plants with nitrogen salts made from nitrogen of the air. But in return, they expect sugary materials to be supplied to them by the plant. To make these sugars, leguminous plants need plenty of potash.

In the century that has passed since Lawes and Gilbert showed the value of potash as a plant food, farmers have learned what potash can mean to them in terms of increased crops. As cultivation has intensified, they have been unable to rely on supplies of natural dung and manures to return the necessary potash to the soil. And potash in the form of artificial fertilizer has established its place in agriculture.

PHOSPHORUS

The amount of the second "fertilizer" element, phosphorus, varies greatly from one soil to another. There are few phosphorus-containing minerals, and the phosphorus in a soil often comes from animal and human remains which have become mixed into it throughout the centuries.

Some soils are rich in phosphorus, with as much as two tons to the acre. But in many parts of the world, for example in South Africa and New Zealand, soils are deficient in phosphorus, and heavy additional supplies are needed to maintain good crop yields.

Deposits of phosphate rock are mined in many countries to provide the phosphorus needed by agriculture. Much of the world's phosphate comes from North Africa.

Clays are generally deficient in phosphorus. The element is not present in the igneous rocks from which clays are formed. But chalky soils or those that have come from limestone are often well supplied with phosphorus. These are sedimentary rocks, formed from the remains of once-living things. The phosphorus from their bodies is liberated in the soil as the rocks weather.

Calcium phosphate is the chief constituent of all animal bones, and ground bones have been added to the soil for centuries. But the hard calcium phosphate of bones does not readily dissolve in water. Its phosphorus is not available to the plant until it has turned into more soluble materials. This is a process that takes place slowly under natural conditions, particularly in acid soils. Bones provide a long-lasting supply of phosphorus to the soil. Mixed with the soil in which a shrub or tree is planted, they will go on releasing small but steady supplies of phosphorus to the growing plant for years afterward.

Disappearance of Phosphorus

Today, the superphosphate discovered by Lawes is more widely used than any other artificial fertilizer. It supplies phosphorus that is lacking in so many soils. It must be applied regularly, as phosphorus loses its "availability" very quickly. In the United States, more than a million and a half tons of superphosphate and other phosphorus fertilizers are used every year. This is only about a half of the amount the soil could use.

The "disappearance" of phosphorus from the soil is one of the major problems facing the soil scientist today. Superphosphate is washed down into the soil by the first rains after it has been applied. It is immediately available to the plant. But in many soils, particularly those containing iron and aluminium salts, the soluble superphosphate changes back into insoluble compounds. Once this has happened, it is no longer available to the plant as food.

PHOSPHORUS—

Phosphorus is intimately associated with all life processes, and is a constituent of every living cell. All plants need phosphorus in considerable quantities for proper growth.

Phosphorus is never found in soils as the native element. It is present in certain rocks in the form of phosphate, in which it is combined with oxygen and other elements.

Many soils are deficient in phosphorus, and much of the phosphorus that *is* present is "bound" or "fixed" in very insoluble forms. Only a very small quantity of the total supply becomes available in any one cropping season. For this reason, even soils with a high total phosphorus content may fail to provide supplies adequate for maximum crop production.

Unsatisfactory plant growth is more often due to shortage of this element than to any other, excepting nitrogen. Applications of phosphorus fertilizers will often bring remarkable results.

Phosphorus is commonly applied in the form of superphosphate, which is produced by treating ground phosphate rock with sulphuric acid. Superphosphate is more soluble in water than the rock phosphate itself, and is more readily available to the plant.

In recent years, a number of other phosphatic fertilizers have become of importance. Triple superphosphate, mono- and di-ammonium phosphates, ammonium phosphate sulphate, and nitric phosphates are coming into use on an increasing scale.

Other phosphatic fertilizers include basic slag, bone meal, colloidal phosphate and calcium meta-phosphate.

WHAT PHOSPHORUS DOES

* **Stimulates early root formation and growth.**

* **Gives a rapid and vigorous start to plants.**

* **Hastens maturity.**

* **Stimulates blooming and aids in seed formation.**

* **Gives winter hardiness to autumn-seeded grains and hay crops.**

* **Encourages sound germination of seedlings.**

PHOSPHORUS IN THE SOIL

Plants obtain their supplies of phosphorus from phosphorus-containing compounds dissolved in soil water. As the compounds are absorbed by plant roots, fresh supplies are formed from the store of undissolved material in the soil. This store consists of phosphates and other substances produced by breakdown of phosphorus-containing minerals, by the decay of organic matter, and from phosphorus fertilizers previously applied to the soil.

(*Continued opposite*)

THE ROOT MAKER

Phosphorus in the soil (*continued*)

Phosphorus chemicals produced in the soil do not dissolve readily; the soil water will commonly contain only about 1% of the total phosphorus. Plants will often use the dissolved phosphorus faster than it can be replaced by natural processes, and extra supplies must be given by adding soluble fertilizers such as superphosphate.

On the face of it, this seems a simple enough matter. But in fact, it presents many problems. Almost every soil contains materials that will react with soluble phosphates to produce insoluble substances which remove the phosphorus from the soil solution. Phosphorus applied as soluble phosphate will be lost from the soil solution before it can be used by the plant; it is added to the store of insoluble phosphate in the soil, of which there may be ample already.

In acid soils, hydrated iron and aluminium oxides are the chief culprits. They react with soluble phosphate to form insoluble iron and aluminium phosphates. These phosphates are least soluble at pH 4.0, the solubility (and availability) increasing as the pH increase to pH 8.5. Liming an acid soil may increase the concentration of phosphorus in the soil solution by as much as 10 times.

Unfortunately, liming an acid soil is not the simple answer to increasing the availability of phosphorus. At pH 6.0, calcium phosphate begins to form, and this too is insoluble in soil water. Its solubility decreases as the pH increases to 7.5, and then increases from 7.5 to 9.0.

In general, the availability of phosphorus is at a maximum at about 6.5 to 7.0. But even at best, it remains low.

POINTS TO NOTE

* **Most cultivated soils will contain more than enough phosphorus to serve the needs of a crop, but in a form which is not available to the plant. The problem facing the farmer or gardener is to provide readily-available phosphorus which will remain dissolved in soil water, and so feed the plant.**

* **If superphosphate is scattered on the soil, or sprayed on the soil as a solution, it is being given every opportunity of reacting quickly with substances that render it insoluble. This is the least efficient method of using superphosphate. By placing superphosphate in bands beside the seeds or plants, contact with reactive constituents of the soil is kept at a minimum. An area of concentrated superphosphate solution is maintained around the band, and plant roots will find a rich source of available phosphorus provided for them.**

* **If fertilizer must be broadcast, it is best to use granulated material. Each granule forms a small region of concentrated superphosphate solution which makes contact with only a small amount of reactive soil material.**

* **Phosphorus does not move readily in the soil. It will usually remain in the top 12 inches.**

Long-lasting Sources

Often, less than a fifth of the phosphorus applied as fertilizer can be accounted for in the first three crops grown in the soil to which it was applied. The rest has been turned into insoluble and unusable phosphorus chemicals in the soil. One of the advantages of keeping a soil well limed is that it slows down this chemical imprisonment of soluble phosphorus fertilizers.

Although superphosphate has now become the chief source of phosphorus needed as a plant food, bones are still used in various forms to supply a "background" of phosphorus chemicals. Rock phosphate is also applied as a slow-acting phosphorus supplier, and there is another important source of phosphorus in basic slag. This is a slag that is formed on the top of molten steel in the steel furnace. It comes from the lime which is added to the steel to remove phosphorus and other impurities. After it has been cooled and solidified, basic slag is ground up and used as a phosphorus-containing fertilizer.

An average crop will use up to 10 pounds of phosphorus to the acre. With plenty of available phosphorus in the soil, a young plant is able to develop an extensive root system. Phosphorus therefore gives a plant a particularly good start in life. Crops reach maturity more quickly and the harvest is earlier.

Every living cell contains phosphorus. In human beings and animals, this phosphorus, and that needed to provide the calcium phosphate in bones, comes from the food we eat. Like every other food constituent, it is provided by plants which in their turn have derived it from the phosphorus chemicals in the soil.

NITROGEN

The problem of enriching the soil with extra supplies of simple nitrogen chemicals is fundamentally different from that of providing it with potassium or phosphorus.

There are few deposits of natural nitrogen chemicals in the world. We have therefore had to make these chemicals for ourselves.

The tremendous demand for soil nitrogen today is, to some extent, a consequence of the industrialization of the modern world. The manufacture of nitrogen chemicals is now an integral part of the industrial machine in many countries.

Up to the beginning of the Industrial Revolution, food production was very much the direct concern of every member of the community. The small mixed farms and gardens were carefully tended. Crops were grown in rotation, which by experience had been found to improve fertility; and every available bit of compost and manure was returned to the soil.

But as the mills and factories began to spread over the countryside, men left the land and started making engines and textiles, ships and bicycles. People stopped helping to grow the food they needed for themselves. Instead, they had money in their pockets with which to buy food that someone else had grown.

At the same time, the population of the world during the eighteenth and nineteenth centuries was increasing at an alarming rate. The demand for food intensified—food in bulk to supply the people thronging the great cities and industrial areas.

Large-scale Agriculture

To provide the food, the world turned to countries like America and Canada, where vast prairie lands could be harvested in thousands of acres at a time. In place of the little balanced farms of bygone days, we had intensive cultivation on a major scale. Farming became a mechanized industry as our demands on the soil increased.

Year after year, crops took food from the soil, and insufficient was put back in return. Slowly, the land became

NITROGEN—

Nitrogen is a constituent of most of the chemical substances of living matter, including the proteins which are to be found in every cell. It is needed in large amounts by all crop plants, which obtain their supplies in the form of simple nitrogen-containing chemicals dissolved in soil water.

HOW NATURE MAINTAINS NITROGEN SUPPLIES

Nature replenishes the soil with nitrogen-containing chemicals in the following ways: —

* *Leguminous Plants*: Clover, alfalfa and other leguminous plants support colonies of bacteria in the nodules on their roots. These bacteria can fix atmospheric nitrogen, combining it with other elements to form simple chemicals.

* *Nitrogen-Fixing Bacteria in the Soil*: Some soil bacteria can fix atmospheric nitrogen, contributing a small but valuable amount of nitrogenous chemical to the soil solution.

* *Lightning Discharges*: When electric discharges flash through the air, they stimulate the chemical union of nitrogen and oxygen gases. Oxides of nitrogen are produced, which are washed into the soil by rain, ultimately to form nitrates.

* *Organic Matter*: Plant and animal remains are attacked by decay organisms. The nitrogen locked up in proteins and other complex organic chemicals is released into the soil as ammonia and nitrates. This is a slow process, and a soil may be rich in total nitrogen, including that in the organic matter, and yet be unable to supply the plant with simple nitrogen chemicals it can absorb. Soils may contain as much as 7000 lb. of nitrogen to the acre altogether, yet only a few lb. an acre will become available annually in the form of plant nutrients.

HOW NITROGEN IS LOST FROM THE SOIL

Nitrogen chemicals are removed from the soil in the following ways: —

* *Leaching*: Nitrates and other nitrogen-containing chemicals dissolved in soil water are lost by leaching. They are carried away by water draining from the soil. Nitrates are very soluble in water, and are carried to and fro by capillary water. They are lost in large amounts by leaching. Ammonium salts, such as ammonium sulphate, are more resistant to loss by leaching. The ammonium ion is held on the surface of colloid particles, and is released to the roots by ion-exchange processes.

* *Erosion*: Water and wind erosion are responsible for considerable loss of nitrogen and other soil chemicals, especially in certain parts of the world.

* *Denitrification Bacteria*: In acid soils, and soils especially rich in manure and other organic fertilizers, denitrifying bacteria will attack nitrates, and release nitrogen as gas which finds its way back into the air.

* *Crops*: Every crop that is harvested contains nitrogen that has come from nitrogenous chemicals in the soil. An acre of wheat which produces a crop of 40 bushels is taking 50 lb. of nitrogen from the soil.

THE LEAF MAKER

MAKING UP THE SHORTAGES

Modern agriculture makes heavy demands on the soil, and nitrogen supplies, in particular, are likely to be inadequate. Extra nitrogen chemicals must be provided if crops are to grow properly. These are in the form of either organic or inorganic fertilizers.

* *Organic Fertilizers* are plant or animal by-products, such as manure, compost, dried blood, slaughterhouse waste, seed meals, fish meals, peat etc. The nitrogen they contain is locked away in complex chemicals that form part of their once-living matter. They are released slowly as the organic material decomposes in the soil, and organic fertilizers alone may be unable to release nitrogenous chemicals fast enough for intensive cultivation. Also, they are generally expensive in terms of cost per unit of nitrogen.

  Substantial quantities of organic nitrogen can also be added to the soil by digging in cover crops and crop residues. Low nitrogen organic materials such as straw and corn-stubble need extra nitrogen to aid in their decomposition, but all the nitrogen they contain, as well as the extra added to speed decay, is ultimately available to growing crops.

* *Inorganic Fertilizers* are generally simple chemicals, which are commonly made synthetically (and are often called Synthetic Fertilizers). They include such substances as ammonium sulphate and sodium nitrate, which dissolve in soil water and are readily available as nutrient chemicals to the growing plant.

WHAT NITROGEN DOES

1. Gives dark green colour to crops.
2. Induces rapid growth.
3. Increases yields of leaf, fruit and seeds.
4. Improves quality of leaf crops.
5. Increases protein content of food and feed crops.
6. Feeds soil micro-organisms during their decomposition of low-nitrogen organic materials.

SOME COMMON FORMS OF COMMERCIAL NITROGEN FERTILIZERS

Nitrates (NO_3)
- Ammonium nitrate
- Nitrogenous solutions
- Potassium nitrate
- Sodium nitrate

Ammonia (NH_3)
- Ammoniating solutions
- Ammonium nitrate
- Ammonium phosphates
- Ammonium sulphate
- Anhydrous ammonia
- Calcium cyanamide
- Nitrogenous solutions
- Urea

Organic Materials
- A. Vegetable Organics, such as cottonseed meal, soybean meal, pomace etc.
- B. Animal Organics, such as fish meal, animal tankage, process tankage etc.

exhausted of its simple chemical foods. They were being removed faster than nature could replace them. And, by the end of the nineteenth century, the outlook for the world had become desperate indeed.

By this time, the work of Lawes and Gilbert at Rothamsted had presented the problem in fundamental terms. The struggle to grow more food had become identified with the problem of providing the plant with the simple chemical "foods" it absorbed from the soil.

As far as potassium and phosphorus were concerned, the raw materials were available in almost unlimited supply in the form of minerals. Phosphorus could be given to the soil as superphosphates, and potassium as potash from the Stassfurt mines. But providing suitable nitrogen chemicals was a different matter.

Chile Saltpetre

At the end of the nineteenth century, when the problem of providing nitrogenous "fertilizers" became acute, natural supplies of suitable nitrogen-containing chemicals were to be found in only one part of the world. High up on a sun-baked plateau of the Andes in South America, there was a great bed of mineral salts. The main constituent was sodium nitrate—Chile saltpetre. This desert of crystals formed a reservoir of nitrogen for agriculture. The nitrates from it are similar to those released by organic manures as they decay in the soil. And they can act equally well as food for growing plants.

Chile became the world's chief source of nitrogen fertilizer, with additional supplies coming in the form of by-products from the growing coal-gas industry. But Chile lay halfway round the world from Europe, where the need for fertilizers was greatest. And output from the nitrate beds was unable to meet the mounting needs of agriculture.

The problem facing agriculture at the beginning of the

present century was primarily that of supplying suitable nitrogenous fertilizers to the soil in the vast amounts that were required. Only in this way could farmers hope to grow the increasing quantities of food needed by the expanding population of the world.

Sir William Crookes' Warning

The situation was summed up dramatically by Sir William Crookes, one of Britain's greatest scientists, at the British Association meeting in 1898:

My chief subject is of interest to the whole world—to every race—to every human being. It is of urgent importance today, and it is a life and death question for generations to come. I mean the question of food supply. Many of my statements you may think are of alarmist order, certainly they are depressing, but they are founded on stubborn facts. They show that England and the civilized nations stand in deadly peril of not having enough to eat. As mouths multiply, our food resources dwindle. Our wheat-producing soil is totally unequal to the strain put upon it. It is the chemist who must come to the rescue of the threatened communities. It is through the laboratory that starvation may ultimately be turned to plenty.

In 1871, the bread-eaters of the world numbered 371 millions. At the present time (1898) they number 516,500,000.

Up to recent years the growth of wheat has kept pace with demands. As wheat-eaters increased, the acreage under wheat expanded.

But, should all the wheat-growing countries add to their area to the utmost capacity, on the most careful calculation the yield would be just enough to supply the increase of population among bread-eaters till 1931.

I have said that starvation may be averted through the laboratory. All crops require what is called a dominant manure. Wheat pre-eminently demands nitrogen in the form of ammonia or nitric acid. . . .

The situation may be summed up briefly thus: The world's demand for wheat—the leading bread-stuff—increases in a crescendo ratio year by year. Gradually all the wheat-bearing land is appropriated to wheat-growing, until we are within measureable distance of using the last available acre. We must then rely on nitrogenous manures to increase the fertility of the land under wheat.

In the air, there is an unlimited supply of nitrogen gas. Thirty-five thousand tons of it press down on every acre of the earth's surface. In every breath of wind that stirs its leaves, the plant could find the nitrogen it needs to keep it alive. But in its elemental form, this nitrogen is useless. Before the plant can absorb nitrogen, the gas must be changed into simple chemicals which can be scattered on the soil and taken up in solution through the roots.

This was the problem that faced the chemists of the world half a century ago. An economical method must be found of combining atmospheric nitrogen with other elements, in such a way that it could be imprisoned inside compounds suitable for adding to the soil.

Nitrogen Fixation

By 1914, when the First World War broke out, the problem had been solved. Several methods of "fixing" nitrogen in the form of simple chemicals had been discovered. Many countries contributed to the successful development of large-scale fixation, but it was in Germany that the new industry first became established on a major scale.

It has been said, with some truth, that Germany had to wait before starting the First World War, until her chemists had succeeded in building up a nitrogen-fixation industry. Nitrogenous chemicals were needed in tremendous amounts, not only to enable the Central Powers to grow their food, but as raw material for explosives as well. Once war broke out, Germany would be cut off by the blockade from the Chilean nitrate beds. She must therefore depend on atmospheric nitrogen for her needs.

Nature pointed the way toward the successful fixation of atmospheric nitrogen. Lightning discharges in the atmosphere are constantly bringing about the chemical union of nitrogen and oxygen gases. The nitrogen oxides produced are carried down to the ground as nitric acid, forming nitrates with the lime and similar materials in the soil. Every year, an acre of soil receives as much as 11 pounds of combined nitrogen in this way. In tropical countries, where electric discharges are more intense, the amount is much greater.

Following Nature's lead, chemists developed a method of making nitrates by passing nitrogen and oxygen gases through electric discharges. This process is still used for making nitrates, but it has been largely superseded by a different process in which the nitrogen is made into ammonia. This is the basis of the huge synthetic fertilizer factories which are now a part of the economy of every industrial country. Nitrogen from the air is united with hydrogen gas from water to form ammonia. From this ammonia, nitrogen-containing materials such as ammonium sulphate and sodium nitrate are made for use as nitrogenous fertilizers. Ammonium sulphate applied to the soil is turned by bacteria into nitrates; nitrate fertilizers are ready for immediate use by the plant.

A Major Industry

Hundreds of tons of nitrogen are sucked into these huge modern factories every day to provide the fertilizers needed so desperately by a hungry world. Great man-made mountains of shining crystals fill the concrete silos of the nitrogen factories; crystals in which nitrogen from the air has been imprisoned to feed the wheat and potatoes, the rice and corn, barley and grass that must serve the world as food.

Altogether, more than two million tons of nitrogenous fertilizer are being made every year from atmospheric

PARENT ROCKS

The mineral matter of soils is formed from the parent rocks of the earth's crust, which serve as a store of elements from which the growing plant obtains its nutrients. Most of these elements are united to form compounds, which form the mineral constituents of rocks.

1. Igneous Rocks

These are rocks formed by cooling of molten matter from the earth's interior. If cooling took place slowly, the constituents would form large crystals which may be seen in many igneous rocks. If the material cooled quickly, it would form small crystals, or a non-crystalline glass such as obsidian.

Igneous rocks contain a great variety of mineral constituents, including the following:—

QUARTZ   Silica. SiO_2

FELSPARS
- (a)   Orthoclase and microcline. Aluminium potassium silicate. $Al_2O_3,K_2O,6SiO_2$
- (b)   Albite. Aluminium sodium silicate. $Al_2O_3,Na_2O,6SiO_2$
- (c)   Anorthite. Aluminium calcium silicate. $Al_2O_3,CaO,2SiO_2$
- (d)   Labradorite. Aluminium calcium sodium silicate. $Al_2O_3,CaO,Na_2O,6SiO_2$.

MICAS   Aluminium potassium (or sodium) silicates, which may contain many other constituents including iron and magnesium.

AMPHIBOLES   (hornblende) Calcium magnesium silicates, which may contain aluminium and iron.

PYROXENES   (augite) Calcium magnesium silicates, which may contain aluminium and iron.

OLIVINE   Magnesium iron silicates.

Different igneous rocks contain some or all of these and other minerals in varying proportions.

GRANITE contains quartz, felspar and mica, often with hornblende and pyroxene.

BASALT contains felspar, pyroxenes (augite) and often olivine.

RHYOLITES are similar to granite in mineralogical composition.

SYENITES do not contain quartz.

DIORITES and ANDESITES lack potassium minerals.

Accessory minerals are present in most igneous rocks to varying degrees, including

MAGNETITE Iron oxide Fe_3O_4

APATITE Calcium phosphate and fluoride

PYRITE Iron sulphide FeS_2

(Continued opposite)

2. Sedimentary Rocks

These are rocks formed by deposition of materials from water. The sediment may result from particles of suspended matter, including sand, silt and clay; it may come from dissolved substances which have undergone chemical change to form insoluble materials, such as calcium and magnesium bicarbonates which have been converted to insoluble carbonates.

Sedimentary rocks exist in a great variety of forms, depending upon the nature of the sediments from which they have arisen, and the treatment they have received. Some sedimentary rocks are cemented firmly; others are relatively weak and unconsolidated. Iron compounds often act as binding materials.

SANDSTONE This is chiefly quartz, the particles being cemented together with calcium carbonate, silicates and iron compounds. WHITE SANDSTONE has calcium carbonate, and RED SANDSTONE has iron oxide as binding material.

SHALES These are clays mixed with felspars, quartz and other minerals, which have been hardened by pressure. They were formed from sediments laid down in deep, still waters.

BOULDER CLAY was carried along and deposited by moving ice.

MARL AND CHALK These are essentially calcium carbonate, but contain clay, sand, magnesium carbonate and organic matter in varying quantities. They are, in effect, impure and unconsolidated forms of limestone.

LIMESTONE This rock is essentially calcium carbonate which has been formed by the deposition of the remains of marine organisms. It may contain varying amounts of other constituents, including iron oxides, silica, magnesium carbonate and clay. It dissolves readily in water containing dissolved carbon dioxide.

DOLOMITE is a calcium magnesium carbonate, which is harder than limestone itself.

3. Metamorphic Rocks

These are rocks which have resulted from the effects of heat and/or pressure on other rocks.

GNEISS is formed from granite; MARBLE from limestone; SLATE from clay shales.

C

nitrogen. But even this enormous tonnage is only a fraction of the amount that could be used with advantage to give the soil the nitrogen it needs.

In many Asian countries, the same earth has been providing food for centuries and getting insufficient in return. Its output is limited by the amount of nitrogen and other chemical nutrients it contains. This output often represents only a small proportion of the crops the earth could yield if it were properly supplied with food in the form of fertilizer.

The transition of agricultural ideas from traditional to scientific understanding is not an easy thing for the farmer to accept. Agriculture has always been an endeavour whose strength lay in experience and traditional skills. Crops are still very largely at the mercy of the weather and other factors beyond mere man's control, and the farmer must rely constantly upon his individual judgment to bring his crops safely to harvest. It is not easy, therefore, to persuade him to depart from procedures and techniques which he knows from experience will yield at least some result. An experiment that goes wrong can mean the loss of a year's income.

The introduction of chemical fertilizers into farming practice has inevitably been a gradual process. Even today, it is only in its infancy by relation with agriculture as a world-wide industry. There are still many people who will take sides in an imaginary struggle between "organic" fertilizers and "chemicals," without realizing that the plant foods supplied by each are fundamentally the same.

Role of Fertilizers

In modern techniques of soil management, chemicals and organic manures each have their part to play. For the supply of chemical plant foods is only one aspect of efficient cultivation. The soil is all-important as a medium in which the plant can grow, and good soil is more than just soil with an adequate amount of essential chemical foods in it. Good soil is soil that will in every sense encourage proper growth. It must be firm enough to allow the plant to support itself against the weather. It must be friable and porous to allow the air and moisture to circulate freely through it. And without an adequate amount of organic matter in it, no soil will meet these needs. Chemical fertilizers can never be a substitute for good husbandry; their use is part and parcel of it.

During the nineteenth century the population of the world was doubled. It is still growing at an alarming rate today; and the demand for food increases from year to year. The soil must be made to produce to maximum capacity if the peoples of the world are to be fed.

Even in a rich and fertile soil, the natural weathering and decay processes are too slow to meet the needs of the growing crop during successive annual cultivations. Inevitably, the point is reached where reserve supplies are used up, and the crop yield falls.

Experiments carried out at the experimental station established by Lawes at Rothamsted have shown dramatically what can happen. Wheat has been grown on the same strip of land for over a century. One strip has been fully manured, whereas the other has received nothing. The yield from the unmanured strip dropped quickly and remained steady at an average of about a third to a quarter of that from the manured strip.

The top foot-thick layer of a good soil will often contain more than five tons of nitrogen to the acre. This is more than enough to provide for the needs of a hundred crops of wheat. But most of this nitrogen is held in the form of complex substances in the organic matter of the soil. It is set free too slowly to sustain a rapid succession of crops.

To enable the soil to do its job efficiently under modern conditions, we have to provide it with additional supplies of chemical plant foods in the form of fertilizers.

SOIL PARENT MATERIALS

The mineral matter of a soil has not necessarily been derived from the rocks on which the soil is lying.

RESIDUAL MATERIALS

If the mineral particles forming the parent materials of a soil have come from the soil beneath, they are called residual materials. The soil is known as a *sedentary soil*.

The chemical nature of a sedentary soil is related to the parent rock on which it lies. Soils of this type are found usually where the land is flat, and conditions are such that the parent material is not subjected to the effects of moving water, ice or wind.

TRANSPORTED MATERIALS

Often, the parent material of a soil has been moved from its place of origin.

1. **Water-moved Materials**

Alluvial deposits are those which have been left by moving water, including rivers and streams. The soils on these deposits often show little or no modification of the material by soil-forming processes. The deposited material (alluvium) is sorted by the water according to the size of the particles. The large particles of sand and gravel are deposited first, followed by the silt and then the clay.

Alluvial soils are often fertile, and support flourishing agricultures. They include the flood plains and deltas of great rivers like the Nile and Mississippi.

Lacustrine Deposits are materials deposited from the water of fresh water lakes created by melting glaciers. Many such lakes were formed during the Ice Ages, and as they subsequently dried up, the sediment on the lake floor became the parent material of a soil.

Marine Deposits are materials deposited on the sea-bed, for example near the mouths of rivers. Changes in the level of the land have lifted the bed, leaving the deposits to become the parent material of a soil.

2. **Wind-moved Materials**

Aeolian (eolian) materials are those that have been carried from their place of origin by the wind. Sand dunes are examples of aeolian deposits. *Loess* is a wind-borne material consisting predominantly of silt, but including some sand and clay.

(*continued opposite*)

SOIL PARENT MATERIALS

(*continued*)

3. Ice-moved Materials

During past Ice-Ages, sheets of ice moved like huge bulldozers over the earth's land surface. As the ice melted, water carried away much of the finer material pushed along by the ice, leaving the rocks and stones and larger particles.

Moraines, in the form of hills of stones, were left at the edge of the ice as the sheet moved forward.

Till Plains were created as the ice melted faster than it was moving forward, leaving its burden of rock material in the form of a smooth, flat plain.

4. Gravity-moved Materials

Colluvial deposits are formed where rocks and stones have been moved from their place of origin by the force of gravity. They are common in mountainous districts.

5. Cumulose Materials

These are the deposits formed by accumlation of plant remains in conditions where the normal processes of decay cannot take place. *Peat* is a cumulose material in which the form of the plant matter can still be seen; *muck* is a material in which the original matter can no longer be distinguished.

4

The Living Soil

Over the entire land surface of the earth, the soil is still being formed and modified by the weather. New mineral particles are slowly being split from the parent rock, reaching the soil as stones. Under the effects of heat and cold, the stones expand and contract, splitting into smaller pieces as time goes on. They become gravel, the gravel turns to sand and the sand to silt.

Within these little particles are imprisoned elements that were present in the original bedrock. Some are bound together so tightly that they remain unchanged through thousands of years. Others are more easily modified by the chemical influences of the soil into simpler chemicals that become food for growing plants.

As the particles break into smaller and smaller pieces, they become more easily affected by their surroundings. The total area of surface increases as the rock breaks into finer particles. And the greater the surface, the more readily can weathering bring about chemical changes in the minerals forming the rock. Between them, the air and water that permeate the soil can muster a formidable array of chemicals to attack the soil particles. Oxygen, carbon dioxide and acids formed by lightning are brought to the soil by the air; water in the soil is often strongly acid and can corrode and decompose many of the mineral substances in the rock.

Clay

In the upper layers of the soil, the chemical changes caused by air- and water-borne chemicals are intensely active. Soluble substances are formed, many of them containing the essential elements needed by the plants. But from the hard igneous rocks come the superfine particles of solid matter that we describe as clay. These particles, less than one twelve-thousandth of an inch in diameter, are insoluble in water, but they have many of the characteristics of dissolved substances. Clay particles, for example, will remain floating in water without settling out. They can be carried along by water from place to place, almost as though they were dissolved in it.

The particles of gravel and sand in a soil are simply pieces of the parent rock, but the tiny particles of clay are the result of chemical changes that have taken place through the weathering of soil particles by air and water. Although they are not dissolved in the soil water, as are other chemicals liberated from the rock, the clay particles are chemically extremely active, and they play a supremely important role in feeding the plant.

Clay particles are not only incredibly small, but have a loosely built laminated structure as well. The total surface of a clay particle is immense, and on this surface a sequence of interchanges between the soil elements is continually going on. A cubic foot of clay has several acres of surface on its particles.

Particles of clay are charged with electricity; they carry a negative charge, and tend to repel each other. This helps them to float around in water without collecting together into aggregates that would settle out. But the negative electric charge serves another purpose too; it attracts the positively charged particles of elements such as calcium and potassium which are present in the water of the soil. These elements cling to the immense surface of the clay particles, and resist being washed out by the rainwater flowing through the soil.

When the root hairs of the plant lie close alongside the particles of clay, they breathe out carbon dioxide generated during cell respiration. This dissolves in the soil water forming an acid, and the acid is able to release the food elements held against the surface of the clay particle. In this way, clay acts as a collector of essential nutrients for the plant, holding them until the roots can seek them out.

Soil Texture

The nature of any soil is determined very largely by the proportion of particles of different sizes that it contains. The largest particles are the stones, followed by the gravel, sand, silt, and clay, in that order of diminishing size. Arbitrary size limits have been fixed by soil scientists so that any particle can be classified in one or other of these categories.

The relative proportions of the three categories – sand, silt and clay – determine the texture (see page 274).

Often, three-quarters or more of the particles consist of gravel, sand or silt. Most of these particles are simply bits of rock which weather slowly to provide the clay and soluble food chemicals on which the plants depend.

Soil Profile

The true personality of a soil depends on more than the characteristics of its surface layer. Soil extends from the surface to the bedrock. It varies greatly at different depths, and the lower levels of the soil influence the fertility of the soil as a whole.

Most of the weathering effects take place in the surface layer, where air and water can combine to attack the mineral particles, and bacterial activity is at its height. But when rainfall is heavy, the soluble chemicals and the fine clay particles may be washed down into the lower layers of the soil. Some of the soluble chemicals are carried away by drainage water, the clay being filtered out in the subsoil.

THE SMALLER THE PARTICLES, THE GREATER
THE SURFACE AREA

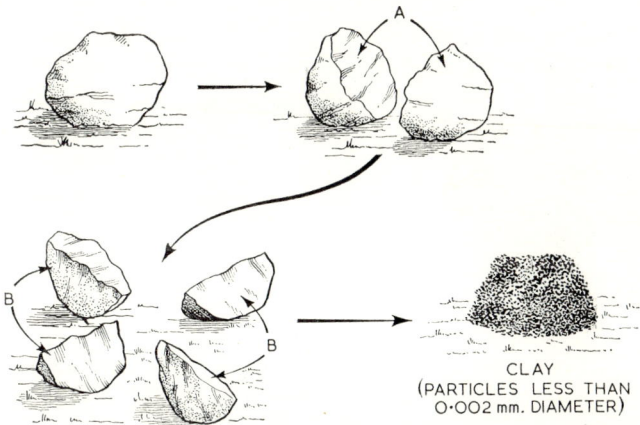

CLAY
(PARTICLES LESS THAN
0·002 mm. DIAMETER)

If a rock is split in two, the surface area is increased by the two areas marked A. If these two pieces are split again, the new surfaces marked B are added. As the subdivision is continued, more and more surface is added in this way.

If subdivision is continued until the particles are of diameter less than 0.002 mm diameter, the rock will be converted into particles equivalent in size to particles of clay. The total surface area of a spadeful of clay particles may extend to several acres.

This continual leaching in humid climates creates a changing pattern in the soil at different depths. On the top is the highly weathered material from which the rain has washed soluble chemicals and fine clay particles. Below this lies a layer of less-weathered soil where much of the clay is often deposited. Still farther down is slightly weathered soil similar to the parent rock. The pattern of layers created in this way is called the *soil profile* (see page 66).

The depth of soil from surface to bedrock varies greatly from one part of the world to another. On a rocky, wind-

c*

A SOIL PROFILE

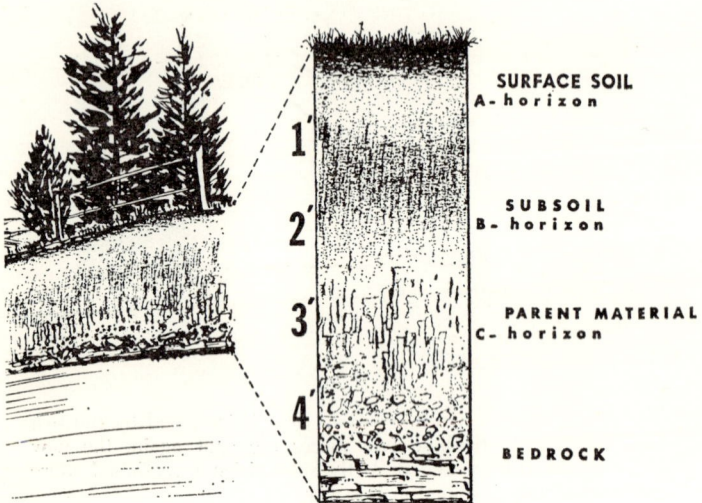

SURFACE SOIL
A-horizon

SUBSOIL
B-horizon

PARENT MATERIAL
C-horizon

BEDROCK

If a hole is dug in almost any soil, a series of horizontal soil layers of varying thicknesses will be seen. These layers are very noticeable, for example, in road cuttings.

The soil layers or *horizons* (see page 239) differ from one another in such properties as colour, texture, structure and other physical and chemical characteristics. Together, they make up the soil *profile* (see page 237).

A soil profile consists usually of three major divisions, designated as A, B and C horizons.

TOPSOIL

The A horizon includes the upper part of the profile in which life is most active. This horizon, which commonly includes the ploughed or dug layer, is the most productive due to its normally higher organic matter content and crumbly structure. It is the gardener's "topsoil".

(*Continued opposite*)

A SOIL PROFILE (*continued*)

The topsoil is usually darker in colour than the lower layers of soil, largely owing to the humus it contains. It is teeming with life, and is the home of countless millions of bacteria, fungi, protozoa, insects, worms and other forms of vegetable and animal life.

The topsoil is the layer in which weathering and decay are most active, producing the nutrient chemicals that are needed by plants. This is the most fertile region of the soil, with which the farmer and gardener are most concerned.

Rainwater percolates into the topsoil, dissolving many of the chemical nutrients that have formed naturally, or have been added as fertilizer. Carbon dioxide liberated by roots and decaying humus tend to make the soil water acid, increasing its power of attacking and dissolving minerals.

As water flows through the topsoil, it carries away dissolved nutrient salts, together with lime and very fine particles of clay and humus. The loss of lime results in an acid topsoil, even where the soil is lying above chalk, limestone and other "lime" materials.

SUBSOIL

This is the gardener's name for the B horizon, the layer that lies immediately beneath the topsoil. It is often plastic and sticky when wet, containing clay which has been washed from the topsoil. It is hard and tough when dry.

The subsoil is often coloured red or yellow by iron oxides which have been washed from the topsoil, and there is little organic matter to darken it. Salts and particles washed from above will sometimes form hard layers which resist penetration by plant roots, and prevent water flowing deeper into the soil. These 'pans' should be broken up when soil is being prepared for plants, and every effort made to loosen the subsoil, making it penetrable by plant roots. It should not, however, be mixed with top-soil, except in very small amounts at a time; it dilutes the rich topsoil with lower grade material.

PARENT MATERIAL

This layer, the C horizon, is the partly-weathered rock from which the soil above has formed. It may result from breakdown of the bedrock on which the soil rests, or it may have been carried to its present site by wind, water or ice (see page 60). It contains little humus, and is infertile. It should not be mixed with the topsoil during cultivation.

swept outcrop, there will be no soil at all; in Arctic regions, the soil is often an inch or two deep and only a few thousand years old; in tropical Africa, where weathering is intense and temperature changes are high, the soil may lie in a layer forty feet thick.

In an average British or American soil, the surface layer may be less than a foot or two in depth; the second layer, the subsoil, may be up to two feet deep; and the third, lightly weathered layer as much as five feet deep.

The rock particles within these different layers are undergoing the slow, steady breakdown that releases supplies of mineral elements. Only one of the soil-borne elements needed by the plant is lacking from the minerals forming the rock. This is the element nitrogen; and for nitrogen, the plants depend mainly upon the living creatures of the soil.

Life and Decay

Life in the soil is part of Nature's all-embracing cycle of life and death. Into the soil go the remains of animals and plants that have lived and died. These remains sustain the feverish, frantic round of life in the soil itself.

When anything dies, the substance from which it was made begins to decay. Complex substances that formed the living body of the plant or animal are changed. Gradually, they disintegrate and disappear, returning in the form of simple chemicals to the soil and air from which they came.

Decay is not a spontaneous chemical change. It is the result of an attack upon the dead material by myriads of living things. The soil is thronging with micro-organisms of many kinds which depend for their source of food on matter that has lived and died. They attack it and digest it, breaking it down and making its constituents available once more in the form of simple chemicals. A fertile soil is usually one that supports a vigorous microbe population.

This cycle of life and death in the soil is a continuous

WEATHERING.
FREEZING AND THAWING

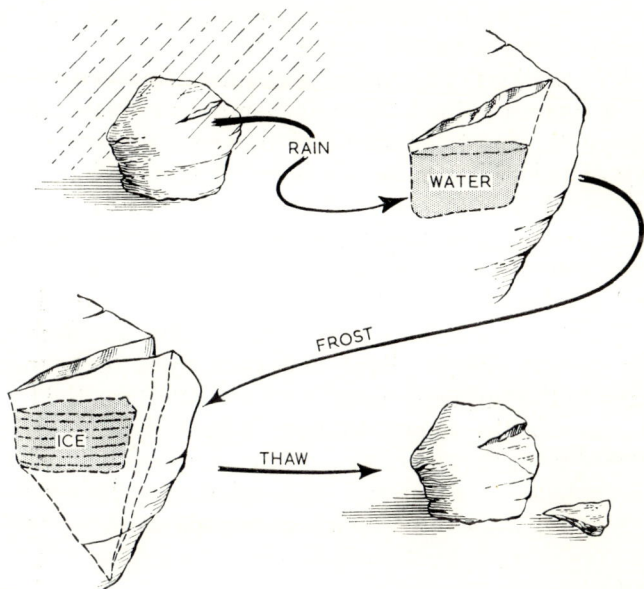

RAIN

WATER

FROST

ICE

THAW

Above: Rainwater fills cracks in the rocks. If the water freezes, it expands, forming a wedge of ice that pushes the walls of the crack apart. When the thaw comes, a flake of rock falls away to the ground.

Right: The effect of freezing and thawing may be shown by filling a jar with water, capping it tightly and allowing the water to freeze. Expansion during freezing breaks the glass walls of the jar.

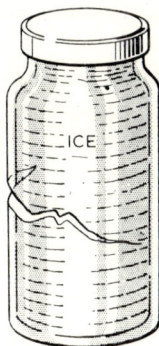

ICE

one. From atmospheric carbon dioxide, water and simple soil chemicals the plant builds up its complex body substances. These return to the soil when the plant dies, or are used as food by animals, returning inevitably to the soil in the form of animal remains. In the soil, through the attack of millions of microbes, this once-living matter can become again the food of new generations of plants. Bacteria are the most important of these soil microbes. An ounce of soil will often be the home of 1,300 million bacteria, together with some 30 million moulds and fungi. The remains of these micro-organisms are, themselves, important sources of plant food.

In humid regions, most of the bacteria live in the layer of soil between one and three inches below the surface. They do not like the light, but they want to be near enough to the surface to get the air and moisture, the food and warmth they need to live. Where the ground is sheltered from the direct rays of the sun, they will collect an inch below the surface. In sun-baked soil they will congregate two or three inches farther down.

Humus

From the sugars and starches and cellulose in the plant or animal remains, bacteria draw the energy that gives them life. Carbon dioxide that was used to provide so much of the bulk of the living plant is liberated into the soil and makes its way back into the air above. When anything dies, microbes attack the dead matter, which begins to lose its original physical form, turning slowly into the dark material we call humus. Humus is a halfway stage between the substances of life and the simple chemicals into which all living matter is eventually resolved. Humus is a vitally important constituent in any soil. It can come only from matter that has lived, and as the food of living organisms in the soil it brings life to a soil that would otherwise be dead.

WEATHERING.

EXPANSION AND CONTRACTION

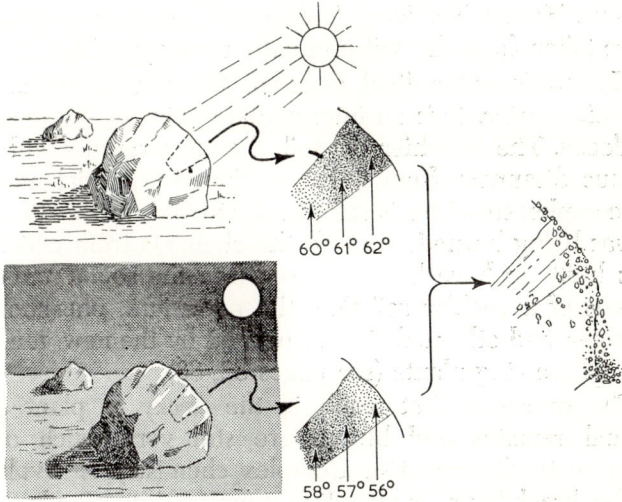

Above: During the day, the sun heats the surface of rocks (*top*). Most rocks are poor conductors of heat, and the surface reaches a higher temperature than the layers below. This causes unequal expansion of the rock at different depths.

At night, the rock cools (*bottom*), heat escaping more rapidly from the surface than from the layers beneath. This causes unequal contraction.

The effect of these unequal forces is to weaken and break up the surface of the rock, which crumbles into particles.

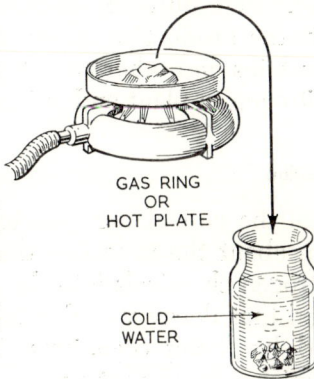

Right: The effectiveness of this weathering process can be demonstrated by a simple experiment. A small piece of limestone heated in a tin, and then dropped into cold water, will break into pieces.

The other soil materials, the sand and clay and stones, all come from parent rocks in the earth's crust. Not so the humus. Humus has lived. And in it are food elements that were taken from the soil originally to support life.

Humus is not a final stage in the decomposition of organic matter. It is an intermediate point in the process of decay. The healthier the soil, the more rapidly will the humus disappear from it by continued bacterial attack. Its complex structure is steadily destroyed, just as though it was being burned, until all the elements from which it was built up have been released into the soil. From the humus of a healthy soil flow the potassium, phosphorus, nitrogen and other substances needed by the new generation of growing plants (see pages 82, 83).

The processes that result in the decay of plant and animal remains and humus are still very much of a mystery to the scientist. Complex chemistry is involved in the breakdown of once-living matter into simple substances that serve as food for plants. In most cultivated soils, humus is of particular importance as a source of much-needed nitrogen chemicals. Bacteria play a vital role in the production of simple nitrogen chemicals from the proteins and other complex substances which contain the nitrogen in plant and animal bodies.

Nitrification

Until the end of the nineteenth century, little was known about the processes that enable humus to release its nitrogen chemicals into the soil. But in 1873, scientists showed that decay was due to biological activity; it was caused by living organisms. Experiments were carried out which proved that nitrate production stopped when the soil cooled below 37° F. or was heated above 87° F. Between these temperatures, micro-organisms were able to maintain their activity. Also, antiseptic substances stopped

TERRACING

PLATE 1

Above : Cultivation of steeply-sloping ground may cause serious erosion unless special techniques are used to hold the soil in place.

Below : Rock-walled bench terraces in Lebanon have been in use for thousands of years. Construction of terraces of this type today would cost as much as £2,000 ($6,000) per acre. Such expensive methods of protecting land are practicable only where people have no other land on which to raise their food.

THE
PLOUGH

PLATE 2

This crude wooden plough was in use in the Mediterranean regions before 6000 B.C.

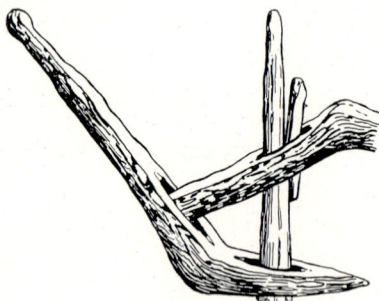

For thousands of years, the plough remained basically unchanged. In mediaeval times it was drawn by oxen, and had an iron share – *The Science Museum, London.*

The modern plough is mechanized, and is commonly drawn by tractor.

But the crude wooden plough is still used today in some parts of the world, just as it was thousands of years ago. This one is being used on the Andean Plateau, Ecuador – *F.A.O.*

PLATE 3

PLATE 4

CRUMB STRUCTURE

These two samples of soil were taken only 25 feet apart. The one on the left is from a field in which intensive cultivation has removed much of the humus that held soil particles together; the sample on the right came from an undisturbed fence row, showing the crumb structure that has been built up in the soil. The fence-row soil absorbs moisture 20 times faster than the cultivated soil.

Below : The crumb structure of this cultivated soil has been damaged by intensive cultivation, and the topsoil is being carried away by water flowing down the slope. A layer of soil 8 inches deep has been removed – *U.S.D.A.*

the production of nitrates in the soil; they killed the micro-organisms causing decay.

As experiments continued, it was found that nitrates were only the final stage in a succession of chemical changes. The first simple nitrogen chemical to appear from the decaying humus was ammonia. This was then turned into nitrites, which were changed in their turn into nitrates. Each of these chemical changes is controlled by different bacteria. In healthy soil, all the necessary bacteria are there, and nitrate production, or "nitrification," can go on steadily so long as there is humus on which the bacteria can feed.

Although ammonia is normally the first stage in the release of nitrogen from humus, it is rarely present as such in the soil. The ammonia-producing bacteria work more slowly than those which carry out the changes from ammonia to nitrates. Conversion of humus nitrogen to ammonia may, in fact, take years. No sooner does ammonia appear than it is grabbed and changed into nitrates by the nitrifying bacteria.

These natural processes of nitrate production will operate efficiently only under certain conditions, when the whole process from humus to nitrates can be complete in a few weeks. The ammonia-making and nitrifying bacteria must be present in the soil in sufficient numbers. The soil must not be so cold as to inactivate the bacteria, nor so hot as to destroy them. There must be sufficient moisture for the bacteria, and plenty of air. Also, some chemical must be present in the soil to neutralize the acids that are produced as the bacteria multiply. This is a job we normally entrust to lime, which acts as a stimulant to nitrogen production from humus in the soil.

Effect of Soil Conditions

If the soil can fulfil these conditions, its humus will be an efficient nitrogen provider, and the soil has every en-

WEATHERING. CHEMICAL ACTION

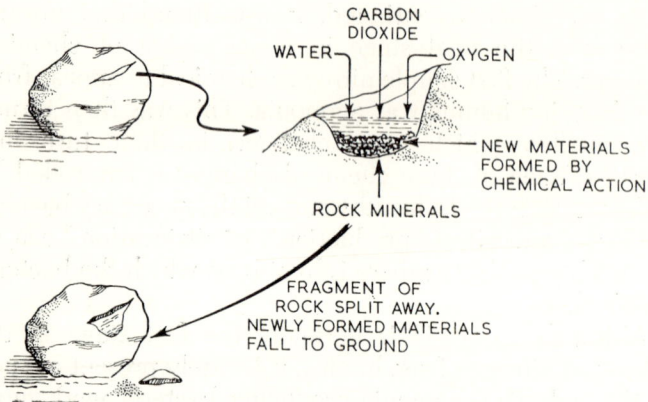

Many rocks are attacked chemically by oxygen, carbon dioxide, water and other constituents of the air and soil. New materials are formed, and the pressure exerted by these in cracks and confined spaces may break away portions of the rock.

In the soil itself, this chemical attack continues. Carbon dioxide is released by plant roots, and by decaying organic matter. The gas dissolves in water to form carbonic acid, which attacks rocks such as limestone and marble. New substances are formed, and particles of resistant material are released from the rock.

---

couragement to produce in plenty. If, on the other hand, the soil is unable to meet the needs of its microbe population, it will tend to be infertile; nitrogen will be locked away inside the humus as securely as the potassium and phosphorus and other minerals are held inside their parent rocks.

Waterlogged soil, for example, cannot maintain its nitrogen output, as the bacteria are denied their supplies of air. A swampy soil will often contain a lot of humus. In the absence of air, the humus cannot undergo its nitrification process. And, for all the good it does in the waterlogged soil, it might as well not be there.

Nitrification rarely take place in subsoils, where the particles are tightly compacted and compressed, and air cannot penetrate. Even when a subsoil is turned over and cultivated, it will take time to establish a healthy bacterial life that will bring to the soil the fertility needed for good crop cultivation. Clay subsoils, in particular, are difficult to aerate; skilful cultivation is needed to change the dead clay into a healthy living soil.

Cultivation of pasture land tends to increase the natural rate of humus decay in the soil. Cultivated land normally contains less humus than similar land alongside it which has been left as pasture. The aeration of the soil which follows cultivation encourages nitrification bacteria. Humus decomposes more quickly, and the ground becomes richer in available nitrogen.

For the same reason, sandy soils lose their humus faster than clays. Plants in sandy soils respond more rapidly to added manure. Its food elements are released quickly.

Warmth will stimulate the fertility of a soil by encouraging bustling activity amongst its microscopic inhabitants. Cold winds blowing over a growing crop can slow its growth almost to a standstill. The bacteria of the soil, which have been plying the crop roots with nitrates from the humus, will slow down until their surroundings become warm again. The effect can often be seen as a colour change in the crop; the fresh green of healthy, lush growth will turn yellow as a cool breeze blows over the field, cutting down nitrogen supplies from the discouraged bacteria.

In the spring, bacterial activity is often low in soil which has cooled during the winter. Yet it is in the spring that plants need a supply of nitrogen to sustain a vigorous early growth. Nitrate fertilizer can have a remarkable effect in early spring, giving the plants the nitrogen food they need to tide them over until the earth warms up and the humus bacteria can settle down to work.

SOIL TEXTURE

The basic constituents of any soil are the mineral particles that have been formed by weathering of parent rocks. These may range in size from stones and gravels to particles so small that they cannot be seen even through the most powerful optical microscope.

In general, the mineral particles of a soil do not change rapidly, and they can be regarded as a near-permanent feature. The relative proportions of particles of different sizes determine the *texture* of the soil.

In modern scientific terms, the texture of a soil is defined by measuring the proportions of particles falling within three size-ranges, which are described as *sand*, *silt* and *clay*.

There are twelve textural class names in common use, and each one indicates that the proportions of sand, silt and clay fall within a certain range (see page 273).

Summer Warmth

During summer, when the soil is warm, nitrate production will be at its height in a moist, healthy soil. If the summer is too hot and dry, lack of moisture will slow up the bacteria. By autumn, there will often be a good store of nitrates waiting to be used. But much of this will be washed out in the heavy rains of winter unless an autumn follow-up crop is planted to make use of the nitrate before it is lost.

Any treatment that loosens up the soil will stimulate nitrogen production by improving the air supplies needed by the bacteria. The more a soil is cultivated and stirred up, the better will its useful bacteria thrive. Summer cultivation of a soil is a first-rate way of increasing nitrate production in preparation for an autumn crop.

Summer crops which involve a lot of soil movement can improve soil fertility. Cultivation of a turnip crop, for example, requires a thorough working of the soil. Though turnips need plenty of nitrogen, they will grow happily without demanding additional supplies. Provided that the soil has adequate amounts of humus in it, nitrogen foods will be released by high-powered bacterial activity that follows the working of the soil which bears the turnip crop.

Though nitrification bacteria are so essential in providing plants with the nitrogen they need, they may compete with crop plants for the food available in the soil. Fresh manure or plant residues ploughed into the soil will often cause a temporary lowering of soil fertility. Bacteria attack the dead material with feverish activity, flourishing and multiplying at a great rate. But these bacteria are themselves plants, and they make sudden demands on the soil for supplies of some of the foods they need. In the presence of freshly ploughed manure or compost the soil may be denuded of some of its food constituents.

The effect is only temporary. As decay goes on, the bacteria settle down to a more humdrum existence and lose their early enthusiasm. In due course, they release more plant food than they are using, and the nitrogen and other materials of the manure and dead bacteria are fed to the growing crop. For this reason, it is best to use rotted manure or compost, rather than fresh material. The first ecstatic bacterial excitement has died down by the time the manure is mixed into the soil, and there is no danger of competition between bacteria and crop.

Nitrogen-fixing Bacteria

When vegetation is allowed to grow naturally on the land, the amount of nitrogen in the soil often increases over the years. In all soils, there are bacteria which can fix atmospheric nitrogen and release it ultimately in the soil as nitrates. Two species of nitrogen-fixing bacteria have been found in soils from all parts of the world. *Clostridium pastorianum* works in the absence of air and can be isolated from pond mud. *Azotobacter* likes a supply of air and inhabits ordinary soil.

These nitrogen-fixing bacteria need a supply of sugary materials as part of their diet, and they depend on other micro-organisms to provide these for them from humus. They prefer their nitrogen in the form of simple salts, as other plants do: they will only make use of atmospheric nitrogen if "fixed" nitrogen is not available. The nitrogen is stored in the body of the bacterium as proteins or other body substance. It is then either used as food by attacking protozoa or released into the soil when the bacterium dies; the nitrogen is then turned into ammonia or nitrates by the micro-organisms which do the same in the case of higher plants.

Where plenty of organic matter is available, *Azotobacter* will flourish and fix its own nitrogen from the air. *Azotobacter* is responsible for the steady increase in nitrogen fertility of many soils carrying natural vegetation. The entire remains of the growing plants are returned to the soil, providing plenty of humus. In the soil, *Azotobacter* draws sugary materials from the humus and fixes its nitrogen supplies from the air. The nitrogen resources of the soil are increased from year to year.

If land of this sort is cultivated, potential humus is carried away in the form of the growing crop, and *Azotobacter's* work is restricted. That is why virgin ground will build up its nitrogen content much more than a patch of the same ground which is being cultivated. *Azotobacter* does its best work on soil that is left alone for a year or two.

Although *Azotobacter's* contribution of fixed nitrogen is not spectacular, it is of very great importance to the world. These soil bacteria can fix as much as 20 pounds of nitrogen to the acre every year; under favourable conditions they will provide half of the nitrogen needs of a cultivated crop.

Leguminous Plants

The ancient Carthaginians and Egyptians knew that by growing certain crops – peas, beans, alfalfa – they could improve the fertility of their soil. These crops, instead of depleting the food resources of the soil, appeared to increase them. But it was not until some two thousand years later that scientists discovered how these so-called leguminous plants performed their useful trick.

In 1886, two German chemists showed that leguminous plants could flourish in soil containing supplies of potassium and phosphate but no nitrogen. They grew to maturity, obtaining somehow the nitrogen needed for their proteins and other living substances. It seemed as though the plants were able to use nitrogen gas direct from the air.

In a sense this proved to be the answer. But it was not the plant itself that was doing the job; it was a species of micro-organism which was able to absorb nitrogen gas and "fix" it in the form of simple chemicals. This organism is called *Rhizobium*. It makes its home in little wartlike nodules which it builds on the roots of leguminous plants. In its ability to fix atmospheric nitrogen, *Rhizobium* is similar to *Azotobacter*. But it does not live a free life in the soil. Inside its nodules, the nitrogen-fixing bacterium sets up a happy relationship with the plant. Each works to the benefit of the other. The crop plant supplies the bacteria with sugary materials that they need as food; in return, the bacteria absorb atmospheric nitrogen and turn it into nitrogen chemicals, some of which are handed over to the plant and some released into the soil.

As they feed on the sugary foods provided by the plant, absorbing nitrogen and turning it into chemicals, most of the bacteria grow fat and lazy. They develop into oversized, degenerate bacteria called bacteroids, which are digested and absorbed by the crop plant. In this way, the plant obtains the nitrogenous substances that it needs. Some of the bacteria, however, remain small and tough. When the plant roots and the nodules decay, these bacteria are released into the soil ready to inoculate the next crop. If necessary, they will survive in the soil for several years.

Inoculation with Nodule Bacteria

Scientists have grown leguminous plants in sterile soil containing insufficient nitrogen chemicals. As the plants reach the point of nitrogen starvation, they can be revived and will continue growing if a watery extract of ordinary cultivated soil is provided. In this extract are bacteria which can set up house in nodules on the plant roots. Soon they are manufacturing the nitrogen chemicals that the plant needs, and in return are being plied with sugary foods. The activity of these bacteria can be stimulated by adding sugars direct to the soil.

When long-standing natural soil is broken up, it is often short of nodule-forming bacteria. This applies particularly to peaty soils, which are full of acid humus. When soils like these are being reclaimed for cultivation, they are often inoculated with nitrogen-fixing bacteria. This can be done by scattering supplies of cultivated soil onto the virgin ground, or by supplying an extract containing the bacteria themselves. Farmers in the Netherlands have been using this technique for centuries, having found out by experience that soil which has grown legumes can pass its fertility on to other soils. Methods have been developed for inoculating legume seed with root bacteria.

Like other soil bacteria, these nitrogen-fixing nodule bacteria normally dislike an acid soil. Lime, which will neutralize the acids, is a useful stimulant on soil that has become too acid for bacteria to flourish.

The value of a leguminous crop as a nitrogen supplier to the soil depends upon its fate after it has been grown.

Much of the nitrogen fixed by the bacteria is in the stem and leaves of the plant itself. If the crop is harvested, a large part of the nitrogen is removed, and the land that has carried the crop is richer only by the amount of nitrogen left in the stubble and roots and that which the bacteria released into the soil.

If clover or alfalfa, on the other hand, are grown as green manure and ploughed into the soil, the nitrogen fixed by the nodule is returned to the soil and becomes available for future crops.

Individual Strains

The amount of nitrogen fixed by nodule bacteria can be impressive. A four-ton clover crop will add more than a hundred pounds of nitrogen to the acre. With some legumes, the amount is almost twice as much. Nodule bacteria exist in several strains. Each strain has its preferred leguminous plant, though some are less particular than others. The nodule bacteria of beans will inoculate peas. But they are not keen on lupins. Similarly, clover bacteria are of little use to alfalfa.

It is possible that, given time, strains of these bacteria will adapt themselves to a leguminous plant they normally ignore. But it may take several years for the bacteria accustomed to alfalfa, for example, to learn to live to mutual advantage with clover.

Inoculation of a field of leguminous plants with its appropriate bacteria may not show any immediate effect. Two or three successive crops may be needed before the bacteria have settled down in sufficient strength to be of real value in increasing the fixed nitrogen of the soil.

The ability of certain regions to grow good crops of leguminous plants is often thought to be due to climate, whereas in fact it can be caused by a rich population of nodule-forming bacteria in the soil.

HUMUS

WHAT IS HUMUS?

Humus is a descriptive term for organic matter which has undergone partial decomposition in the soil. Humus is not a definite chemical compound, but is a complex mixture of materials. It represents a part-way stage in the breakdown of organic matter into simple chemicals.

Humus will commonly contain up to 45% of lignin, a material from the cell walls of plants, with some 30% of protein. The rest is made up of fats, waxes, carbohydrates and other materials.

HOW IS HUMUS FORMED?

The decay of organic matter is brought about by bacteria and other micro-organisms in the soil. When plant or animal remains fall to the soil, they are attacked by hordes of micro-organisms which draw on the organic matter as a source of food.

Bacteria, which play a major role in the decay of organic matter, are tiny plants. And like other plants, they require supplies of essential nutrients including nitrogen, phosphorus and potassium. As they attack fresh organic matter, they will draw on the soil for supplies of nutrient elements.

When fresh organic matter is added to the soil, it may be depleted of essential nutrients by bacteria which attack their food material. This withdrawal of available plant foods by bacteria (which are themselves plants) may result in a setback to a crop growing in the soil.

This is a temporary effect of adding fresh organic matter to the soil, as the bacteria will eventually die and release the material of their bodies as nutrient chemicals. The effect may be avoided by using well-rotted manure and compost, in which the initial decomposition has already taken place, or by supplying readily-available nitrogen with the fresh material.

The vigorous attack of bacteria transforms the mass of organic matter into the partly-decomposed material known as humus. If the soil is well aerated, the humus will continue to decay, but more slowly than it did initially. Eventually, its constituent elements are released as simple chemicals which the plant may use as nutrients. Humus thus acts as a store of nitrogen, phosphorus, potassium and other essential plant foods which are released steadily into the soil.

If there is insufficient air, as in a waterlogged soil, the decomposition of organic material stops at an early stage. An acid form of humus is produced, which does not readily undergo further decay. This is the type of material found in swamps and peat bogs. It occurs widely in the moorlands of upland Britain.

(*Continued opposite*)

HOW MUCH HUMUS?

A waterlogged soil may be almost 100% organic matter, for example in the form of peat. A sand dune, on the other hand, may contain no organic matter at all.

A typical cultivated soil may contain about 5% of humus. The better cultivated it is, the more rapidly will the humus decay as bacteria flourish in the well-aerated soil.

For the same reason, sandy soils will lose their humus more rapidly than clay soils. Organic manures thus act more rapidly on sandy soils, but need supplies more regularly to keep them in good heart.

Lime, too, will encourage bacteria, and speed up the decay of humus in the soil.

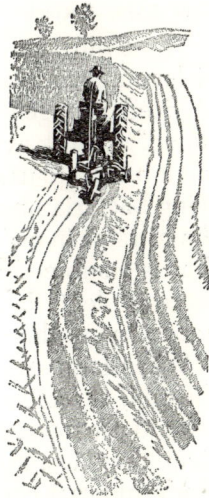

WHAT HUMUS DOES

Humus plays a vital role in shaping both the physical and chemical characteristics of the soil.

* It acts as a storehouse of plant nutrient elements, including nitrogen, phosphorus and potassium, which are released slowly but steadily into the soil.

* It is a colloidal material, and it holds many essential elements on the surface of its particles, releasing them to plant roots as a result of ion-exchange processes.

* It absorbs moisture like a sponge, adding to the water-holding capacity of the soil.

* It helps to build and sustain a desirable soil structure, loosening clay soils and binding the particles of sandy soils to form aggregates which resist erosion, facilitate cultivation and tillage, improve drainage and aeration.

Denitrifying Bacteria

These nitrogen-fixing bacteria in the soil and in the roots of leguminous plants are continually stocking up supplies of fixed nitrogen in the soil. But there is an "awkward squad" at work as well, feeding on fixed nitrogen and turning it back into useless atmospheric nitrogen. These denitrifying bacteria operate especially in acid soils. They attack the nitrates in order to supply themselves with the oxygen that is combined with the nitrogen in these chemicals. If there is plenty of air available in the soil, the bacteria are happy to use the oxygen in it, leaving the nitrates alone.

When large quantities of manure or nitrates are used in the soil, shortage of air will encourage denitrifying bacteria to use nitrate oxygen, and crop returns will be smaller than they would have been on smaller nitrate rations. Under normal conditions, the soil is rarely rich enough in organic matter for this to happen; nor is it so sealed off from supplies of air.

Sterilization

When crops are grown intensively, the bacterial population of the soil can be controlled by sterilization. Nurserymen have found that they can double their crops by heating the soil in steam for two hours before using it. Plants grown in this soil will have three or four times as much nitrogen in them as plants grown in unsterilized soil.

Experiments carried out on soil sterilization have shown that the steam destroys most of the bacteria, leaving only a few particularly tough spores, or "seeds." Within a few days after sterilization, these bacterial spores can multiply until the soil is carrying more than five times its normal bacterial population. Sterilization has destroyed the protozoa, amoebae and other larger organisms which normally prey on the soil bacteria and help to keep their numbers down, and has killed harmful bacteria that cause plant diseases.

HUMUS-MAKERS

Almost anything that lives, or has lived, is a source of organic material that can produce humus in the soil.

ANIMAL MANURE
The fertile black soils of old, well-cultivated gardens owe their granular, easily-worked structure to the use of ample quantities of animal manure or compost. Nowadays, supplies of good manure are difficult to obtain, but they are worth their weight in gold to anyone with an interest in the soil. Information on the preparation and use of animal manure is given on page 190.

Farmyard manure is best for sandy soils, and stable manure for clayey soils. Both are suitable for general use.

GREEN MANURE
Green manures are crops grown specifically to serve as a source of organic material for the soil (see page 197). The crop is dug or ploughed in, and as it rots it provides humus. Mustard is commonly used for this purpose; it grows quickly, and seed is cheap. The seed is sown in August, and the crop is ready for turning into the soil in the autumn. Green manuring of this type is especially useful in sandy or chalky soils.

PEAT
Peat is partly rotted organic matter which has accumulated in waterlogged soil. It is spread on the surface of the soil in a layer about 1 inch thick, and dug or ploughed in during the autumn. The main benefit of peat lies in its ability to hold moisture.

HOP MANURE
The basis of this is spent hops, a waste material from brewing. Mixed with fertilizers to form a balanced plant food, the material forms an organic fertilizer which is popular with gardeners. It is dug into the top spit during late winter or spring, at the rate of a handful (about 4 – 6 oz.) per square yard. Areas in which plants are growing may be top-dressed with hop manure at the rate of 2 to 4 oz. per square yard.

Hop manure is used as a mulch for roses, fruit trees and shrubs, using 2 to 6 oz. per plant, depending on size.

COMPOST
See page 194.

Nitrifying bacteria appear to be particularly susceptible to destruction during sterilization. When the soil bacteria are flourishing again, there is usually a build-up in the concentration of ammonia, as there are not sufficient nitrifying bacteria to bring about the final stages in the nitrification process, the change from ammonia into nitrites and then nitrates. Plants growing in sterilized soil, however, are able to take up the nitrogen they need in the form of ammonia.

Fungi

Although bacteria will often outnumber fungi by as much as fifty to one, fungi play an essential and often specialized role in the round of life in the soil. Fungi can live under conditions that bacteria do not like. They will thrive in the high temperatures generated inside a compost heap, breaking down the dead material into simple substances. In the acid soil of the forest floor, fungi will come to an arrangement with the trees. In exchange for a supply of ready-made sugars, they will provide the tree roots with the nitrogenous substances they need.

Without the micro-organisms that live in this world of putrescence and decay in the soil, higher forms of life would not be able to continue on earth. Dead material would accumulate and litter the surface of the soil. Living things would be smothered and stifled; there would be no food for plants in the exhausted soil. Without plants, there would be no food for the animal world.

After millions of years of the cycle of life and death, the soil has turned into a living layer that throbs with its micro life. Every acre of soil in a fertile field contains up to four tons of living micro-organisms. There are more tiny living things in a spoonful of this soil than there are living human beings on earth.

Although bacteria and other micro-organisms play such a vitally important role, they do not represent the entire life of the soil. There are mites and springtails, insects in endless variety, eelworms, earthworms and slugs.

In the soil of pastureland, mites and springtails can reach a population figure of more than a billion to the acre. In the hot, damp lands of the tropics, insects infest the soil in numbers so vast that we cannot even guess how many are there.

Helpful Earthworms

In temperate lands, much of the fertility of the soil depends upon the earthworm. The importance of the earthworm was recognized by Charles Darwin, who estimated that worms bring fifteen tons of soil to the surface in the form of worm casts on every acre of agricultural land during a year. This is equivalent to a layer of soil one-fifth of an inch thick; it is the work of as many as a million earthworms which inhabit each acre of fertile soil. The soil in the worm casts has been ground and mixed during its passage through the alimentary tract of the worms.

Only two of the twenty-five species of worms in British soil bring casts to the surface in this way. As they tunnel into the soil, they drag dead leaves and other decaying material underground, mixing it with the soil and helping to grind and cement the particles together. As they wriggle through the surface soil, the worms promote aeration and drainage. They usually abound in pasture that is old and mellow.

In tropical countries, termites take over from the earthworms and help to break up and aerate the soil.

5

Water, Air and Warmth

Life needs Water

Wherever there is life, there must be water. Every living part of every plant, from a seed to the trunk of a tree, contains a supply of water in which the complex processes of the plant take place. Some plants, like cabbages and turnips, are almost entirely water, with the other constituents making up less than a tenth of the total weight. Water is indeed the elixir of life.

One of the most important jobs of any soil is to maintain an adequate supply of water to the plants which it supports. It is this, more than anything else, which determines the fertility of a soil. A plant can survive only so long as a flow of water is moving constantly through it; water that is taken from the soil by the roots which wriggle down amongst the humus and the mineral particles.

To the growing plant, water is a chemical raw material, similar to the nitrates and other fertilizers. Sugar, which the plant manufactures as its basic food, is built up from water and carbon dioxide gas absorbed from the air. But only a small quantity of water is used as raw material in this way. Prodigious quantities of water flow through the plant. Drawn in through the roots, this water sweeps upward through the stem, bearing in solution the soil chemicals that are needed by the plant as food. Reaching the leaves, the excess water is evaporated and escapes into the air through tiny pores, or stomata, that puncture the surfaces of the leaves.

The Marvel of Transpiration

Transpiration, this constant flow of water from the leaves into the air, is one of nature's minor miracles. It is a function of every higher plant, whether it be a tiny daisy or a massive forest tree.

As the water turns to vapour inside the leaves, it needs heat. This heat is taken from the plant, which is in consequence cooled. Transpiration is used by the plant as a way of keeping cool in the summer sun. Experiments have shown that the evaporation of transpired water from the leaves can account for 30 per cent of the sunshine energy falling on the plant.

Most of the water absorbed through the plant roots is water used in transpiration. Only a very small amount is needed as raw material for making sugar. For every ounce of sugar that is produced inside the plant, as much as two and a half gallons of water is transpired. In a field of beet carrying, say, thirty tons to the acre, over a thousand tons of water are transpired by the crop. This is equivalent to more than ten inches of rain – a good half of the total annual rainfall in some parts of Britain. A ton of hay will use 3,000 barrels of water during growth.

Much of the rain that reaches the soil is inevitably accounted for in other ways. In winter, four-fifths of the water that falls as rain is lost. Some runs off into ditches and streams; some is evaporated from the surface of the soil itself; and some percolates through the soil to collect underground or to drain away. In humid regions, as much as two-thirds of the water that reaches the soil is lost by percolation. Where the soil is not being cropped, the average loss is about half; where crops are being grown the loss is only about a quarter.

D

Water is Wealth

To provide the water needed for transpiration, particularly by crops like beet, turnips and potatoes, a comparatively high rainfall is needed if good crop yields are to be made. Even in climates considered to be humid, lack of water is often the main factor in causing indifferent crops.

The astonishing returns that come from adequate supplies of water, with ample nitrogen, can often be seen on sewage farms or nurseries. Even in a country like Britain, where water is rarely considered as being in short supply, one of the main functions of cultivation is to conserve the wealth of moisture in the soil. It is this abundance of water that, more than anything else, provides the lush rich vegetation that carpets the fields of Britain. Yet, in the drier parts of England – in East Anglia and the south-eastern counties – agriculture is handicapped by a shortage of water. As much as 6 inches more rain a year, arriving at the right time, would be welcomed by the farmer. Scientists have suggested that large-scale irrigation should be considered as a way of increasing output.

Soil stores Water

If rain fell steadily and regularly throughout the year, the soil would need to play a relatively minor role in keeping the plant supplied with its water. As it soaked into the soil, the rainwater would be taken up by the rootlets and forced upward through the plant.

But rain is apt to fall in seasonal cycles in most parts of the world. Some countries get their annual water supplies in a deluge lasting only a week or two; others get a winter of steady rain followed by a hot dry summer. Only rarely does the rain fall steadily throughout the year.

To keep the plant supplied with its water, the soil must be able to collect and store water that reaches it as rain. It must release this water steadily to the growing crops, maintaining the process of transpiration by drawing on its

THE WATER CYCLE

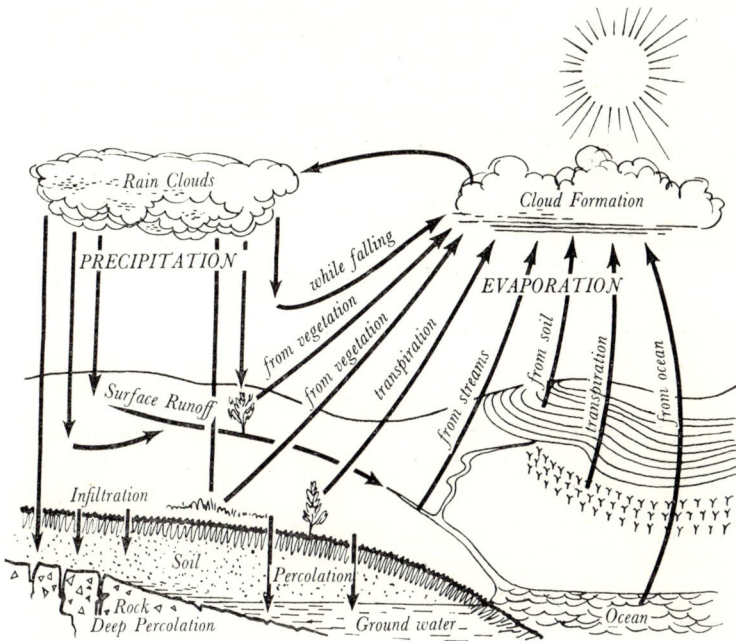

Water travels from the ocean to the atmosphere, and then to the land, from which it finds its way back to the ocean again.

stored reserves. The ability to hold and release supplies of moisture to the plant in this way plays a supremely important part in controlling the fertility of any soil. It depends very largely on the size of the soil particles.

Water Table

When rain falls onto the earth, water begins to trickle

down through the spaces between the tiny particles of soil. It flows under the force of gravity until it collects to form an underground lake. This is called the water table; it is the natural level of water underground at any place. It is the level at which water lies when a hole is dug in the ground – the level of water in a natural well (see page 114).

But not all the water trickles down until it reaches the water table. It soaks into the fine particles of clay or humus, which swell up like sponges until they are holding as much water as they can carry. The colour of the soil darkens; it becomes sticky and plastic.

Surface Film

Some of the water forms a film on the surface of the soil particles. It wets the particles just as it will wet a piece of wood or a stone. This film of water is held tightly. It does not flow down under the force of gravity any more than the surface film of water will drain away entirely from a wet stone. It is gripped by the surface of the particles as though by some invisible magnetic force.

This film of water, called *capillary water*, is the main source of water to the growing plant; billions of root hairs bathe in the film, drinking in the water that flows steadily through the plant. And dissolved in the water are chemicals that the plant uses as its raw material.

Capillary water is able to move about from place to place. The powerful forces that operate at liquid surfaces can make it flow, even against the force of gravity. These are the same forces that lift a little column of water up a narrow glass tube or a drinking straw placed in water; they are the forces that make paraffin flow upward through a lamp wick (see page 97).

As the root hair absorbs its water from the film around a particle of soil, fresh supplies of water flow in from the surrounding film. So long as the film of moisture is thick and continuous through the soil, water can flow upward

SOIL WATER

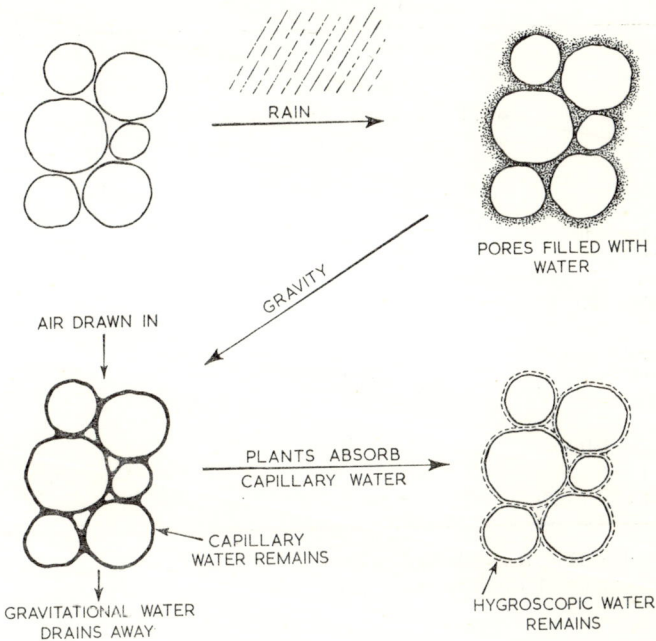

RAIN

PORES FILLED WITH
WATER

GRAVITY

AIR DRAWN IN

PLANTS ABSORB
CAPILLARY WATER

CAPILLARY
WATER REMAINS

GRAVITATIONAL WATER
DRAINS AWAY

HYGROSCOPIC WATER
REMAINS

When rain falls on the soil, water flows into the pores between the particles, and may fill these completely. The soil is then saturated. If the soil is drained satisfactorily, water will flow down through the soil, and the pores will empty after the rain has stopped. Air will flow into the pores to replace the water that has drained away.

The drainage water is *gravitational water*, and it does not provide water directly to the plant.

Water does not drain away completely from the soil under the pull of gravity. A film of water remains on the surface of the soil particles. This is *capillary water*, in which the plant root hairs bathe. It is the plant's source of water.

If capillary water is not renewed, plants will absorb it until there is only a very thin film remaining. This is held so tightly that it is not removed by the plant, which will wilt even though the water is there in the soil. This is *hygroscopic water*.

SOIL WATER AND PARTICLE SIZE

	SAND	SILT	CLAY
Drainage	Large pores; rapid drainage	Medium pores; moderate drainage	Small pores; slow drainage
Storage	Small surface area; low storage of capillary water	Medium surface area; moderate storage of capillary water	Very large surface area; large storage of capillary water
Water held after drainage (% of dry soil)	8.4	29	57
Surface area (acres per cubic foot)	⅓	1.0	2 – 4
Water left as plants wilt (%)	4 – 5	7	10

Note: Humus greatly increases the available surface area, and increases the amount of capillary water held.

from the water table to replenish the supplies.

This movement of water up and down and from place to place within the soil is controlled entirely by the surface film that covers the soil particles. It can take place only so long as the film is continuous. Once it is broken, water is unable to bridge the gap and the supply to the roots cannot be maintained.

The art of cultivation is to a great extent the art of keeping the soil in such a condition that its moisture film remains continuous and effective. So long as the individual particles are covered and connected by their layer of water, the flow of water within the soil can be sustained. Without this continuous film, the root hairs exhaust supplies in their immediate vicinity and the plant will wilt and ultimately die. A crop can fail for lack of moisture even when the water table is only a few feet below its roots.

The surface film does not disappear entirely, even under the driest conditions. In any soil, a stage is reached when the moisture film is reduced to a thickness of about three hundred-thousandths of an inch. This "last stage" film is held so firmly by the particle surface that it cannot be absorbed by the root hairs. The plant will die of thirst even with this water in the soil.

The ability of the moisture film to keep up a flow of water from place to place diminishes as the film becomes thinner. Soil should be encouraged to keep a good thick film of water on its particles, so that it can maintain an efficient flow of water.

Influence of Particle Size

The ability of a soil to hold water depends upon the amount of film water that it can carry. The greater the surface area of solid particles in the soil the greater is the water-holding capacity of the soil. The finer the particles, therefore, the more water the soil can hold (see page 93).

The total surface area in a coarse, gravelly or sandy soil is less than that of a soil made up of fine clay particles; a sandy soil will hold less water in the form of surface film than will a clay soil.

On the other hand, if water supplies are restricted in a time of drought, sandy soil can give up more of its total water supply than can clay soil. By the time the "last ditch" film has been reached and the plants begin to wilt, there will be more water left in the clay than in the sand.

These differences in water-holding and releasing characteristics affect the behaviour of a soil under practical conditions. Clay soil, for example, will store up more winter rainwater than will sandy soil. After a wet winter, it can make more water available to the summer crop. But if the winter has been dry, and the soil has not been saturated with water, the sandy soil has its advantages. It can give up more of the water it is holding when the crop demands it during the growing season. Clay, with its large surface area, clings to a greater proportion of the limited supplies.

Soil particles must be able to pack sufficiently close together to be able to form a continuous water film that links the particles together. Yet, at the same time, they must not be so small that they pack too tightly together, making the spaces between the particles too narrow. If this happens, water will be unable to flow freely from one place to another.

During a summer day, the hot dry air above the ground will evaporate water quickly from the soil. And the plants in the soil will be transpiring at a tremendous rate. Under these conditions, water is often removed from the soil faster than fresh supplies can flow in over the surface film. As the film becomes thinner, so its power of moving water lessens. If, at this point, the soil is given a soaking from a hose, or by rain, the effect will be out of all proportion to the amount of water supplied. The water flowing down through the soil will strengthen the moisture film and help it to carry in fresh supplies more efficiently from its surroundings. The amount of water brought to the plant roots may be very much greater than the quantity that fell on the surface of the soil.

If, on the other hand, the soil dries out to the point where the moisture film becomes thin or discontinuous, the shower of rain will have very little effect. Movement of the surface water into the soil will be restricted, as the "carrier" film is out of action. Air will be filling the spaces between the particles, and preventing still further the flow of water into the soil. The water which has fallen will evaporate from the surface of the soil before it has a chance to penetrate.

This effect is often seen on ground that has been baked

CAPILLARY WATER

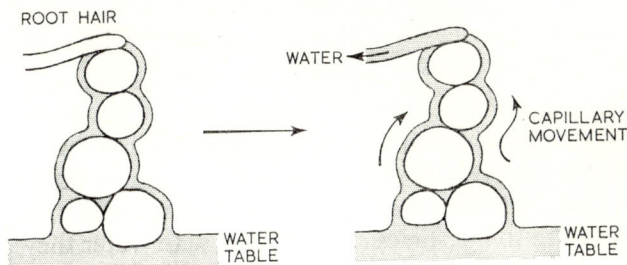

(A)

(B)

The film of water on the surface of soil particles is able to move against gravity by the phenomenon of capillarity. This is a surface tension effect, familiar as the force which lifts a column of liquid up a straw, or the paraffin up a lamp wick. The liquid is drawn along by the attraction of the solid surface.

If a root hair, for example, removes water from the film that coats the surface of a particle, water will flow along the film to replace that which has been lost. This capillary movement will lift water from the water table, the effectiveness depending upon the sizes of the pore spaces. If the pores are too small, the movement of water will be held up by excessive friction. If the pores are too large, there will be insufficient surface to carry large quantities of water.

In practice, capillary movement is a much less significant factor than recurrent rainfall in restoring the film of soil moisture.

D*

dry in the summer sun. Even a heavy shower will do little
more than damp the surface. Once there has been sufficient rain to soak the soil, however, and re-establish the
moisture film, successive showers can have a tonic effect
on the growing crops.

Air is Important

The flow of water in the soil is important, not only as it
affects the supply of water itself, but through its influence
on the air that circulates in the soil. Wherever the spaces
between the soil particles are not filled with water they are
filled with air. Air is needed by the roots of plants growing
in the soil, and by the micro-organisms in the soil as well.

During the hours of daylight, the green parts of plants
are absorbing carbon dioxide from the air to provide the
carbon they need as raw material; oxygen is fed back into
the air. But throughout both night and day, the reverse
process is going on in all the living cells of the plant; oxygen is being absorbed and carbon dioxide exhaled. The
cells of the plant are, in fact, breathing like the cells of
animals and human beings.

In the plant, there is no centrally organized system for
carrying oxygen from "lungs" to the various cells in the
body. Oxygen has to be absorbed locally, where it is
needed. And the roots of the plant, like any other living
tissues, are always breathing in oxygen and exhaling carbon dioxide. This process of respiration provides the
energy that the tissues need to keep alive.

For plant roots to flourish, the soil must be able to supply
them with the air they need. And it must be able to carry
away the carbon dioxide that is exhaled from the roots.

In the same way, air is needed by the billions of micro-
plants, the bacteria that do so much to maintain fertility.
Most of the useful soil bacteria need air to breathe.

Movement of Air

In many fertile soils, as much as half the volume of the

soil consists of pore space, filled partly with water and partly with air. As water fills the pores, air is forced out of them; as water drains away, fresh air from the atmosphere flows back in. This continual to and fro movement, together with a steady diffusion flow, keeps the soil air fresh and sweet.

Inevitably, the air in the soil tends to be richer in carbon dioxide than the air above the earth. This carbon dioxide dissolves in the soil water forming acid which helps the weathering of the mineral particles.

If the air of the soil grows stale, and too much carbon dioxide collects in it, the life of the soil is slowed. Anything that helps to open up the soil and encourage the flow of air between the particles will help to sustain fertility. Tillage of the soil affects the porosity that is essential to air and water flow. In a clay soil, it loosens the fine particles that tend to cake together; in a sandy soil it can compact the particles that are often too loosely packed.

In a porous soil, air will flow freely between the soil and the atmosphere, following the rise and fall of water in the pore spaces. Other natural changes will encourage it; variations in temperature and pressure, for example, will help the soil to breathe.

Soil Temperature

Like all other living things, plants will not grow if they are too cold, nor if they are too hot. Every plant has a growing temperature it prefers, at which it will grow its fastest. Each plant has also a low temperature limit below which it will stop growing, and a high temperature limit above which it must wither and die. These preferences for certain temperatures apply not only to the parts of the plant above the ground but to the roots as well. The warmth of the soil has a major effect on the growth of the plant.

Soil temperature affects the germination of the seed as

well as the roots of the growing plant. It controls the rate at which soil bacteria work and so plays a large part in rationing out the food that reaches the plant roots.

There are big differences in soil temperature between one part of the world and another. On a summer's day in Britain the soil may heat up to 100° F.; in South Africa, soil temperatures of 150° F. are quite common.

The effect of soil temperatures on plants can be remarkable. For most cultivated plants, growth stops altogether below 41° F. At 63° F., the roots of a corn stalk will grow about one-twentieth of an inch a day; at 93° F., they will grow more than two inches.

All plants have a minimum germination temperature below which the seeds will not begin to grow. For wheat, this may be as low as 40° F., but for other seeds, such

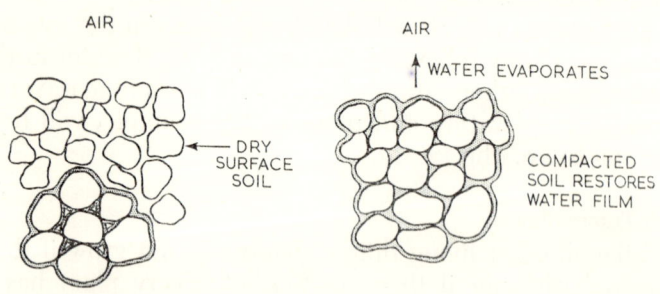

SOIL MULCH

If the surface soil is loosened to a depth of a few inches, contact between particles is minimized, and the capillary film broken or destroyed. As water evaporates from the surface particles, it cannot be replaced rapidly by movement through capillary action. The loose soil helps to conserve moisture in the lower layers.

If the soil is compacted by rolling, contact between the particles is restored, and a water film may be created which extends to the soil surface. Evaporation of the moisture from the surface will lift water from deep in the soil, and loss of water will be heavy.

as cucumbers, the germination temperature is as high as 60° F. Nitrification bacteria in the soil will stop work altogether at a temperature a few degrees above freezing point. Their best work is put in at about 100° F.

Heat from the Sun

The soil's heat supply comes mainly from the sun. Shining down vertically from a clear sky, the sun can deliver almost a million calories of heat an hour to every square yard of the earth's surface. This terrific quantity of heat can build up an extremely high temperature, as it often does in the tropics. But heat is constantly being lost from the soil as well, and the soil temperature is a level determined by the difference between heat going into the soil and heat lost.

In tropical countries, the sun shines down from directly overhead. The amount of sunshine reaching every square yard of soil per hour is at its maximum. In countries farther away from the equator, the sun shines obliquely onto the earth, and the amount of sunshine reaching every square yard is progressively less as the distance from the equator increases. The soil in equatorial regions is generally warmer than the soil in countries far from the equator.

In non-equatorial countries, the amount of sunshine reaching any area of soil can be increased by arranging the angle of the soil so that the sun's rays fall more vertically on it. The southern slope of a hill, for example, can catch the sunshine less obliquely than level land in the same district. The quantity of sunshine per square yard is higher, and the soil is warmer in consequence. The northern slope, which receives the sunshine at a more oblique angle, is correspondingly cooler (see page 106).

Radiation Losses

Although the earth receives all this sunshine to warm it up, it also loses heat by radiation. But the radiations sent

SOIL TEMPERATURE

The productivity of a soil is influenced greatly by its temperature and heating properties. The temperature of field soils shows definite changes at different depths and different seasons of the year (see below). The changes are determined by the amount of radiant energy that reaches the soil surface and by the thermal properties of the soil. The amount of radiant energy reaching the surface is determined by the angle at which the sunlight strikes the earth (see page 106), and by the nature of the atmosphere. Only the part of the energy that is absorbed causes changes in soil temperature.

Dark coloured soils having a low reflecting power capture a much higher proportion of radiant energy than do light-coloured soils. Thus a fallow Brunizem absorbs nearly 80 percent of the radiation that reaches the soil surface. A grass-covered soil and quartz sand absorb, respectively, 65 percent and 30 percent.

The energy that has been absorbed by the soil surface is disposed of in one or more of the following ways:—

(1) by re-radiation to the atmosphere as longwave radiation.
(2) by heating of air above the soil by convection
(3) by increasing the temperature of the surface soil
(4) by conduction to the deeper soil layers.

(*Continued opposite*)

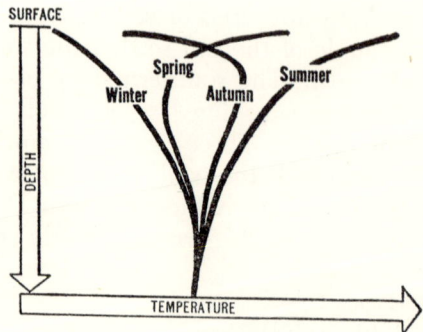

In temperate regions, soil temperatures show characteristic seasonal variations, which decrease with depth.

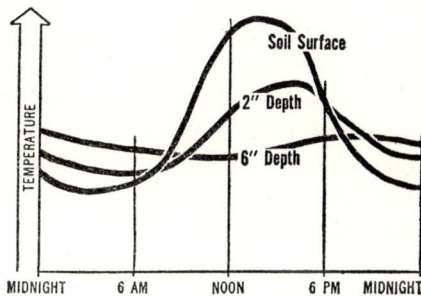

During a 24-hour period, the soil temperature fluctuates widely. Variations become smaller below the soil surface.

SOIL TEMPERATURE (*continued*)

During daylight hours there is normally a net influx of heat to the soil surface. This situation is reversed during the night. Consequently, the temperature of the exposed surface shows wider daily fluctuations than those of the air.

Soil temperatures vary in characteristic manner both on a daily and seasonal basis. The fluctuations in both instances are greatest at the surface and decrease in size at lower depths. A well-defined time-lag, which increases with the depth in the soil, also occurs in both the daily and seasonal variations.

The observed fluctuations in soil temperature are related to the heat capacity and to the thermal conductivity of the soil. Both of these properties are strongly affected by the proportions of the total soil volume that are occupied by the solid, liquid and gaseous soil constituents.

The thermal conductivity of water is greater than the corresponding value for he solid soil particles, which in turn is higher than that of air. Consequently, the rate of heat flow in a soil is increased when the volume occupied by air is decreased. Such a reduction in the volume fraction of air can be obtained either by compacting the soil or increasing its moisture content.

back by the earth are of a longer wavelength than those reaching the earth as sunshine. And they have less penetrating power than the rays in sunshine. Glass, for example, will stop them.

A frame or greenhouse is a sunshine trap. It allows most of the sun's rays to penetrate and reach the soil. Here, they are absorbed and partly emitted in the form of waves of longer wavelength. But the new waves are held back by the glass of the greenhouse, so that there is more energy coming into the greenhouse than there is going out. The temperature rises. In a similar way, the radiations from the earth are trapped by water vapour. Clouds will allow some of the sun's rays through them, but prevent the earth's rays from getting back into space. Clouds, in this way, can act as a super-greenhouse and help to keep the soil temperature high.

Colour plays an important part in trapping sunshine that reaches the soil. Just as black clothes are hotter in the sun than white. so is black soil warmer than light-coloured soil. Anything black will absorb the sun's rays; white tends to reflect them. A field of black soil will often be warmer than a neighbouring field of paler soil by as much as 20° F., simply as a result of the difference in colour. The warmth of a red soil is intermediate between the two.

The temperature of the soil is affected also by water changing to vapour, and vice versa. When water turns into vapour, heat has to be put into it. Water in the soil thus needs heat when it evaporates into the air, and it takes this heat from the soil. A wet, undrained soil is a cold soil, heat being taken from it by the water as it evaporates.

When the reverse process takes place, heat is put back into the soil. Dew forming on the ground will warm up the surface soil. Heat put into the water when it turned to vapour is released by dew as it turns to liquid water again.

*   *   *

Heat from Humus

Humus is another heat provider in the soil. When humus decomposes, it is undergoing a process similar to burning. Some of the energy locked up in it is released as heat into the soil. A heap of manure or humus will heat appreciably as it rots, forming a hotbed on which early crops can be grown. Spread thinly through the soil, humus provides only an insignificant amount of heat. It is too small to be of any great value by comparison with the sunshine and the dew.

Both the sunshine and the dew, and their reverse processes of radiation and evaporation, operate at the surface of the soil. The effect of soil temperature on plant growth is felt as far down as the roots travel; but it is particularly important in the topsoil where bacterial activity is at its height. The structure of the soil affects not only the give and take of the heat processes, but the soil's ability to conduct heat to and fro as well.

In most soils, day-to-day changes in soil temperature reach down only to depths of six inches to a foot. The soil's ability to conduct heat is so small that the subsoil tends to remain at a fairly steady temperature, changing only with the changes in the seasons. But it is within the topsoil that the effect of temperature changes on the plant are most important. And the ability of any soil to conduct heat can have a great influence on the day-by-day changes in the warmth of this upper layer of soil (see pages 102, 103).

As the surface of the soil receives a supply of heat from the sun or from the dew, heat flows down into the cooler soil below. The little particles of soil are the conductors, heat flowing through them, and from one to the other, wherever they are touching. If there is a good close contact between the particles, it is easier for the heat to flow from one to the other. A sturdy moisture film will ensure that contact between the particles is as efficient as can be. Compact, moist soil will warm up quickly as the heat flows into it from the surface layer.

SOIL TEMPERATURE

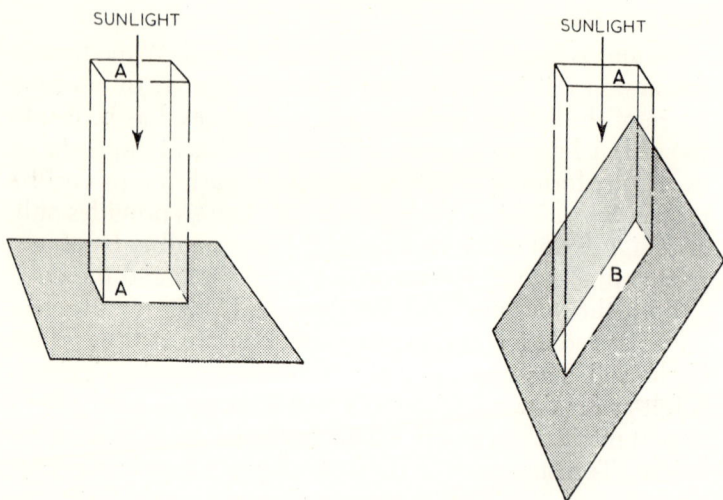

SUNLIGHT

SUNLIGHT

The amount of heat reaching the soil depends upon the angle at which the sun's radiation strikes the surface.

An imaginary "column" of sunshine of definite cross-sectional area, A, for example, will illuminate this same area if it strikes the surface from directly overhead.

SUNSHINE

EQUATOR

If the same column strikes a sloping surface, however, it will illuminate a larger area, B. This means that the radiant energy it carries is spread more thinly over the soil.

SUNSHINE

For this reason, the sun heats the earth more strongly near the equator than in the higher latitudes. And the southern slope of a hill receives more heat than a northern slope.

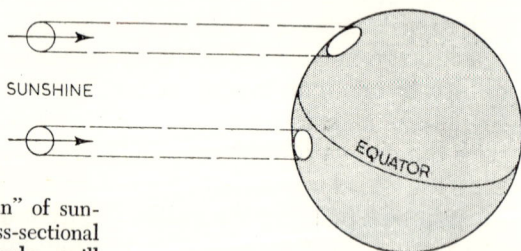

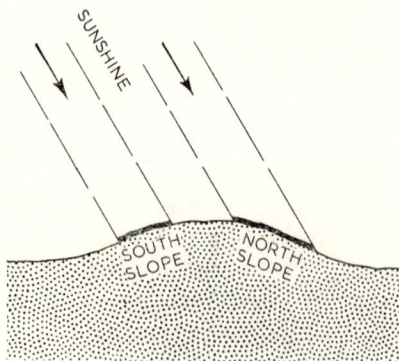

SOUTH SLOPE

NORTH SLOPE

Water and Warmth

Too much water, on the other hand, makes for a cold soil. Water is slow to heat up compared with the solid particles of soil. More heat is needed to raise the temperature of water than to raise the temperature of an equal weight of soil. Water in the soil has a shock-absorbing effect on the soil temperature. It slows up the temperature rise by absorbing a lot of heat; but, on the other hand, it stops the temperature of the soil from falling too quickly when the air is cold. It can lose a lot of heat without cooling unduly.

Clay soils have a high water content in the form of a film surrounding the tiny particles, and they take longer to warm up than sandy soils. But they hold their warmth longer into the autumn, and are shaken less severely by rapidly changing weather.

A loose, well-drained soil is an early soil. It holds a minimum of water, and warms up quickly in the spring sunshine. There is less evaporation to chill the soil by taking heat from it. Moreover, the dryness of the soil allows the farmer to cultivate it early in the year; he can break up the compacted soil and slow the conduction of heat from the surface layers. As a result, the seed bed on the surface is quickly warmed; at the same time the aeration of the soil encourages nitrification bacteria to get to work.

This is the sort of soil that we find so often in the market gardens which cluster round a town. Rich and warm, it enables the gardener to bring on early crops that pay so handsomely. For such advantages, he must be prepared to suffer from the corresponding drawbacks. His soil will lose its heat quickly to the unexpected evening frost, and may suffer more than a heavier soil from a spell of cold dank weather.

The temperature of the soil affects the plant's ability to absorb water. A plant will wilt in a moist soil on a cold night, even with plenty of water at its roots. Trees will die of thirst during a prolonged frost, as they cannot take up the water they need from the soil.

6

Cultivation and Crops

Food and water, shelter, air and warmth; these are the essential needs of everything that lives. They are the things we human beings strive for; they are, no less, the aim of every plant that sends its roots into the soil. It is the balance and supply of these requirements that control the health and heart of the growing plant.

Under natural conditions the vegetation comes to terms with its environment. If the soil is rich and the climate warm and welcoming, plants grow apace and the vegetation is lush. As it lives and dies, it adds its humus to the wealth of the soil. And from the remains of past generations, the living plants can draw the nitrogen and other nutrients they require.

If the soil is poor, or the climate harsh and unrewarding, plants will not grow at a generous rate. Humus is limited and the soil will sustain a growth that is sparse and restricted compared with what it would support if conditions were more favourable.

Where man comes with his agriculture, he disturbs the natural balance achieved between the plant world and the soil. He wants to grow plants more suitable for his needs than those that grow under natural conditions. He wants the return of food to be at a maximum; he imposes his will on the equilibrium established by nature and adjusts the conditions and environment to give him what he wants. Agriculture, in this sense, is an unending struggle against nature. And the skill and experience of the farmer in his handling of the soil have been inherited through thousands of years of this continuing fight.

Digging and Ploughing

The first, fundamental act in the development of agricultural technique took place when primitive man began to turn the soil. He moved it with his digging stick and then with his plough. This was the beginning of all cultivation, and it remains the basic act in agriculture today.

Behind this digging and ploughing lies the needs to sustain and improve the richness of the soil. Nature herself does no digging. But our needs are greater than those of nature, and to achieve more intensive production the soil needs cultivation. In the early days, the digging stick was dug into the ground to clear away weeds and to break up the soil so that useful seeds could be sown effectively. These are important results of digging and ploughing today. But modern techniques have gone further than that. As soil is turned, it is loosened and broken up. Air can enter and water can soak into it more easily. If the soil is sticky and tough, ploughing and digging enable the weather to get at the lumps. Winter frosts grind up the clods, and the soil crumbles to finer particles that can be more easily penetrated by water and air. Seeds can be sown effectively and the roots of growing plants can establish a good firm grip on the soil itself.

A field of three acres will have some four thousand tons of soil in its top 9-inch of surface. Moving and turning the soil of a large field is therefore a tremendous task for the farmer. But it is a job of work that pays handsome dividends. It is the top layer of the soil which benefits by being moved during digging and ploughing. Experiments have shown that ploughing to a depth of 12 to 14 inches helps to control the weeds, but shows no other benefit compared with ploughing to a depth of only 6 or 7 inches.

SOIL STRUCTURE

One of the most important factors in a soil's physical condition, from the practical point of view, is the way in which individual particles are bound together into crumbs or aggregates. This characteristic is described as the *structure* of the soil (see page 283). Much of the effort put into cultivating a soil is expended in improving its structure. In the main, this consists in binding together the particles into aggregates that will resist disintegration by water, and by the effects of cultivation. A well-aggregated soil is easily worked, allows water and air to circulate freely, and provides a suitable roothold for plants. It is not carried away easily by flowing water, nor will it be blown away by the wind.

Several types of material play an important part in the binding of soil particles into aggregates.

CLAY

Neutralization of the electric charges on clay particles may be achieved by adding mineral acids, salts or lime to the clay. This brings about a flocculation of the particles, and the clay settles out from the water. Mudbanks and deltas at the mouths of rivers are formed by flocculation of clay particles neutralized by the salts in seawater.

When lime or gypsum are added to a sticky clay soil, the particles are neutralized, and the clay becomes a crumbly mass. The soil is more easily worked, and air and water can circulate between the crumbs.

The addition of lime to a soil rich in clay thus helps to create and sustain a crumb structure.

HUMUS

Like clay, humus is a colloidal material. It coats the particles of soil with a gummy layer, which holds them together like glue. When lime is added to the soil, humus colloids are coagulated, and stable crumbs are formed.

Humus is especially useful in that it binds together the particles of any sort of soil. It is as useful in a sandy soil as in a clay.

Humus is, however, a part-way stage in the decomposition of organic matter. It is itself decomposing, and the more a soil is cultivated, the more rapidly will the humus disappear. Fresh supplies must be added continually to maintain the crumb structure.

LIME

In some soils, lime is deposited from soil waters containing dissolved calcium bicarbonate, and acts as a mortar that holds soil particles together.

IRON OXIDE

Iron is present in many igneous rocks, and red iron oxide is formed as the rocks are weathered. The granular structure of many red or brown soils is due in part to the iron oxide they contain, which serves as a cement holding aggregates together.

MICROBES; ROOTS

The micro-organisms in a soil play a part in the creation of a crumb structure. Gummy materials produced by bacteria and other organisms help to bind particles together. These gums form part of the humus material that is involved in soil structure. The excellent crumb structure commonly found in grassland is due in part to the gummy materials produced by bacteria which flourish in association with plant roots, together with the binding action of the roots and root hairs themselves.

Crumb Structure

The entire movement of water and air in the soil is affected by the physical structure achieved in cultivation. The ideal which every gardener and farmer strives to attain is the so-called crumb structure, where the individual soil particles are bound together in the form of spongy particles or crumbs. This is the structure that is so often found to perfection in the rich and fertile soil of a well-cultivated nursery plot, or an old cottage garden that has been tended carefully for generations. Ploughing and digging, which make possible the enrichment of the soil, are essential steps toward the attainment of the crumb structure (see page 110).

In the early days of farming, when the three-field system was bringing its indifferent returns from the land, ploughing was carried out inadequately. Tools were poor, and the long-term value of proper cultivation was not understood. It was not until Jethro Tull, in the early eighteenth century, began to improve his crops that the effects of good cultivation were appreciated.

Though digging and ploughing are the basic processes of soil management, modern cultivation involves the use of many processes and products on the soil. With the soil ploughed and weathered, for example, it is usually broken down further by physical processes. Harrowing pounds the lumps of soil and helps the frost to break them into finer particles.

Rolling

In the spring, soil that is to receive the seeds is firmed and compacted by rolling. This presses the particles together and makes good contact between them. Rolling helps the capillary water to flow from particle to particle. It maintains a supply of moisture round the germinating seed, and by improving the contact between particles it enables the heat of the sun to flow more easily into the ground. By bringing water to the surface, rolling can be the cause of rapid chilling if the soil is subjected to a drying wind.

Hoeing

When plants are growing, the surface of the soil is still kept moving with the help of the hoe. The main service performed by hoeing is in keeping down the weeds. Not only will weeds take the natural foods from the soil, denying them to the plant; they cause the greatest harm by transpiring vast quantities of precious water from the soil into the air. Weeds will often stunt a crop by soaking up the water from the soil. And water is the commodity that is often in short supply.

It has been claimed that hoeing prevents water loss from the soil by breaking up the capillary movement in the surface layers. The loose, pliable layer of hoed earth acts as a water stop. There is some doubt now as to the part this process plays. Modern theory holds that it is in weed control that hoeing is most valuable.

Drainage

The supply of air and water to the plant is controlled very largely by the drainage of the land. The introduction of effective drainage into farmland during the last century or so has greatly contributed to the improved fertility of the soil.

In bogland, the water level is close to the soil surface, or even above it. In many soils, the level is a long way down, as shown by the depth to which a well must be sunk to reach it. Often, the level will be a foot or two beneath the surface.

If the water table is too near the surface, the soil will become waterlogged. The spaces between the particles are filled with water that cannot flow away. With water in the pores of the soil, air is unable to penetrate and the living soil is choked to death. Without air, the humus in the soil cannot decompose and release its mineral plant foods. Bacteria which control this decay need air to keep them active. In the absence of air, decay will go only to a halfway stage under the attack of bacteria which can operate without air. Acid humus is formed, which is inimical to plant life. An extreme result of a waterlogged soil is the formation of a bog. In it, half-decayed organic matter accumulates in the form of peat. And although this peat may consist almost entirely of a form of organic humus, it is useless acid soil. With adequate drainage and cultivation air can enter the soil, and useful life returns. Bacteria can get to work on the humus and the soil becomes rich once more.

One of the strangest results of draining the land is that it makes plants better able to resist a drought. Plants do not take in moisture from the bulk supplies of water below the water table. They absorb it through the tiny root hairs that bathe in the thin film of water around the soil particles. When the water level is high in the soil, plant roots are shallow and restricted to the aerated surface layers. In a drought, these shallow-rooted plants have a thin layer of surface soil from which to draw their water. This surface layer of soil dries quickly, and the plant goes thirsty.

In drained ground, on the other hand, the level of the water in the soil is low. Plants growing in the soil have plenty of room in which to spread their roots, and there is a greater depth of soil from which to derive supplies of moisture. They can look after themselves more effectively during the drought (see page 114).

By removing excess of water from the surface, drainage warms a soil as well. Water takes a lot of heating up by the sun to raise its temperature. A wet soil is slow to warm up in spring. Moreover, as water evaporates from the sur-

WATER TABLE

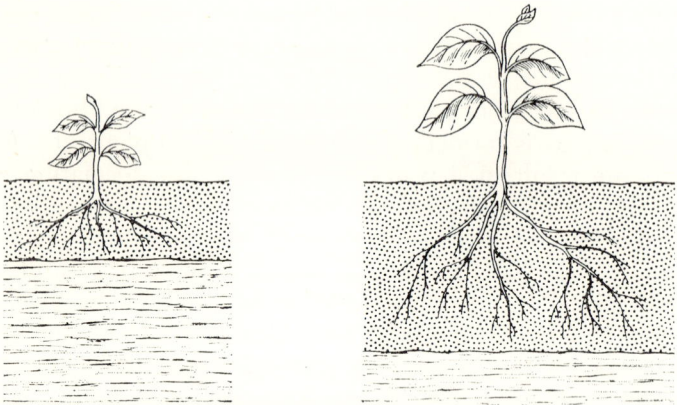

If water lies near the surface of the soil (*left*), roots of crops cannot reach deep into the soil. Plants become shallow-rooted and growth is restricted. In times of drought, when the water level falls, these plants are unable to draw on an extensive region of the soil for their water supplies, and are liable to suffer from lack of water.

In a properly drained soil, the water table is at a lower level (*right*), and roots are able to reach deep into the soil. They are better able to withstand times of water shortage, as they are more extensive, and can draw on a deeper layer of soil.

face of the soil into the air, it takes heat from the soil and chills it. By getting rid of water that is not needed, drainage helps to warm the soil.

Importance of Humus

In a soil that is warm and aerated, the myriad forms of life are able to quicken their activities, carrying the decay of humus to its final stage. Humus supplies the plants with food but it does another equally important job in the soil. A soil without humus is a dead, sterile soil composed of nothing but mineral particles. It may contain the simple chemical foods needed by the plant, and will on that account support plant growth. These foods can be provided in the form of chemical fertilizers. But for practical farming purposes, soil must do more than supply the necessary chemical foods. It must have a physical structure that enables the farmer to cultivate it properly; it must provide a root hold for the plant; it must hold water and retain supplies of chemical nutrients against the leaching effect of the rain; it must provide the plant with warmth. It is in these ways that humus plays its second role. Humus in the soil has great water-holding power. It can swell and hold its moisture like a sponge. In loose sandy soils, water will flow easily between the large particles, and the amount of film moisture held in the soil is limited. If there is plenty of humus in the soil, it forms a sticky, stodgy layer that coats the surface of the particles and helps them to hold an adequate supply of moisture.

Humus affects the essential structure of the soil by helping to form the crumbs that are so beneficial. Water and air can percolate through well-crumbed soils; such soils are easy to cultivate and do not set hard in wet weather. They combine the unique characteristics of clay particles with good drainage and aeration. The crumbs are too heavy to be easily washed away or caught up by the wind, and they give a good firm root hold to the plant. In a sandy soil, humus acts as a glue that encourages inert soil particles to hold together in this way. In a thick clay soil, humus helps to stop the fine clay particles from gumming up together into a solid cement-like mass.

This function of humus in affecting the physical structure of the soil is no less important than its service as a chemical provider. Chemical fertilizers are not alternatives to manure or compost except as feeding substances. They provide the soil with the essential nutrients, similar to those it derives from decomposing humus. But that is the only function of a fertilizer. Humus is a builder of soil structure as well.

Humus is dark in colour, particularly when it is wet. By darkening the soil, it encourages absorption of heat from the sun's rays and helps to warm the soil.

The amount of humus that a soil can take is virtually unlimited. Peat soils are almost entirely humus. Sandy soils may contain none. Even in a good growing soil, humus may account for only a twentieth of the total. The better cultivated the soil is, the more rapidly does the humus decompose and disappear as bacteria attack it. Good husbandry encourages the quick removal of humus from the soil, its nutrients being released as simple chemical foods and as carbon dioxide gas. As a soil improves with proper attention, therefore, the more necessary it is to maintain a supply of humus in it.

The mere presence of a lot of humus, on the other hand, does not necessarily imply that soil is fertile. As in the case of a peat bog, it may be the result of inadequate drainage and bad aeration. The humus remains in a semi-decomposed acid state with its nutrients still locked up inside it.

Liming

When a waterlogged soil has been drained and aerated, bacterial action can continue. But before decay can flourish, the acidity of the soil must be removed. From Roman times, lime has been used for improving soil that has become acid. This chemical, produced by burning limestone rock, will neutralize acids formed in badly aerated soil. Trails in the hills of Derbyshire, England, can still be seen, beaten out in Roman days by people carrying lime to the fertile plains of Cheshire.

By helping the decay of humus and encouraging nitrification, lime is most effective in the surface layers of the

DRAINAGE

If the water table lies too near the surface, it is necessary to lower the water level by laying drains. The draining of a large area of farming land needs careful planning with the help of experts, but the siting of drains in a small garden plot is usually a straightforward operation. A simple plan showing the topography is a great help (see page 152).

Drainage trenches are commonly dug to a depth of 2 to 3 feet, in the form of V-shaped trenches with gently sloping floor leading towards the lowest point of the land. Earthenware or porous concrete pipes of 3 to 6 inches diameter are laid on the bottom of the trenches, leaving a gap of about ⅛ inch between the ends. This allows water to seep into the drainage pipes and flow along them to the outlet.

Branch drains are laid to link with the main drain forming a herring bone pattern, the exits from the branches being spaced at intervals along the main drain. The slope of the drains should be gentle and smooth.

Clinker, rubble, stones, brushwood or other coarse material is used to cover the pipes before the trench is filled in with soil. Often, drains are constructed without pipes, clinker and similar material in the bottom of the trench providing a free run for the drainage water.

If there is a natural outlet, such as a stream, ditch or storm drain, the main drain is led into this. If an outlet is not available, it is necessary to build a soakaway pit.

WHAT DRAINAGE DOES

* Removes excess water and allows air to enter soil
* Encourages more extensive rooting system
* Permits earlier and less arduous working of soil
* Encourages decay of humus, and release of plant nutrients
* Makes for warmer soil
* Removes *cause* of acidity, by allowing air into soil
* Encourages nitrification bacteria in soil and legume nodules
* Improves soil structure by encouraging crumb formation
* Discourages denitrification bacteria
* Removes harmful chemicals from soil.

soil. It is here that bacteria and compost are usually to be found. But lime tends to sink down through the soil, carried away by rainwater in which it can dissolve. It must be applied regularly to the soil, a succession of small dressings being more effective than an occasional large one.

Lime is now known to improve the land in other ways. The calcium it contains is needed by the plant as a food chemical. But the amounts required are small, and weathering processes acting on the soil mineral particles are usually sufficient to keep the soil supplied with calcium needed by the plant.

Lime is particularly useful when the soil is heavy and sticky with clay. The electrically charged clay particles push each other apart as they float around in water. Wet clay cannot easily turn into larger particles formed by the agglomeration of many small particles. Clay soils tend to remain as slimy, plastic masses that are difficult to cultivate and control.

Lime is able to neutralize the electric charges from the particles of clay, allowing them to come together and form the crumbs that the farmer is always trying to encourage in his soil.

In sandy soils, lime can also help to build up these soil crumbs in a different way. Lime dissolved in the water of a soil can bind the particles together as the soil dries out. It acts like the cement mortar that holds the bricks together in a wall.

Rotation of Crops

In the very early days of agriculture, people learned that it was best to change the crop that grew in the soil from year to year. To grow one crop continually on the same piece of ground was to invite trouble. The returns from the soil would drop to a minimum and ultimately the crop might fail completely.

The dangers inherent in single-crop cultivation were

recognized by the Romans. In their three-year rotation system, wheat was followed by barley and then by a year of fallow. Using this system, the yield from the land was greater than it was if the wheat was grown year after year in the same field and barley in another.

The reasons for the improved returns from such a rotation of crops are well understood today. All crops take the same essential nutrients from the soil, among them the "big three" – nitrogen, phosphorus and potassium – together with traces of other elements. But some crops need a lot of one nutrient compared with another. Phosphates, for example, are taken up greedily by a root crop such as turnips; wheat needs plenty of nitrogen, and potatoes use a lot of potash. By growing one crop year after year on a piece of land, the nutrient that is needed most is taken rapidly from the soil. The crop will tend to starve itself of its essential food.

By using a carefully planned rotation, the balance of nutrient needs can be maintained and the crops can make the most of the soil foods that are available to them. During the year of fallow in the old three-field rotation, supplies of mineral nutrients such as phosphorus and potassium were released by weathering of the soil particles. And bacterial activity was able to regenerate a supply of nitrogen chemicals, topped up by those brought into the soil by rainwater from the air.

With the introduction of leguminous crops like beans and alfalfa, the soil was given an added opportunity to enrich itself. A leguminous crop grown in a rotation will provide increased supplies of nitrogen where other crops would reduce them.

When the Norfolk rotation came along, root crops such as turnips were introduced into the cultivation scheme. These crops broke up the soil; they let in the air and helped to develop a finer tilth, bringing the benefits of thorough cultivation to the land.

Today, we retain the principles of crop rotation in the cultivation of our farms and gardens. In addition to the advantages it brings in soil enrichment, we find that insects cannot settle down to enjoy their favourite crop year after year. And the cultivation of different crops in successive years helps to keep down weeds which can become accustomed to life with one particular crop.

Cause and Effect in Cultivation

The simple principles behind these aspects of cultivation are now becoming increasingly understood. The modern farmer knows what he is doing to his soil when he drains and limes, ploughs and manures. He can relate causes to effects.

In our cultivation of the soil, we now know what we are aiming at. Our ideal is the fine crumb structure which is easily ploughed or dug, and which will provide a firm and healthy root hold to our crops. Through this ideal soil, water will drain away without sweeping the surface soil into the rivers; and air can percolate between particles too heavy to be caught up by the wind.

In such a soil, with a high proportion of decomposing humus, we have the supplies of chemical foods needed by the growing plant. The natural breakdown of mineral particles can take place, releasing supplies of potash and phosphorus and the essential trace elements. And within this soil, bacteria have the air they need to produce simple nitrogen chemicals by direct fixation, or by decay of humus in the soil.

Fertilizers mean Food

The soil in many parts of the world is now producing more than ever before. In Britain, the average yield of wheat was twenty bushels to the acre in 1840 and thirty bushels in 1870. It has now risen to about thirty-three.

FERTILIZER HELPS CROPS MAKE BETTER USE
OF MOISTURE

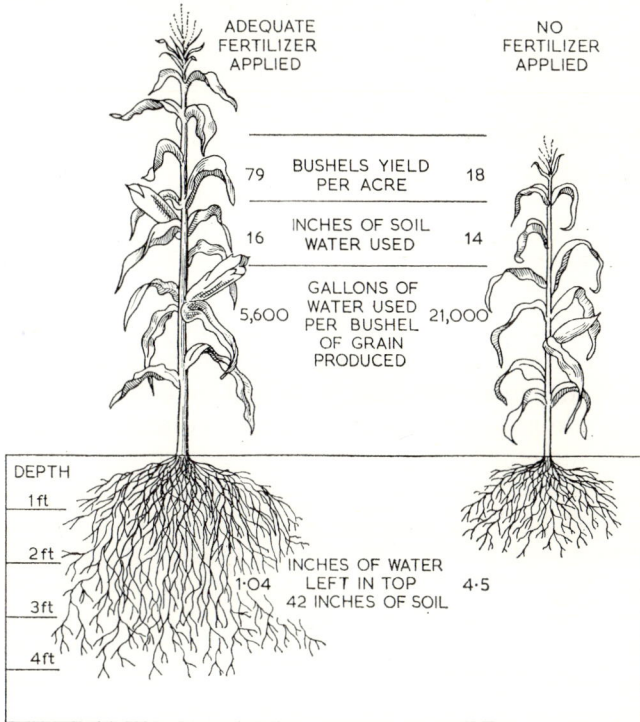

	ADEQUATE FERTILIZER APPLIED		NO FERTILIZER APPLIED
BUSHELS YIELD PER ACRE	79		18
INCHES OF SOIL WATER USED	16		14
GALLONS OF WATER USED PER BUSHEL OF GRAIN PRODUCED	5,600		21,000
INCHES OF WATER LEFT IN TOP 42 INCHES OF SOIL	1·04		4·5

DEPTH: 1ft, 2ft, 3ft, 4ft

There is increasing evidence from research that well-fertilized crops use water more efficiently. When subsoil moisture is good, adequate fertilizer enables the crop to grow vigorously and send its roots deep for water. The diagram above is based on tests carried out in Missouri, U.S.A., in a year with only 5 inches of rain during the growing season. The corn which received no fertilizer (*right*) left much of the soil moisture unused.

This does not mean that fertilizer can substitute for water as such. It means that fertilizer helps a crop to make better use of the moisture that is already available.

E

Much of the credit for this must go to the increasing use
of plant foods in the form of simple chemical fertilizers.
Phosphorus, potassium and nitrogen needed by the plant
are now being returned to the soil from which the growing
plant has removed them. In some cases, traces of other
essential elements are applied to make up a deficiency in
the soil. Used carefully and with a proper understanding,
these fertilizers are enabling us to sustain a level of
production that can provide us with the food the world
needs.

Meanwhile, new methods and techniques are being developed to make the use of fertilizers more effective. With
some crops, the fertilizer can be used to better advantage
when it is placed close to the seed in the soil. Quick-grow-
ing, shallow-rooted crops like spinach, peas and beans
give improved returns when fertilizer is applied in this
way. With cereal crops, this technique has halved the superphosphate requirements of the crop (see page 213).

Although the effect of fertilizer placement is so spectacular, it is a technique that must be used with care. Some
seeds have a flimsy coat that offers little protection against
the effects of fertilizer placed too near them in the soil.
Some seedlings are particularly delicate, and are easily
damaged or destroyed by high concentrations of nitrogen
or potassium salts. Yet cereals, which derive such benefit
from fertilizer placement, can be sown with the grain in
contact with the fertilizer without taking any harm.

While agricultural scientists are now studying the finer
points of the techniques of applying fertilizers in this way,
we have yet to make the most of what Lawes and Gilbert
discovered a century ago. In the world as a whole, we have
hardly made a start on the job of returning to the soil the
nutrient chemicals it needs to give us a generous return
of crops. Proper cultivation and the use of chemical fertilizers could provide food for hundreds of millions of people
who are living on a subsistence diet.

Shortage of Nitrogen

More often than not, it is the element nitrogen that is lacking. Properly used, a pound of combined nitrogen will provide enough food for a man for a week. The world uses over two million tons of nitrogenous fertilizer a year. But this is only a fraction of the amount that is needed by the hungry soil.

Only in a few isolated regions – for example, Holland and Belgium – is the value of nitrogen as a fertilizer thoroughly appreciated. As a result of proper attention to soil feeding and management, Dutch farms produce more food to the acre than any other land in the world. Dutch grassland supports twice as many cows as British land; and Dutch cows can produce one and a half times as much milk.

Most of the world's agricultural soils are desperately short of chemical plant foods, and the job of replenishing them is a difficult one. Many factors combine to slow up progress; apathy, prejudice, economics, politics and ignorance all play their part.

In spite of the growing understanding of the principles of modern agriculture, there is still a deep-rooted suspicion of chemical fertilizers. Many growers regard them as a substitute for the "real thing"; they have not yet learned to think of plant nutrition in chemical terms; they do not realize that the chemicals supplied by artificial fertilizers are essentially the same as the chemicals that come from compost and manure, and from the minerals in the soil.

Farmers are often troubled by the possibility of chemical fertilizers injuring the soil. Used indiscriminately, without any understanding of the needs of the soil or its crop, some fertilizers can be harmful; too much fat or protein is equally unhelpful if crammed into a human being. But used with proper attention to the needs of the soil, fertilizers will restore the balance of nutrients without doing any harm to the soil itself. Superphosphate, for example, has been

LIME — THE SOIL

Most soils in humid regions are acid or "sour" as a result of leaching, which removes calcium, magnesium, potassium and other acid-neutralizing elements from the soil. Even in a temperate climate, rain will wash calcium from the soil equivalent to a ½ ounce of lime for every square yard every year. Removal of calcium is the chief cause of soil acidity, and regular addition of lime to the soil is necessary to make good the losses, and neutralize the acidity.

Lime improves the soil in many ways, as seen below.

WHAT LIME DOES

* *Lime sweetens a sour soil* by correcting acidity. Few plants will grow well in a very acid soil.

* *Lime supplies calcium,* which is an essential nutrient for all plants. Dolomitic lime supplies magnesium too.

* *Lime speeds the decay of organic matter,* including humus, liberating plant food chemicals into the soil. It sets free elements needed for healthy growth.

* *Lime increases the availability of phosphorus.*

* *Lime brings life to the soil* by encouraging earthworms, bacteria and other living things. Beneficial bacteria flourish, including those that fix nitrogen and so increase fertility of the soil.

* *Lime improves the physical properties of the soil.* It breaks up heavy clay soils, binding the clay particles into crumbs. Soils become easier to work, warmer and better drained.

* *Lime reduces the activity of toxic substances* which are detrimental to plants.

* *Lime discourages pests and diseases.* Some soil diseases, such as Club Root, are checked by liming. Many soil pests, including slugs, leatherjackets and wireworms detest a well-limed soil.

AVOID OVER-LIMING –

Too much lime can be as bad as too little. Humus breaks down too quickly, and the structure of a soil may be destroyed. Iron is locked up in the soil, and plants may suffer from iron-deficiency.

– AND USE LIME BY ITSELF

Do not mix lime with other soil dressings. Apply it at least 2 – 3 months after manuring, and 1 month after fertilizers, to avoid loss of plant foods.

Manures, composts, fertilizers and seeds can be safely added to soil 1 month after liming.

CONDITIONER

HOW MUCH TO USE?

The amount of lime needed to raise the pH value of a soil by one unit, e.g. from 5.0 to 6.0, depends largely on the type of soil, organic matter content and fineness and type of material used for liming. Clay and silt loam soils require more lime than sandy soils. Also, soils high in organic matter require more lime than those low in organic matter. Examples of the rates to use are as follows:

Soil	Liming material (lbs per acre)		
	Ground Limestone or Marl	Quicklime	Hydrated Lime
Sandy	1,500	840	1,110
Sandy Loam	2,000	1,120	1,480
Loam	3,000	1,680	2,220
Silt Loam or Clay Loam	3,500	1,960	2,590

Note: For soils low in organic matter, reduce the above by 25 per cent. For soils high in organic matter, increase 100 per cent.

Hydrated or slaked lime is handiest to use on a garden soil. It is easy to handle, quick-acting and safe near growing plants. The following table is a guide:

AMOUNT TO USE (LBS. PER SQUARE YARD)*	Sandy soil	Loam	Clayey or Peaty soil
Very sour	$\frac{3}{4}$	1·0	$1\frac{1}{4}$
Sour	$\frac{1}{2}$	$\frac{3}{4}$	1·0
Nearly neutral	$\frac{1}{4}$	$\frac{1}{2}$	$\frac{3}{4}$
Alkaline	–	–	–

*If the acidity of the soil is not known, a good general rule is to apply ½ lb. of hydrated lime per square yard on sandy or loamy soils, and ¾ lb. per square yard on clayey or peaty soils.

WHEN TO LIME?

Lime is most effective if applied in the autumn, after digging or ploughing. If the soil is manured in the autumn, the liming is best left until February. It is spread evenly on the surface, leaving the rain to carry it into the soil.

The Vegetable Garden usually needs liming every 3 years. If crops are being grown in rotation, liming should be carried out in preparation for the cabbage family, but not for potatoes.

The Flower Garden should be limed every 2 years if the soil is sandy, or every 3 years if it is a loam or clayey soil.

applied for more than a hundred years to some of the soils at Rothamsted. The structure of the soil has remained undamaged and there has been no deleterious effect on microorganisms in the soil.

Fertilizers and Health

It has often been suggested that the use of chemical fertilizers is injurious to the health of the crops and the animals and human beings who eat them. Such doubts can only be answered by reference to statistics of world health. People the world over are in better health today than they have ever been before. They are living longer. And there is no evidence at all that they are suffering any injurious effects from the food they eat, even though much of it has been grown for years with the help of chemical fertilizers. Indeed, if it was not for the help we get from these fertilizers the soil would be quite unable to produce the food that the world needs. Millions would starve.

It has long been known that plants tend to take up minerals indiscriminately from the soil. Under natural conditions of growth, chemicals dissolved in the soil water will find their way into the plant, whether they are needed by the plant or not. In some parts of the world certain minerals taken up in this way can be harmful to animals or human beings who use these plants as food. Teart disease of cattle, for example, is caused by their eating plants containing too much molybdenum that has come from soil containing excessive quantities of the element. Selenium in the soil can make the pasture harmful in a similar way.

Just as nature can cause damage by releasing undesirable chemicals in the soil, so could the indiscriminate application of such chemicals by man affect the composition of growing crops. But in making use of chemical fertilizers the farmer is applying those chemicals to the soil that the plant derives in any case from other sources. He is maintaining the balance of foods needed by the plant. He would no more apply anything harmful to the soil than would a baker mix a dose of arsenic into his dough.

In many parts of the world, deficiencies of one or more of the main elements needed by the plant are the cause of plant and animal diseases associated with definite regions. By making up these soil deficiencies with the help of fertilizer chemicals, the farmer makes a practical contribution to the improvement of his neighbour's health.

Wheats have been grown for many years at Rothamsted, some being fed continually on natural manure, some on chemical fertilizers and some with nothing added to the soil at all. Analysis of the wheat has shown that there is little difference in the chemical composition of grains grown under different conditions of soil feeding.

Erosion Dangers

The use of chemical fertilizers has often been quoted as a major cause of soil erosion that has become such a difficult problem in many countries. But soil erosion is not a consequence of the use of fertilizers; it is the result of careless farming practices and overproduction of food on land that has gradually been stripped of its natural humus.

During the nineteenth century, when cheap food for the workers was demanded by the industrial countries of the world, the soil of many of the great food-producing countries was steadily worked to death. On the great plains of Canada and the United States, in Australia and in Africa, crops were taken from the soil year after year; cattle and sheep were turned on to the pastures and left to nibble the grass down to its roots.

For years, the land gave the farmer his crops and meat. But in doing so, the soil became steadily more exhausted. The insistence on quick returns burnt the humus from the land, and as the humus went, the structure of the soil was gradually destroyed. In place of the spongy crumbs that nature had built up in her prairie soils there remained a

TERMS USED IN LIMING

ACID-FORMING FERTILIZER A fertilizer that tends to increase the acidity of the soil (lower the soil pH).

ACID-NEUTRALIZING VALUE (A.N.V.) See Calcium Carbonate Equivalent.

AGRICULTURAL LIMING MATERIAL A material whose calcium and magnesium content is capable of correcting soil acidity.

AIR-SLAKED LIME See page 184.

BASE (a) The metallic element combined in a salt, as sodium in sodium chloride or calcium in calcium sulphate, or (b) the alkaline compounds formed by such elements, as calcium hydroxide or oxide, or sodium hydroxide.

BOG LIME Marl.

BUILDER'S LIME See Calcium Oxide.

BURNT LIME See Calcium Oxide.

CALCAREOUS Consisting of, or containing, calcium carbonate.

CALCITE The common crystalline form of calcium carbonate.

CALCIUM One of the metallic elements. It never occurs in nature in the free form but only in combination with other elements. It is an essential constituent of teeth, bones, shells, and plants.

CALCIUM CARBONATE (CARBONATE OF LIME) $CaCO_3$. A compound which occurs in nature as limestone, marble, chalk, marl, mollusc shells, coral, eggshells, and similar substances.

CALCIUM CARBONATE EQUIVALENT The sum of the calcium and magnesium oxide contents of a liming material when both are expressed as their equivalents in calcium carbonate. It is usually expressed as a percentage. For pure limestone the value is 100 percent, for pure dolomite it is 108.6 percent. The calcium carbonate equivalent is also referred to as the neutralizing value, or acid-neutralizing value (A.N.V.).

CALCIUM HYDROXIDE $Ca(OH)_2$, made by the chemical combination of calcium oxide (quicklime) and water. See Hydrated Lime.

CALCIUM OXIDE CaO. Quicklime. (See page 184). Also known as unslaked lime, burnt lime, lump lime, stone lime, caustic lime, or builder's lime. It does not occur in nature.

CALCIUM OXIDE EQUIVALENT The percentage of calcium oxide in a liming material plus 1.39 times the magnesium oxide percentage. For pure limestone the value is 56.0 percent; for pure dolomite it is 60.8 percent

CARBONATE OF LIME See Calcium Carbonate.

CAUSTIC LIME See Calcium Oxide.

CHALK See page 185

DOLOMITE See page 184.

EXCHANGEABLE BASE A basic element held on the surface of a colloid but capable of being replaced or exchanged by other basic elements or by hydrogen.

GROUND LIMESTONE See page 184.

GYPSUM A hydrated form of calcium sulphate, also known as land plaster. It supplies calcium to the soil, but it does not correct acidity; hence, it is not a liming material.

HYDRATED LIME See page 184.

LAND PLASTER See Gypsum.

LIME See page 184.

LIME EQUIVALENT Same as Calcium Oxide Equivalent.

LIME REQUIREMENT The quantity of lime required to bring an acid soil to neutrality or to some desired degree of acidity or pH.

LUMP LIME   Quicklime as it comes from the lime kiln. See Calcium oxide.

MAGNESIAN LIMESTONE   Limestone containing varying proportions of magnesium carbonate. See Dolomite.

MAGNESIUM CARBONATE $MgCO_3$. It occurs in nature as the mineral magnesite, and as a constituent of magnesian limestone and dolomite.

MAGNESIUM OXIDE   MgO. It is formed from magnesium carbonate (magnesite) by heating to drive off the carbon dioxide, or, in mixture with calcium oxide, by heating magnesian limestone or dolomite. Also known as magnesia, it occurs in nature as the mineral periclase.

MARBLE   A compact, hard, polishable form of limestone.

MARL   See page 184.

MECHANICAL ANALYSIS   Indicates the percentage of the particles of a material that fall within predetermined size limits, or between certain mesh sizes. Also referred to as screen analysis, sieve analysis, and particle-size distribution.

NEUTRALIZING VALUE   See Calcium Carbonate Equivalent; Calcium Oxide Equivalent.

OXIDE OF LIME   See Calcium Oxide.

pH   A measure of the degree of acidity or alkalinity of a soil. Specifically the numbers $(1 - 14)$ of the pH scale are the logarithms of the reciprocal of the hydrogen ion concentration expressed in gram molecules of hydrogen ion per litre.

PULVERIZED LIMESTONE (FINE-GROUND LIMESTONE)   A product made by grinding either limestone or dolomitic limestone fine enough to pass through a 20-mesh sieve, with at least 75 percent passing through a 100-mesh sieve.

QUICKLIME   See Calcium Oxide.

SCREEN ANALYSIS   See Mechanical Analysis.

SHELL MARL   See Marl.

SIEVE ANALYSIS   See Mechanical Analysis.

SLAKED LIME   See Hydrated Lime.

SOIL REACTION   The acidity or alkalinity status of a soil. Soils that are acid are said to have an acid reaction; those that are alkaline are said to have an alkaline reaction.

TOTAL OXIDES   A term applied to the simple sum of the percentages of calcium and magnesium oxides in a liming material.

WASTE LIME   Waste, or by-product, lime is any industrial waste or by-product from such sources as tanneries, sugar mills, and acetylene plants. It contains calcium and magnesium in forms that correct soil acidity when applied to the land.

E*

fine powdery soil that held little but the mineral particles derived from the parent rocks. Exhausted by its efforts to produce too many crops, the soil died.

Much of the industrial wealth of the United States was built up on the fertility stored in its virgin soils. Once this fertility had gone, it was difficult to replace it. And over great areas of the United States and other countries the soil became bankrupt. If it had then been a matter only of returning the necessary chemical foods to the soil, the situation would have been serious, but not desperate. But the crumb structure of the soil is built by nature only after years of slow, steady effort. Once it is destroyed, it is no easy matter to restore it again.

Water Erosion

The fine, loose soil that results from overproduction, particularly when this is accompanied by a run of dry years, is at the mercy of the wind and the rain. Spattering down upon it, the rain beats the surface of the soil into a hard impenetrable cake. Unable to soak into the topsoil, the water sweeps over the flattened earth. In rivulets and streams it flows into the valleys, heading towards the rivers and the sea. As it flows, the water sweeps up the dusty soil, carrying it away as a river of mud. This mud contains the precious topsoil that has been built by nature over hundreds of years of balanced growth. As the soil is removed, deep gullies are formed. In the rivers, banks of silt are raised, blocking the waterways with barriers of priceless soil (see Pls. 1, 4, 12).

In Africa and the United States, vast areas of once fertile land have been destroyed by erosion in this way. With the topsoil gone, crops cannot grow in the dead half-weathered subsoil that is left.

Wind Erosion

In the huge prairie districts of the United States, the

wind has done what water does elsewhere. Bereft of its cover of vegetation, the dusty soil is swept up in great clouds by the wind. In the "dustbowl" districts of the United States, many a farm has been swept in a cloud of dust over the horizon as though by a giant broom. In this dust has gone the topsoil, the farmer's capital (see Pl. 13).

Erosion of this sort, by water and wind, has become a serious threat to food production in many countries. It is at its worst in lands where rain falls heavily, or the wind is able to blow unchecked across the plains that have dried in the hot sun. Erosion tends to be more of a problem in tropical and semi tropical countries than it is in temperate lands. But even in Britain, where the climate is relatively mild, and farming is more varied, erosion has begun to nibble at the land. There are places in Wales and Cumberland where water has swept away the topsoil. In Norfolk, where rainfall is low and the winds can blow unchecked across the flat countryside, wind erosion has taken place. Compared with erosion in other countries, that in Britain is not a serious threat. But the fact that it can take place at all is a warning that the soil must be treated with the respect it deserves.

In the United States alone, the annual loss of topsoil through water erosion is equivalent to the soil from 10,000 hundred-acre farms. The cost of erosion has been put at some $4 billion every year, and the quantity of plant foods washed or blown away with the topsoil is equal to more than fifty times the amount of fertilizer used in the United States every year. These figures give an idea of the size and seriousness of erosion as an economic problem in one of the world's great food-growing areas. In other countries, the story is the same; in Canada, wheat has been grown year after year in the same prairie soil until the humus has been used up and the crumb structure of the soil destroyed; in South Africa, ruthless grazing and cropping has allowed the rain to drive huge channels through the land,

FERTILIZER GLOSSARY

ACID-FORMING Capable of increasing soil acidity.

AMMONIATING (AMMONIA) SOLUTION Solution of ammonium nitrate or of urea in ammonia and water. These solutions contain from 37 to 53% nitrogen.

AMMONIATED SUPERPHOSPHATE A product resulting from the treatment of superphosphate with ammonia solution or anhydrous ammonia.

ANHYDROUS AMMONIA Dry ammonia gas compressed into a liquid form. Stored under pressure.

ARTIFICIAL MANURE Product resulting from the composting of waste straw, stalks, leaves etc., with phosphate, nitrogen-bearing material and liming material.

AVAILABLE In a form capable of being assimilated by growing plants.

BASIC SLAG A by-product produced in the manufacture of steel from phosphatic iron ores. It contains about 10% P_2O_5, 30% calcium, 3% magnesium and 2.5% manganese.

BONE MEAL (RAW) A product resulting from the drying and grinding of animal bones that have not previously been steamed under pressure.

BONE MEAL (STEAMED) The product resulting from grinding animal bones that previously have been steamed under pressure.

BORAX Hydrated sodium tetraborate ($Na_2B_4O_7 \cdot 10H_2O$), which contains slightly over 11% boron.

CASTOR POMACE The ground residue of the castor bean which remains after extraction of the oil.

CURING The conditioning that takes place when fertilizer materials are mixed and stored, and chemical reactions are completed.

FORMULA The quantities and grades of materials used in making a fertilizer mixture.

GRADE The guaranteed minimum percentage of total nitrogen, available phosphoric acid and/or soluble potash contents.

HUMUS Partly decomposed organic matter in the soil.

MANURE SALTS Potash salts containing a high percentage of chloride and from 20 to 30% of potash (K_2O).

MICRO NUTRIENT A term used in referring to boron, manganese, molybdenum, copper, zinc and iron, which are essential plant food elements required in very small amounts.

MURIATE OF POTASH Potassium chloride, KCl.

NITRIFICATION The process by which nitrates are formed in the soil by bacterial oxidation of ammonium nitrogen.

NON-ACID FORMING Not capable of increasing the residual acidity of the soil.

(*Continued opposite*)

ORGANIC   Containing carbon (other than as carbonates) as an essential ingredient. The term usually refers to material derived from plant or animal sources.

PEAT   Partly decayed organic matter of natural occurrence.

PHOSPHATE ROCK   A natural rock containing one or more calcium phosphate minerals of such purity as to permit its use in the manufacture of commercial products.

PRIMARY NUTRIENTS   Nitrogen, phosphorus, potassium; essential nutrients used in large amounts by plants.

SECONDARY NUTRIENTS   Calcium, sulphur and magnesium; essential nutrients used in moderate amounts by plants.

SOLUBLE POTASH   That portion of the potash of fertilizers that is soluble in an aqueous ammoniacal solution of 0.8% ammonium oxalate.

SUPERPHOSPHATE ORDINARY (normal or standard): a product containing 18 to 24% available P_2O_5 formed by treating phosphate rock with sulphuric acid.

SUPERPHOSPHATE DOUBLE   (triple or treble): a product containing about 40 to 50% of available P_2O_5 formed by treating phosphate rock with phosphoric acid.

SULPHATE OF POTASH (MAGNESIA)   A double sulphate of potassium and magnesium containing not less than 21% of potash (K_2O), not less than 53% of sulphate of magnesia and not more than 2.5 chlorine.

TANKAGE   *Garbage Tankage* is the rendered, dried and ground products derived from waste food materials.

Process Tankage is a product made under steam pressure from ground inert nitrogenous materials with or without the use of acids for the purpose of increasing the availability of the nitrogen.

TRACE ELEMENTS   See Micro Nutrients.

THE IDEAL SOIL

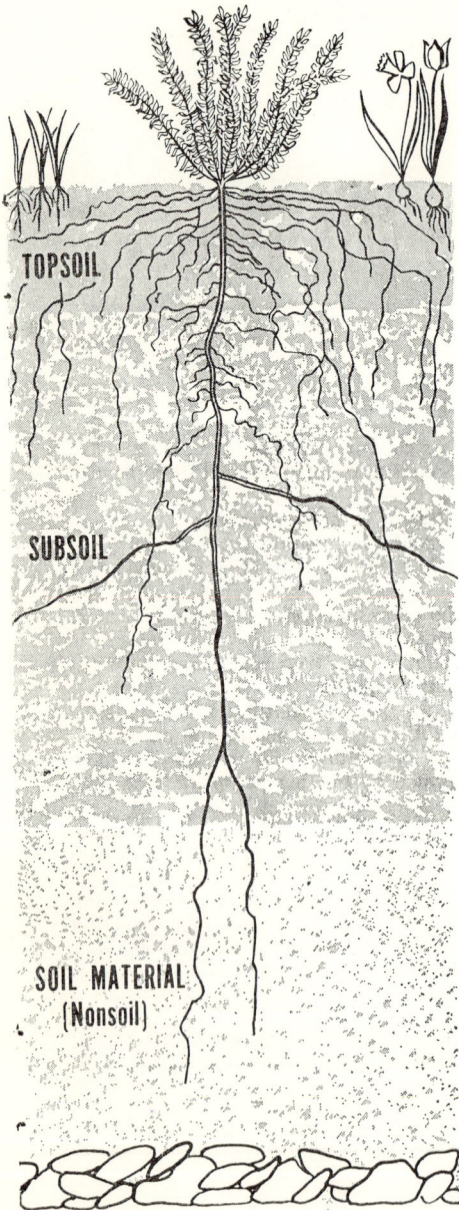

TOPSOIL

SUBSOIL

SOIL MATERIAL
(Nonsoil)

1. The Ideal Soil has a deep rooting zone from which plants can take both water and nutrients. This zone is at least 18 inches deep; most plants do better if it is thicker, even 4 to 6 feet. A shallow soil cannot hold enough water and nutrients to keep plants growing at their best.

2. The Ideal Soil is loamy in texture; that is, it consists of a favourable mixture of sand, silt and clay particles. Sands take in water readily but retain only a small part of it. Clays hold a great deal of water, but unless handled carefully they tend to become hard and massive when dry.

3. The Ideal Soil has good structure. The particles of sand, silt and clay are grouped into granules or crumbs, permitting water to enter easily, roots to penetrate deeply, and air to move in and out freely. The surface is moderately cloddy, not fine and dusty. The soil is firm enough to hold moisture and make close contact with seeds and roots. It allows excess water to drain through promptly but holds a good supply for plants to use between rains and irrigations.

4. The Ideal Soil contains much organic matter in various stages of decomposition. It also contains many micro-organisms and small animals, such as earthworms, that help decompose the organic matter. In the process they release nutrients for use by new plants. The partially decomposed materials that make up humus produce a stable organic structure in the soil. Since the organic matter in the soil is constantly being broken down, new supplies must be added regularly to maintain life in the soil. *(continued opposite)*

The Ideal Soil (continued)

5. The Ideal soil has an adequate and balanced supply of nutrients for the plants that are to be grown. Most vegetables do best in soil of high fertility, and most flowers in soils of moderate fertility. The herbs and some flowers and shrubs prefer soils of low fertility.

6. The Ideal Soil has proper reaction (acidity) for the plants to be grown. Roses, most annual flowers and vegetables, and most lawn grasses should have a slightly acid to neutral soil. Some plants, like azaleas and rhododendrons, require an acid soil.

---

down which the topsoil has been washed away; in Australia, sheep have been left to nibble the grass down to its roots, destroying the natural pasture that sustains the structure of the soil.

We tend to think of erosion as a modern agricultural phenomenon. But in fact it has been going on since man began cultivating the soil. Intensive cultivation during the last century has allowed it to get out of hand. Whenever we are taking crops from the ground, we are tending to destroy the crumb structure of the soil. But by treating our soil carefully and thoughtfully we can ensure that it will retain the porous crumb structure that enables it to resist being swept away by wind and water.

Erosion Prevention

Where the damage has been done, and the soil is fine enough to be carried away, much can be done to minimize the loss. If water is sweeping over the surface of the soil, the land can be protected by contour ploughing. This is nothing more than a development of the terracing of hillsides that has been in use for thousands of years. The land is ploughed in such a way as to follow the natural contours of the sloping ground. The channel cut by the plough remains on a level, forming a little terrace that collects the water and prevents it flowing rapidly downhill. Water is given every chance to sink into the soil (see Pl. 12).

If wind is the danger, every effort must be made to prevent its sweeping unchecked across the land. Trees can break its strength, and fields planted out in strips with different types of crops can hold on to the soil more firmly than an unprotected expanse of powdery soil.

Wherever possible, an adequate cover of vegetation is grown to grip and hold the topsoil. Rain cannot beat so heavily on a soil that is carrying a crop as it does on an uncovered soil. In many regions, the land is stubble-mulched instead of being ploughed; sharp disc harrows are dragged over the stubble, cutting through the roots of weeds but leaving the stubble itself to hold on to the soil.

With every precaution taken to prevent erosion carrying off the powdery topsoil, the aim must always be to restore the crumb structure of the soil. Humus is ploughed in and special crops are grown which are known to contribute to the build-up of soil structure. Under natural conditions, the soil beneath a healthy pasture is usually in excellent heart. Beneath the turf, the particles of soil are held together in aggregates as big as garden peas. Some grasses and legumes have an unusually binding effect on the soil, and the use of suitable rotation is often a better way of building soil structure than is the use of farmyard manure or compost. The effects remain even after the roots of the plants have died; this may be due to sticky substances produced by the roots themselves, or by bacteria that are associated with them. Some bacteria are known to surround themselves with gummy capsules; soil fungi can also bind soil particles together.

Soil Conditioners

The chemical nature of these sticky materials produced by humus and by bacteria and other organisms in the soil is not known. But they are sufficiently understood for us to know the kind of substances they are. Many similar substances have been made synthetically and some of these have been found to encourage crumb-building in soils that

TREASURE FROM THE FARMYARD !

Until comparatively recent times, farmyard manure was the " fertilizer " on which all farmers and gardeners relied for feeding their crops. Today, the amount of farmyard manure available is sufficient for only a fraction of the quantity of plant foods that are needed. But its value to the soil lies also in providing the humus so essential in building soil structure, and every available scrap should be returned to the soil.

The foods eaten by farm animals come, in the first place, from plants. The excrement of the animals contains some or all of the elements that were constituents of the plant materials they have eaten, and by digging or ploughing animal manure into the soil we are returning elements needed by future generations of plants.

During their passage through the animal, the substances in plant foods have undergone all manner of chemical changes. Their constituent elements are rearranged into new combinations, before being excreted in the urine or the solid excrement. Some of the substances in the manure can serve immediately as plant foods. Others must undergo further changes to form chemical combinations that the plant can use. These changes take place as the manure decays.

The value of a farmyard manure depends to a large extent upon the nature of the food that the animal has eaten. If the food is easily digested, much of the nitrogen will have been absorbed into the animal's body, and it will pass out in the urine. Nitrogenous chemicals dissolved in urine are readily available as sources of nitrogen to the plant.

If the animal has been fed on indigestible food, on the other hand, much of the nitrogen will remain in the undigested solid matter. It will become available as plant food only after being broken down by decay organisms.

A ton of good manure will contain 10-15 lbs. of nitrogen, 4-9 lbs. of P_2O_5 and 9-18 lbs. of potash.

PLATE 5

PLATE 6

MAN AGAINST THE SOIL

When primitive man roamed the earth, he relied upon his own individual efforts to provide himself with food he needed. As agricultural skills developed, the production of food per man increased, and people began to give up the production of their own food. They left the job to others, and the farmer came into being.

As civilization has progressed, the farmer has learned to produce food from the soil with ever-increasing efficiency, and the extent to which he can feed other people is a yardstick by which the progress of civilization can be measured.

The increase of agricultural productivity has been especially marked in the U.S.A., where science and mechanization have made their greatest impact. In 1800, the U.S. farmer was feeding himself and also meeting one third of the needs of one other person. Today, he has increased productivity to the point where he feeds himself, his family and *14 other individuals*. This increase symbolized in the photograph above, showing (*left*) farmer with 1 unit of food for his own family, and (*right*) 14 additional units to feed others – *du Pont*.

MECHANIZATION. Cultivation of the soil and the growing of crops has now become a highly mechanized industry.

Below left : The equipment used on a modern 78 acre U.S. farm. In 1910, there were 1,000 farm tractors and 25 million horses and mules on U.S. farms. Today, there are more than a million farm tractors and less than 5 million horses and mules, many of which do no farm work.

Below right : The modern tractor and plough in the foreground do as much work as ten horses, five ploughs and five men in the background.

PLATE 7

CHEMICALS ON THE FARM.

In the last half century, production has doubled on farms in many western countries, despite the reduction in the number of farm workers by one third. About one quarter of this vast increase may be attributed to mechanization, and the release of land which was previously being used to provide feed for animals that were replaced by the machine. The rest of the increase is due to scientific progress, especially the growing understanding of the role that chemistry plays in agriculture.

The picture above gives an indication of the amount and variety of chemicals used on a 78 acre U.S. farm in the course of a year. Fertilizers for the soil make up a high proportion of the total.

Even in a highly productive agricultural country like the U.S., however, much more could be done to increase farm output by the proper use of fertilizers. In 1956, only one quarter of all U.S. crop land was treated with fertilizer.

PLATE 8

are deficient in naturally-formed gums. These synthetic substances have become known as soil conditioners; if they can be produced cheaply and in quantity they could play a vitally important part in helping us to restore the structure of soils that have been denuded of their humus. They enable the farmer to fight back effectively against the threat of soil erosion.

In a world that is so short of food, we can ill afford to lose any of the precious topsoil that has often taken a thousand years or more to form. Erosion is a threat long before it has reached the stage where it is bringing total destruction to the land. The loss of less than an inch of topsoil can mean five bushels of corn less to the acre.

Maintaining the fertility and structure of our soil has become one of the most urgent problems of our time.

PART 2

YOU AND YOUR SOIL

7

Know Your Soil

The soil in your garden is an asset that can bring you a regular income in the form of plants. You may measure this income in terms of valuable foods, such as vegetables and fruits. You may prefer to take it as the sheer enjoyment of gardening, with the beauty of flowers providing an attractive environment in which to follow your hobby. No matter how you approach your gardening, you will want to go about it in such a way as to bring a good return of healthy plants. And to do this you must know your soil.

The modern farmer can call on the help of official agricultural advisers, who will assess his soils scientifically. Experts will prepare soil maps of his land, and by considering these in relation to situation and climate will work out the most effective way of using the farm's soil resources (see page 323).

A detailed scientific study of this sort is generally beyond the scope of the average gardener. But there is a great deal that the enthusiastic gardener can do for himself in assessing the soil of his garden. And with an increased understanding of his soil to help him, he can decide how best to use his soil resources.

See for Yourself

Your soil is a three-dimensional body. It has depth as well as length and breadth, and to understand it properly you must know what lies beneath the surface layer. If possible, you should examine the soil profile right down to bedrock, or at least to the bottom of the normal rooting zone to a depth of about 3 feet.

To the expert, the nature of the soil profile tells the story of the soil's long history. Many cultivated soils have a profile that records the soil's development over thousands of years. Other soils may be so young that they do not have discernible horizons at all. The flood plains alongside rivers, and the sand dunes bordering desert areas are examples of soils which have been moved into place so recently that they have not yet developed a layered profile.

The nature of the soil profile may vary considerably from one place to another, even in a small garden. It is not sufficient to dig a hole at random and examine a single profile; you must dig holes at intervals on your land and study the profile to be seen at every hole. In a small garden, this will mean perhaps three or four holes; in a large garden it may mean twenty or more. The holes should be spaced out systematically, and should include any parts of the land which have obviously been subjected to any sort of special treatment in the past.

Often, you can save unnecessary work by examining the soil profile in holes that have to be dug anyway, for example, in planting trees or putting in posts. Remember always that a hole in your garden is a window through which you can see the soil beneath. Make sure of having a good look through it when the opportunity arises!

If a hole is dug carefully, the profile of the soil will be seen quite clearly on the side of the hole. You should make a careful record of the characteristics of the profile, noting especially the thickness of the layers, and the texture, structure and colour of the soil in each layer. You will not be able to assess these characteristics as accurately as the expert soil scientist would, but you can learn enough to understand the sort of treatment to which your soil will respond.

DEPTH AND HORIZON THICKNESS

In some soils, there is a clear-cut boundary between one layer and the next, and it is a simple matter to measure the thickness of the layers. In other soils, you will find one layer merging gradually into another, and you will have to make an estimate of where the boundary lies.

You should examine the subsoil carefully for signs of hard, impenetrable layers. These layers may form when substances such as iron oxide are washed from above, cementing soil particles together into a rock-like "pan". Pans are also formed by the pressure of feet or heavy implements on the soil surface.

Soil pans act as a barrier to the free run of plant roots, and to the flow of air, water and plant nutrients in the soil. They convert what could be a deep and porous soil into a shallow soil, and you must make plans to break them up wherever they are found.

The total depth, including topsoil, subsoil and parent material, is an important characteristic of your soil. In general a deep and porous soil enables your plants to draw on greater reserves of water, air and nutrient materials. A thin soil covering, on the other hand, will provide only a severely restricted space in which roots can forage.

TEXTURE

A Simple Test

The texture of each layer is a vitally important characteristic of your soil, and you should make every effort to assess it. If you want an accurate determination of the textural class of your soil, you must have it analysed in a laboratory. But you do not need such precise information for normal purposes. You can judge the texture of the soil for yourself simply by rubbing and squeezing a sample of moist soil between your fingers. With a little practice, you will be able to assess soil texture with sufficient accuracy for most practical purposes.

The naming of a soil texture with accuracy can be done only by carrying out a mechanical analysis to determine the relative proportions of sand, silt and clay (see page 274). But for practical purposes, it is possible to judge the texture broadly by picking up a handful of moist soil and moulding it with the fingers.

* If the soil feels gritty and tends to crumble easily, it is probably a *sandy* soil.
* If the soil does not feel gritty, and moulds without feeling plastic or sticky, it is probably a *loam*.
* If the soil does not feel gritty, and moulds into a sticky ball, it is probably a *clayey* soil.

The advantages and disadvantages of these soils, and suggestions for improvement, are given below.

Soil Texture	Advantages	Disadvantages
Sandy Other names: light soil, Warm soil, Hungry soil.	Warm — most suitable for early crops. Easily worked, even when wet. Free draining, due to open texture.	Hungry — often short of plant foods. Dries out quickly; needs frequent watering during summer.
Loam	Advantages, to a lesser degree, of sandy and clayey soils.	
Clayey Other names: Heavy soil, Cold soil.	Generally well supplied with plant foods.	Cold — not suitable for early crops. Heavy to work under wet conditions. Tends to waterlog in winter. Cakes hard and cracks in dry weather.

Notes on Treatment

Sandy "The soil with the least backache and the most heartache." Sandy soils lose food and water very quickly. As much humus-making material as possible should be added. Sticky manure, such as cow or pig manure, is best, but all humus-makers are valuable. Fertilizers are essential, and should be applied in spring and summer. Humus-makers and fertilizers should not be dug in deeply.

Loam The ideal soil. This is the easiest soil to look after. It will readily acquire and retain a good crumb structure with good management. Regular light dressings of lime, humus-making materials and fertilizers should be given. The ground should be dug over in the autumn.

Clayey The soil may need draining. It should be dug thoroughly in the autumn, the lumps being exposed to winter frosts. A generous dressing of lime will help to build up a crumb structure. Humus-making materials are needed to preserve the

(*Continued opposite*)

SOIL TEXTURE

Notes on Treatment (*Continued*)

crumb structure obtained in this way. Strawy stable manure is best, but all organic materials are useful. Clayey soils are usually rich in plant foods, but the proper use of fertilizers will make for still better results.

SPECIAL SOIL CHARACTERISTICS

The physical nature of many soils is modified by special factors such as stoniness, high content of organic matter and chalk.

Soil	Characteristics	Advantages	Disadvantages
Stony (Burning Soil)	Scores of stones, large and small, per square yard	Usually free draining Workable early in season	Dries out very quickly in summer Difficult to cultivate
Peaty (Acid Soil)	Dark brown or black, very rich in plant remains. Spongy	Easily worked Best soil for acid-loving plants, e.g. Azaleas, Rhododendrons, Heaths, Fertile when limed and drained	Too acid for most plants
Chalky	Dark surface soil, with white sub-soil a few inches below surface	Best for numerous flowers and shrubs, especially rockery plants	Sticky and soft in wet weather

Notes on Treatment

Stony   Remove the larger stones lying on the surface. Do not attempt, however, to free soil from stones completely. Stony soils tend to be free-draining, so that the plant nutrients are quickly washed through. Plenty of manure or compost and fertilizers is essential. These must be applied close to the surface; digging should be kept shallow to avoid bringing up more stones.
If the soil is also noticeably sandy or clayey, treatments recommended for these soils should be used.

Peaty   These are basically very fertile soils, being rich in organic matter, and will give excellent results with proper treatment. Good drainage and generous liming are essential. The addition of loamy top-soil is very helpful.

Chalky   These soils are difficult to manage, but they can be greatly improved. Digging should be kept shallow, and plenty of humus-making materials and fertilizers must be added, as these soils are free-draining and therefore "hungry".
Green manuring is a great help.
Although the subsoil is chalk, liming may be necessary.

Garden soils are usually classified into three broad textural groups, called sandy, loamy and clayey soils. These names coincide roughly with the alternative terms coarse-, medium- and fine-textured soils (see page 147), and they indicate which of the three types of particle is playing the most significant role in the soil.

SANDY SOILS. (Coarse-textured Soils)

If your soil feels harsh and gritty, and the particles barely hold together when moist soil is rubbed between your fingers, it is a sandy soil. It has a preponderance of the largest type of particle.

Sandy soils are usually well-aerated and permeable to water. They dry out quickly, holding little moisture by comparison with soils of finer texture, and they tend to be deficient in plant nutrients. They need plenty of watering in summer, with an ample supply of organic manures and fertilizers to provide plant foods.

Sandy soils are easily cultivated, even when wet. They are "warm" soils, heating up quickly in spring, and are commonly used for producing early crops.

The porous texture of sandy soils allows water to flow freely through them, washing out lime and plant nutrients. They tend to become acid more quickly than other soils, and need regular liming to keep them sweet.

LOAMY SOILS. (Medium-textured Soils)

If your soil does not feel gritty when rubbed, and moulds without feeling plastic or sticky, it is a loamy soil. This is usually a fertile soil, and the easiest to manage. Its properties are intermediate between those of the sandy and clayey soils.

CLAYEY SOILS. (Fine-textured Soils)

If your soil does not feel gritty, and moulds into a sticky, plastic ball, it is probably a clayey soil. You will be able to

GENERAL TERMS FOR TEXTURAL CLASS NAMES

General Terms		Basic Soil Textural Class Names
Sandy soils	Coarse textured soils	Sands Loamy sands
Loamy soils	Moderately coarse textured soils	Sandy loam Fine sandy loam
	Medium textured soils	Very fine sandy loam Loam Silt loam Silt
	Moderately fine textured soils	Clay loam Sandy clay loam Silty clay loam
Clayey soils	Fine textured soils	Sandy clay Silty clay Clay

confirm this by rolling a sample into a long thin rod, which can be bent into a ring without breaking.

A clayey soil is commonly regarded as a "heavy" soil; the plasticity of the wet clay and the hardness of dry clay can make for heavy work on these soils. Clay is a colloidal material (see page 314), and it swells when wet. The clay in a fine-textured soil will tend to seal up the pores between other particles. The soil becomes waterlogged and difficult to cultivate. If it is trodden or compressed by heavy machinery in this condition it coheres into a stodgy mass that hardens like concrete when it dries.

Clay should never be worked when wet, and it is often too hard to work when dry. It should be caught at a half-way stage.

As it dries, clay shrinks. Cracks and fissures appear in the soil surface, allowing water to enter. This expansion and contraction of clay as it becomes wet and dry breaks up large clods into smaller particles. It helps the frosts of winter to pulverise clay that has been dug during autumn.

Although a clayey soil is often difficult to cultivate, a proportion of clay in the soil contributes greatly to the creation of a crumb structure (see page 110). The plastic, sticky clay holds other particles together to form the crumbs that are so desirable in a soil.

Clay aids Fertility

Clay plays a vitally important role too in the fertility of the soil. The immense surface area presented by the particles, and the electric charges they carry, enable clay to hold supplies of many essential elements (see page 318). These elements are released to the plant root hairs that lie in the film of water coating the soil particles. The clay thus acts as a store of plant nutrients, and makes an invaluable contribution to soil fertility.

The fine texture of a clay soil tends to make for low permeability. Water does not flow readily between the particles themselves, and it is essential to create a good crumb structure in a clay soil. Water can then flow between the crumbs.

The immense surface of the fine clay particles, on the other hand, allows a clay soil to hold large quantities of water. A clay soil provides plants with a better reserve supply of water than a sandy soil does. The extra water content makes a clay soil cold. It is slow to warm up in spring, and is less satisfactory for early crops.

STRUCTURE

If you examine any soil, you will find that it has a characteristic structure. The topsoil from an old, well-tended cottage garden or the soil beneath a grassy meadow, for example, will consist of granules or crumbs which hold together quite firmly if you rub them in your hands.

Other soils may have blocky, nut-like aggregates; some

soils will have no aggregates at all, their particles remaining in the form of individual grains.

The structure of your soil has an important effect on its productivity, and much of the work you put into your garden will be expended in improving soil structure.

Crumb Structure

The ideal soil has a structure in which the particles are held together as aggregates or crumbs between the size of a grain of rice and a garden pea. The crumbs are strong enough to resist quite firm pressure, and are not readily disintegrated by water.

A soil of this sort is easily worked, and will withstand the effects of tillage and cultivation without breaking down into its individual particles. It will not "puddle" easily when wet, nor will it become dusty when dry. It offers an excellent roothold for plants, and allows air and water to flow freely through the large pores between the aggregates.

A well-crumbed soil is not easily carried away by water, nor are the crumbs swept up by the wind. It resists erosion much better than a soil in which the individual particles are not bound together.

Although water flows freely in this type of soil it is absorbed by the crumbs themselves. Inside the crumbs, it coats the surfaces of individual particles to provide the capillary water on which the plants depend. If the crumbs contain a high proportion of clay or humus, the available surface area will be very large, and the soil will provide a lavish supply of water and plant nutrients.

Test Your Soil Structure

It is a simple matter to examine the structure of your soil, and you should test the topsoil and the subsoil in various parts of the garden. Dislodge a lump of soil from the appropriate layer, place it on a concrete path and give it a sharp blow with a spade.

If the structure is good, the soil will break up easily into discrete crumbs, between $\frac{1}{4}$ to $\frac{1}{16}$ inch diameter. If the structure is poor, the soil will be tough or hard, forming flat-sided clods with angular corners which show little sign of porosity or granulation.

You can carry out a further test by shaking samples of your soil with water. A soil of good structure will retain its aggregates intact, whereas a soil of poor structure will form a shapeless plastic mass (see Plate 16).

Nature's Crumb Structure

If you are making a garden from a patch of virgin grassland, you will find that nature has already created an excellent soil structure in the topsoil. Beneath the grass, the soil is bound up into crumbs of an ideal size.

This natural crumb structure results from the combined efforts of the plant and animal inhabitants of the soil. Earthworms, for example, tunnel through the soil, dragging leaves and other litter from the surface and leaving it to decay in the topsoil. The maze of channels left by worms allows air and water to flow freely, encouraging organic matter to decay and release its nutrients.

Plant roots follow the earthworms' tunnels, and push downwards into the subsoil. Fibrous roots form a network of threads that bind the soil particles together near the surface. And the roots exude gummy substances that serve as a natural glue.

Countless millions of microbes flourish in a healthy natural soil, feeding on the dead organic matter and bringing about its decay. They too produce a natural gum that helps to cement the particles into crumbs. And they turn the organic matter into humus, which is probably the most important binding material of all.

In a healthy natural soil, these factors all work together to build and sustain the crumb structure that lies beneath a meadow turf. Grass, with its mass of fibrous roots, plays a particularly important part in holding the soil particles together.

If the natural crumb structure remained in this form when we make a garden from virgin soil, all would be well. But the very acts of tillage and cultivation tend to destroy the crumb structure.

Effects of Cultivation

When we dig or plough the soil, we aerate it and speed up the decomposition of organic matter. This is helpful in that it releases plant nutrients that feed our crops. But it is detrimental in that it destroys humus and gummy organic materials that are holding the soil particles together in crumbs.

If soils are cultivated intensively, humus may be removed more rapidly than it can be replaced, and the results can be disastrous. This is what has happened in great food-producing areas of the U.S.A. and other countries, where the natural structure of the soil has been destroyed, leaving fine particles at the mercy of wind and water.

The same thing happens on a smaller scale in a garden that is tended without thought for the soil structure. If we strip the soil of its humus, we may find ourselves with a soil in which individual particles are no longer bound together into aggregates.

The cultivation of soil for crops means inevitably that we must trample on the land, and use all sorts of equipment on it. Pressure exerted on the soil helps to destroy its crumb structure, and to create compacted layers or pans which are impervious to air and water, and present barriers to plant roots.

This problem is especially difficult for the farmer, who must use tractors and other heavy machinery on his land. But it is a problem for gardeners too, and you should avoid any unnecessary trampling of your soil.

CONTOUR PLAN FOR A GARDEN

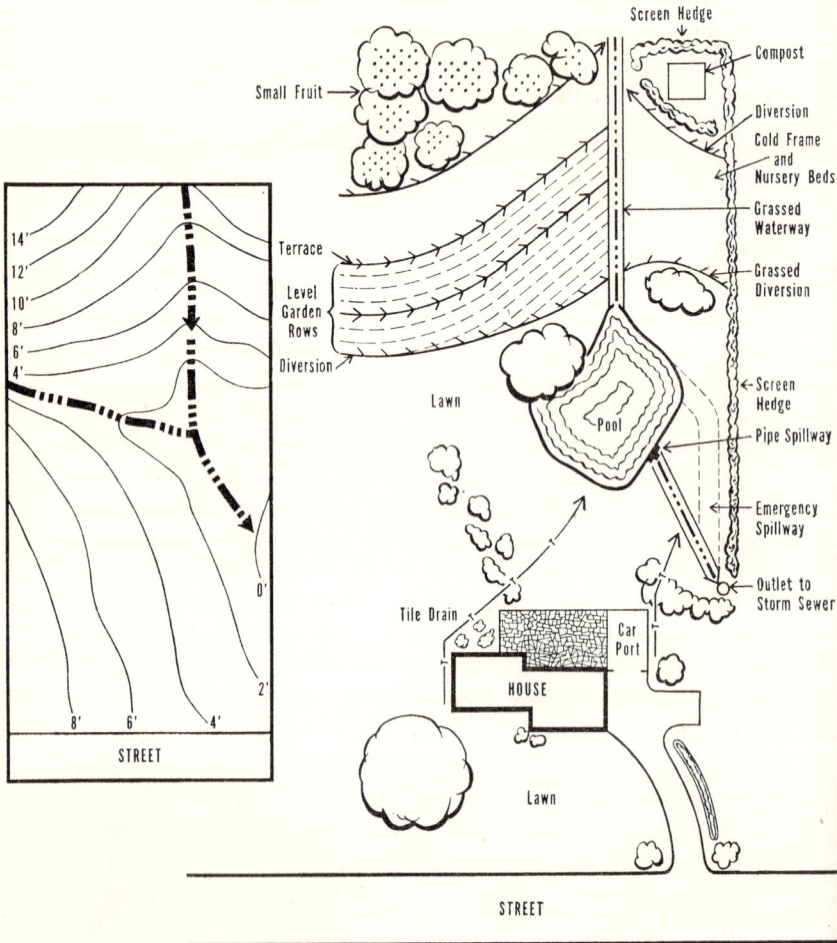

Small Fruit

Screen Hedge

Compost

Diversion

Cold Frame
and
Nursery Beds

Grassed
Waterway

Grassed
Diversion

Terrace

Level
Garden
Rows

Diversion

Lawn

Pool

Screen
Hedge

Pipe Spillway

Emergency
Spillway

Outlet to
Storm Sewer

Tile Drain

Car
Port

HOUSE

Lawn

STREET

14'
12'
10'
8'
6'
4'

0'

2'

8'   6'   4'

STREET

This garden has been planned to make best use of the land with respect to the topography as shown in the contour map on left. The flow of water is controlled in such a way that proper drainage is assured, and soil will not be carried away by water flowing unchecked over the surface.

Rain forms Crusts

When soil is covered with grass and other vegetation, it is protected from the battering of raindrops. Water is able to soak into the surface and trickle down between the crumbs of soil. But by removing the natural cover we expose the soil to the direct effects of the rain. Each drop batters at the crumbs like a tiny bomb, blasting away individual soil particles (see Plate 17). These particles block the pores in the soil, forming a crust that seals the surface. Water runs over it instead of sinking in, and the precious topsoil may be eroded away.

Surface crusts formed in this way restrict the proper growth of plants, especially seedlings which have not established a firm roothold. Germination of seeds is prevented, and seeds are carried away by water flowing across the surface of the soil.

COLOUR

The colour of a soil will often give a useful indication of its properties or condition. It will tell you much about the drainage, the amount of organic matter and the general level of fertility of your soil.

A soil rich in organic matter or humus is usually brown or brownish black. If the soil is well-drained, this dark colour is a sign of high fertility.

A black soil, on the other hand, may signify that drainage is bad. Peat will accumulate on a water-logged soil, and you should always check the drainage of a dark-coloured surface soil. A well-drained soil is commonly brown to brownish red to a depth of 3 to 4 feet.

In low ground, especially where the surface soil is black, a grey horizon may indicate poor drainage. A completely water-logged soil is often a slatey blue colour.

White is usually a sign of chalk or salty deposits, but yellowish-white to grey in well-drained upland soils may indicate severe washing out of nutrients by water.

F

Subsoils and parent materials (C horizons) are often mottled. This may indicate poor drainage, the soil being water-logged part of the time and aerated at other times.

PERMEABILITY

One of the most important characteristics of any soil is its behaviour with respect to water. If your soil is to grow plants effectively, it must be able to acquire and hold water needed by the plants. But it must at the same time, allow excess water to drain away so that the soil does not become water-logged.

This water/soil relationship is a complex one, in which texture and structure play an important role. They influence the way in which water flows into the soil, and is held by it. A soil of good crumb structure, for example, allows water to flow readily through it, and yet retains a supply of moisture on the surface of particles within the crumbs. A soil of poor structure, on the other hand, is readily beaten into a hard crust by heavy rain (see Plate 18), and water flows away across the surface instead of sinking into the soil. It may carry away fine particles of topsoil, causing erosion.

Your examination of the physical characteristics of the soil will tell you much about its permeability. But a simple test will give you a practical confirmation.

Cut the bottom from a can to form an open cylinder. Then push one end of this into the surface of soil which has previously been soaked with water. Fill the can with water. Leave for ½ to 1 hour, and measure how far the water level has fallen in the can.

If the water level drops 3 inches or more in an hour, the permeability is high; if it falls between 1 and 3 inches, it is medium; if it falls less than 1 inch, permeability is low.

If your test confirms that the permeability of your soil is low, this is a further indication that the structure must be improved.

DRAINAGE

For you soil to produce good crops, it must provide the growing plant with nutrients, water and air. Without air, roots cannot breathe, and the plant is suffocated (see page 98).

If air is to flow freely through your soil, it is essential that excess water should drain away readily to a depth that allows a satisfactory root run—usually about 3 feet. It is surprising how many soils fail to meet this requirement. More often than not, water will lie very near the soil surface, and plants will not have the root-room they need to flourish.

It is an easy matter to test the drainage of your own soil. All you need to do is to dig a hole about 3 feet deep at the lowest point of your garden, and fill it with water. If the garden is very well drained, the hole will empty within 30 minutes to an hour. In this case, you need have no worries so far as drainage is concerned.

If water remains in the hole permanently, or for longer than 24 hours, drainage is unsatisfactory, and you should take steps to improve it.

Drainage is one of the things you must attend to if you are going to create satisfactory soil conditions in your garden. The level of the water table controls the effective depth of your soil. If the water is lying too near the surface, plants will be shallow-rooted and cannot flourish. They will be under-nourished, and will lack the extensive root system needed to withstand periods of drought.

The majority of garden flowers and vegetables can make good use of some 3 to 4 feet of soil. This is the depth at which the water table should lie.

Often, the level of water will rise and fall with the changing seasons. The soil will be adequately drained in summer, but partly water-logged in winter. Annual plants may grow satisfactorily in these soils, but the roots of perennials will be suffocated in winter, and the plants will die.

Even annuals will do badly if they suffer periods of poor drainage conditions during the growing season.

WATER RETENTION

If your soil is to support good crops, it must be able to retain sufficient moisture to meet their needs at all times. The ability of a well-drained soil to hold moisture depends very largely on its texture, structure and humus content.

Plants take up moisture from the layer of capillary water that coats the soil particles (see page 97). In general, the greater the area of surface available on these particles, the more capillary moisture the soil will hold.

Surface area increases as the size of particles decreases (see page 65). Clay particles, with their vast surface area, soils are able to hold a greater reserve of moisture than soils of coarser texture.

If you have a clayey soil in your garden, you can depend hold more capillary water than silt or sand. Fine-textured on it holding up to ½ gallon of water per square foot, to a depth of 1 foot. A sandy soil, on the other hand, may hold only half as much, and plants will need more frequent watering.

Humus, like clay, has excellent water-holding properties. The addition of humus to a sandy soil will bring a great improvement in this respect.

CONTAMINATION

Most people create their gardens from the land that surrounds their house, and the soil will often have suffered greatly when the house was built. It may be contaminated with all manner of strange materials left behind by a careless builder. Tarred paper and pieces of wood, broken bricks and rubble, slabs of concrete and plaster will have found their way into the soil.

Some of the rubbish you find will be little more than a nuisance, like broken brick. Some of it, including glass, may be dangerous. Some of it may be chemically active like plaster and concrete, which can be detrimental to acid-loving plants.

All this rubbish should be removed before you settle down to cultivate your soil.

TOPOGRAPHY (Surface Configuration)

In assessing your garden plot, you will need to know the "lie of the land"—its topography. This controls the flow of water across the surface, and influences the relationship between the water and your soil, on which so much depends.

If you know how to use a surveying level and rod, or can enlist the help of a friend who does, you may find it worth your while to make a simple contour map of your land.

For a tract of 5 acres or less, it is usually sufficient to locate a single bench mark and determine relative elevations at points 25, 50 or 100 feet apart around the boundaries of your plot. Choose as the bench mark a point on a permanent and stable structure, such as a manhole cover or corner post, that can be seen from as much of your area as possible.

On a map drawn to scale, plot the elevations of the stations around the boundary, of high and low points within the property, and of other points of interest. Using these fixed points as guides, you can sketch in rough contour lines at 1-, 2- or 5-foot verticals, whichever is practical for the size and steepness of your tract.

Drainageways

Now sketch in the courses of any drainageways that cross your property. Look around you and see how your land lies with respect to the surrounding landscape. Is it at the top of a hill so that water runs only away from it, on a slope where water drains onto it from above and off onto land below, or in a valley where it receives run-in water from

HUNGER SIGNS

Plants show hunger signs which can be detected by careful observation and study. They are an indication that the soil is deficient in one or more nutrients. A disadvantage of this method of diagnosis lies in the fact that it may reveal deficiencies too late for them to be corrected for growing crops. The information can be used, however, in preparing for the following season. Some common hunger signs are as follows:

NITROGEN DEFICIENCY

1. A sickly yellowish green colour.
2. Distinctly slow and dwarfed growth.
3. Drying up or "firing" of leaves, which starts at the bottom of the plant, proceeding upward. In plants like corn, grains and grasses, the firing starts at the tip of the bottom leaves and proceeds down the centre or along the midrib.

PHOSPHORUS DEFICIENCY

1. Purplish leaves, stem and branches.
2. Slow growth and maturity.
3. Small slender stalks in the case of corn. Lack of stooling in small grains.
4. Low yields of grain, fruit and seed.

POTASH DEFICIENCY

1. Mottling, spotting, streaking or curling of leaves, starting on the lower levels.
2. Lower leaves scorched or burned on margins and tips. These dead areas may fall out, leaving ragged edges. In corn, grains and grasses, firing starts at the tip of the leaf and proceeds down from the edge, usually leaving the midrib green.
3. Premature loss of leaves, and small knotty, poorly-opened pods.
4. Plants falling down prior to maturity, due to poor root development.

CALCIUM DEFICIENCY

1. Young leaves in terminal bud become "hooked" in appearance and die back at the tips and along the margins.
2. Leaves have wrinkled appearance.
3. In some cases, young leaves remain folded.
4. Light green band along margin of leaves.
5. Short and much-branched roots.

SULPHUR DEFICIENCY

1. Young leaves light green in colour, with even lighter veins.
2. Short, slender stalks.
3. Slow, stunted growth.
4. Spotting of leaves, as with potatoes.
5. Immature fruit, light green in colour.

IN PLANTS

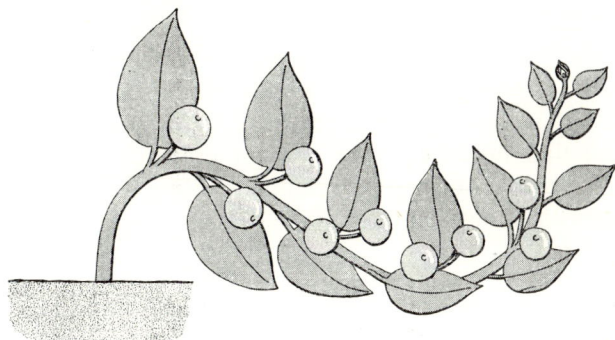

MAGNESIUM DEFICIENCY

1. General loss of green colour which starts in the bottom leaves and later moves up stalk. The veins of the leaf remain green.
2. Purplish-red colour sometimes appears between green veins.
3. Weak stalks with long branched roots.
4. Definite and sharply-defined series of yellowish-green, light yellow or even white streaks throughout entire leaf.
5. Leaves curve upward along the margins.

MICRO NUTRIENT DEFICIENCIES

Boron deficiency is indicated by cracked stem of celery, brown rot of cauliflower, dry rot of sugar beets, heart rot of turnips, yellow top of alfalfa, corky core of apples, and black heart of table beets.

Manganese deficiency is shown by pale green to yellow and red colours between green veins of leaves of tomatoes and beets, resinous spots on leaves of citrus, chlorosis of crops such as spinach and soybeans on overlimed soil, and "gray speck" on oats.

Copper deficiency causes die-back in citrus and, on muck soils, blasting of onions.

Zinc deficiency is indicated by white bud of corn and little leaf of fruit trees.

Iron deficiency is shown by pale-yellowish colour of foliage, in presence of adequate nitrogen, and on soils that are high in lime or manganese.

several directions? Mark the points at which surface water enters and leaves your property and the routes of flow across it.

With this information you can plan your garden in such a way as to make best use of the water that reaches it, avoiding water-logging, flooding or uncontrolled surface run-off that might carry away your precious topsoil.

An example of a garden planned to suit the contours of the land is shown on page 152.

Air

When you are considering the topography of your garden, remember that air is an important constituent of your soil too. The air that lies on your garden can affect its productivity.

If your garden lies high on sloping ground, cold air will drain away from it onto the ground lower down. Plants will escape late-spring and early-autumn frosts that nip plants in the valley below.

A garden situated at the bottom of a valley, for the same reason, will have a shorter growing season than a garden higher up on the side of a hill. And if the soil is peaty, plants will be even more liable to frost damage on low ground.

LIGHT AND SHADE

Plants need light if they are to grow, and the situation of your soil is important in that it controls the amount of light that reaches the plants growing in it. The warmth of the soil, too, depends upon the heat it receives from sunshine.

Study your garden to determine the hours of sunshine received by various parts of it. You will then be able to plan your garden to make the most effective use of its light conditions. And you can modify the soils of different parts of the garden with this in mind.

Most fruits and vegetables enjoy plenty of sunshine, but salad crops need some shade. Some plants, including tomatoes, grow well in only half the sunshine that many fruits and vegetables enjoy. Others, including ornamentals, flourish in the continuous shade on the north side of a building. Some ornamentals do well with winter and spring sun and summer shade, as under an oak tree.

Many grasses prefer full sun, but others enjoy partial shade. Ornamental plants that appear to suffer in too much sun may be, in fact, affected by high soil temperatures. They will flourish in full sun if the soil is covered by mulches that keep the roots cool. Clematis is an example. Azaleas prefer partial shade, but may do well in the sun if kept well mulched with compost or sawdust.

COMPETING ROOTS

Competition for soil space may be fierce in the vicinity of your garden plot, and this too must be considered in making your soil plans. Trees may spread their roots into your garden from considerable distances away, and this will affect some plants more than others.

Azaleas, for example, will grow among oak trees, but roses will not. Azaleas, on the other hand, will not grow well in competition with elm or maple. Lawns, flowers and fine shrubs grow poorly near elms, maples, poplars and willows.

Trees, by their very size, compete effectively against the roots of garden crops. But there are plenty of small plants which exert an influence out of all proportion to their size. Forsythia roots, for example, are notorious soil robbers, and iris too.

PLANT NUTRIENTS

Many of the physical characteristics of the soil may be studied adequately without any special equipment. But soil fertility is concerned very largely with the chemical state of the soil. And this is not a property you can assess without proper facilities at your disposal.

If your plants are to flourish, they must be sure of obtain-
F*

ing as much of the nitrogen, phosphorus, potassium and other elements as they need (see page 26). And these elements must be in the form of simple chemicals that can make their way into the plant roots.

The chemical content of your topsoil will depend upon the nature of the soil-forming materials from which it has come, and the treatment it has received in the past. Crops will have removed chemical nutrients according to their individual requirements (see page 220), and fertilizers added to the soil will have brought materials other than those provided by nature. The only way to find out what your topsoil contains in the way of chemical nutrients is to analyse a sample. On the basis of this analysis, you can estimate the amounts of different fertilizers and manures that should be added to the soil to provide the nutrients that are needed.

Chemical Tests

You can obtain a chemical analysis of your soil by sending a sample to one of the fertilizer manufacturers providing a soil-analysis service, or to your local agricultural advisory department. Experts will assess the chemical content of your soil and advise you as to the amount and type of fertilizer that is needed for specific crops.

Alternatively, you can test the soil yourself by using one of the special soil testing kits which are available. These kits provide apparatus and chemicals necessary for estimating the nitrogen, phosphorus and potassium in your soil, and indicate how much fertilizer should be added to make up the deficiencies.

The sample of soil used in testing should be as representative as you can make it. Samples should be taken from as many sites as possible over the garden plot, including soil to a depth of 6 to 8 inches. The soils are then mixed thoroughly in a clean container, and a sample of the mixture is used in testing.

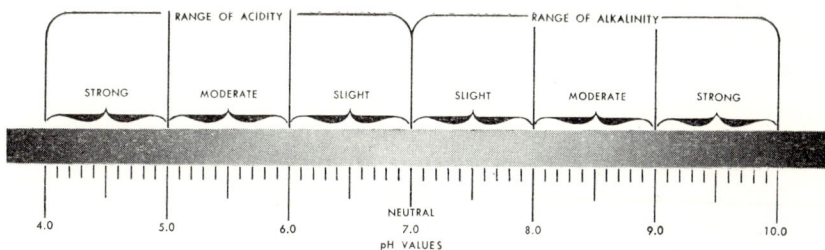

THE pH SCALE. The degree of acidity or alkalinity of a soil is conveniently expressed in terms of pH values. The pH scale is divided into 14 divisions or pH units numbered from 1 to 14. Soils with a pH value of 7.0 are neutral. Soils with a pH value below 7.0 are acid or "sour", while those above 7.0 are alkaline or "sweet". A pH of 5.0 is 10 times more acid than a pH of 6.0, and a pH of 4.0 is ten times more acid than pH 5.0. Thus a soil having a pH of 4.0 is 100 times more acid than one with a pH of 6.0.

The pH of most soils falls in the range between 4.0 and 8.0. The scale above covers part of the pH range, from pH 4.0 to pH 10.0.

Hunger Signs

If your soil is deficient in one or more essential chemical nutrients, the plants will themselves warn you that something is wrong. With experience, you will be able to judge what is lacking and to put it right. Details of common hunger signs in plants are given on page 158.

There is a serious drawback to this method of assessing fertility in a soil; it is often too late to do anything for the crop which is showing hunger signs.

ACIDITY

Soils vary greatly in acidity, and different plants grow best under different acidity conditions. Each plant prefers a particular degree of acidity for vigorous growth. It is important, therefore, that you should know the acidity of your soil, and be able to adjust it to suit the plants you aim to grow.

An acid soil is commonly called a sour soil, and an alkaline one is sweet. These terms describe acidity only in the vaguest way, which is inadequate for a proper understanding of soil requirements. A more precise definition of the degree of acidity is given by means of the pH scale (see page 163).

The pH scale describes acidity in terms of figures ranging from 0 to 14. A pH value of 7 represents neutral point, i.e. neither acid nor alkaline. Any figure *lower* than 7 represents an acid reaction, the degree of acidity increasing as the figure becomes smaller.

A pH value *greater* than 7 represents an alkaline reaction, the degree of alkalinity increasing as the figure becomes greater.

Most plants will grow well over a fairly wide range of pH values, usually on the acid side. Many shrubs and flowers demand an acid soil; others grow best in neutral or even alkaline soils (see page 166).

Most soils become acid as a result of weathering and the release of carbon dioxide by plants and micro-organisms. They have a pH value of lower than 7.

The acidity is neutralized by addition of lime in adequate quantities.

If the degree of acidity is known, the amount of lime needed to neutralise the acidity may be worked out (see page 182). The first step in controlling the acidity of your soil is thus to find its pH value.

Testing Acidity

For most ordinary gardening purposes, pH can be measured adequately by means of an indicator paper. This is a paper impregnated with a special substance which turns a different colour at different pH values, and by

4.0pH 4.5	5.0	5.5	6.0	6.5	7.0	7.5	8.0	8.5	9.0	9.5	pH10

NITROGEN

PHOSPHORUS

POTASSIUM

SULPHUR

CALCIUM

MAGNESIUM

IRON

MANGANESE

BORON

COPPER & ZINC

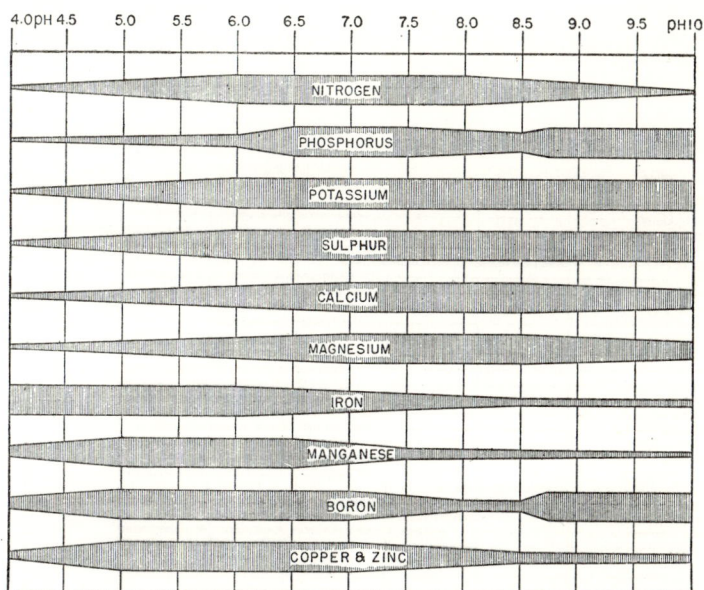

SOIL ACIDITY AND PLANT NUTRIENTS. This chart shows the effect of soil pH on the availability of plant nutrients. For each nutrient, the width of the band is an indication of its relative availability. The region between pH 6.5 and pH 7.0 is best for most nutrients.

dipping it into water in contact with the soil it is possible to judge acidity with reasonable accuracy.

To test the pH of your soil in this way, soil samples should be taken from as many sites as possible on the garden plot, including soil to a depth of 6 to 8 inches. The samples are then mixed thoroughly in a clean container, and a sample of the mixture is tested for acidity.

A similar test should be carried out on your subsoil, and separate tests should be made on patches of soil which differ in obvious ways from the normal soil of the garden.

Most garden vegetables and annual flowers, most lawn

SUITABLE pH RANGE FOR VARIOUS CROPS AND PLANTS

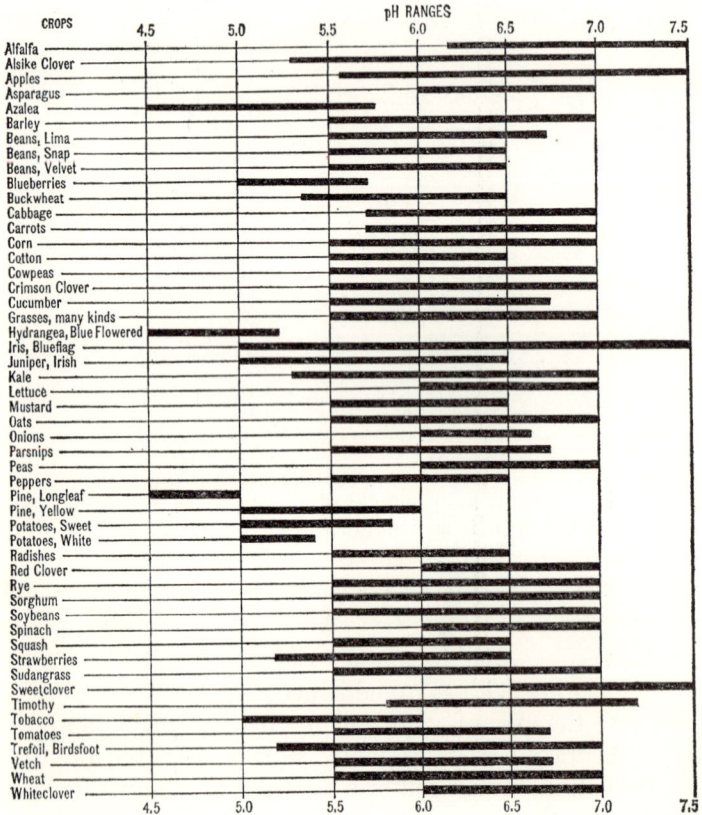

pH RANGES

CROPS	4.5	5.0	5.5	6.0	6.5	7.0	7.5

Alfalfa
Alsike Clover
Apples
Asparagus
Azalea
Barley
Beans, Lima
Beans, Snap
Beans, Velvet
Blueberries
Buckwheat
Cabbage
Carrots
Corn
Cotton
Cowpeas
Crimson Clover
Cucumber
Grasses, many kinds
Hydrangea, Blue Flowered
Iris, Blueflag
Juniper, Irish
Kale
Lettuce
Mustard
Oats
Onions
Parsnips
Peas
Peppers
Pine, Longleaf
Pine, Yellow
Potatoes, Sweet
Potatoes, White
Radishes
Red Clover
Rye
Sorghum
Soybeans
Spinach
Squash
Strawberries
Sudangrass
Sweetclover
Timothy
Tobacco
Tomatoes
Trefoil, Birdsfoot
Vetch
Wheat
Whiteclover

	4.5	5.0	5.5	6.0	6.5	7.0	7.5

Most crops grow and produce best on slightly acid or neutral soils. There are exceptions, however, such as blueberries and cranberries, which do best on strongly acid soils. Other crops, including alfalfa and sweet clover, grow well in slightly alkaline soils.

EFFECT OF pH ON SOIL AND CROP RELATIONSHIPS

	pH SCALE											
	4·0	4·5	5·0	5·5	6·0 6·5	6·7 7·0	7·2	7·8	8·0	8·5	9·0	

ACIDITY	EXTREMELY ACID	VERY STRONGLY ACID	STRONGLY ACID	MEDIUM ACID	SLIGHTLY ACID	NEUTRAL	ALKALINE	STRONGLY ALKALINE
OCCURRENCE	RARE	FREQUENT	MOST SOILS IN HUMID REGIONS WHEN NOT LIMED		LIMED SOILS			OCCUR ONLY IN ARID REGIONS

TONS OF LIME PER ACRE TO BRING pH TO 6·5 (APPROX)

SANDY AND SILT LOAM	6·0	5·0	4·0	2·0	0·5	0
CLAY SOILS	8·0	7·0	5·0	3·0	1·0	0
MUCK SOILS	12·0	10·0	8·0	6·0	3·0	0

SULPHUR SHOULD BE USED HERE

RANGE OF CROP TOLERANCE TO ACIDITY

◄ BLUEBERRIES ►
SWEET CLOVER ◄——— ◄——— BEST ———►
ALFALFA ◄——— ◄——— BEST ———►
RED CLOVER ◄——— BEST ———►
CORN ◄——— BEST ——► ◄——— BEST ——►
POTATOES ◄——— BEST ———► ◄——— SCABBY ———►
TOBACCO ◄——— BEST ———►
TOMATOES ◄——— BEST ——►
ONIONS ON MUCK ◄———————►

SOIL SITUATION

LOW AVAILABILITY OF PHOSPHATE (FIXED BY IRON) LIME (LEACHED OUT) POTASH (LEACHED OUT) BACTERIA DO NOT FLOURISH FUNGI THRIVE ORGANIC MATTER DOES NOT READILY ACCUMULATE	BEST pH FOR PHOSPHATE, LIME, AND FOR NITROGEN FIXATION BY LEGUMES AND ORGANISMS ORGANIC MATTER ACCUMULATES	IN SOILS WITH pH ABOVE 7·5, THE PHOSPHATES ARE FIXED BY CALCIUM (LIME). BORON, IRON, MAGNESIUM, MANGANESE, AND POTASSIUM ARE LIKELY TO BE DEFICIENT

grasses, and many herbaceous perennials and shrubs do best in slightly to very slightly acid soil—about pH 6.1 to 6.9. A more acid soil, of pH lower than 6.5, is better for many plants, especially those that grow naturally under trees among leaf litter.

Plants like these, which prefer an acid soil, do better in soil which does not include free lime within the rooting zone. Free lime occurs naturally in some soils, especially in sub-humid and semi-arid regions. Also, it may have been added accidentally as ashes, or in rubbish. Or it may have been added deliberately to sweeten garden soils to be used for vegetables, lawn grasses and other plants which do not like strongly acid soils.

Effects of pH

The soil microbes which decompose organic materials, and contribute so much to soil fertility, grow best at pH 6.5. And near this pH, conditions are best for the availability of most plant nutrients.

As the acidity increases, the availability of nearly all important nutrients diminishes. Phosphorus, in particular, is held as insoluble compounds in highly acid soils (see page 306).

As the acidity decreases (i.e. pH rises), iron, manganese, copper and zinc become less available. Iron chlorosis, a yellowing disease of plant leaves due to iron deficiency, is a common symptom of acid-loving plants growing on soils containing free lime.

Most upland soils developed under forests in humid regions are too acid for the best growth of lawn grasses, vegetables and many other plants. They need thorough liming.

Soils developed under grass and shrubs in sub-humid or dry districts are seldom highly acid, and may not need liming.

NATURE'S NITROGEN FIXATION.

Nitrogen makes up some 80% of the air we breathe. Each acre of land has 70,000,000 pounds of nitrogen gas pressing down on its surface. But the growing plant cannot draw directly upon these vast reserves of nitrogen ; it absorbs the nitrogen it needs as simple chemicals which dissolve in soil water and pass into the plant via the roots.

These chemicals are formed by union of the nitrogen with other elements, and Nature achieves this union with the help of the lightning flash. Under the influence of this huge electrical discharge, nitrogen and oxygen of the air unite ; nitric and nitrous acids are formed, and these are carried into the soil by rain.

Every day, some 60,000 tons of nitrogen are " fixed " by Nature in this way. Most of it falls on oceans and mountains, and on the uncultivated regions of the earth, where it is wasted – *U.S. Weather Bureau – Noel M. Klein.*

PLATE 9

PLATE 10

PUSHING THE LIMITS

Almost all the world's supply of food is grown on 2,500 million acres of cultivated land. This is only about 2% of the total area of the earth.

The remaining 98% is covered by water (71%), mountains (3.5%), ice or snow, or land which is too wet or dry to be habitable (5%). 12% is very sparsely settled due to rigorous climate, extreme heat, deserts, jungles and other barriers to intensive development. The remaining 6.5% consists of forests, hills, cities, rocks, arid and eroded land, swamps and other areas in which large-scale agriculture is next to impossible.

The area of cultivable land may be extended by conservation, reclamation and irrigation projects, but only at great cost and in small amounts. The problem of providing more food for the world's growing population will be solved primarily by increasing the output from the soil we now farm.

Deserts, such as this wasteland in Tripolitania, grow little apart from a few fruit trees in oases – *Radio Times, Hulton Picture Library*.

Mountains cover 12% of the earth's land surface, and are mostly unfit for farming.

PLATE 11

Water in the form of oceans and rivers covers nearly three-quarters of the earth's surface.

Jungles may often be cleared for agricultural purposes, but only at enormous cost in money and manpower.

Ice and Snow covers vast areas of the earth, and these regions can never be farmed using present methods.

Rocky Soil can be farmed only with the greatest difficulty.

CONTOUR TERRACING

Left : This land was cultivated to produce terraces on the natural contours. After a heavy rain, water is held in the terraces, giving it time to soak into the soil instead of flowing away freely across the surface.

PLATE 12

Right : The soil of this field has been severely eroded by a hard spring rain. The disc tracks are plainly seen running down the slope of the hillside, providing channels along which the water flows downhill.

MODERN CONTOUR FARMING.
Below : An aerial view of contour strips, showing how land is cultivated in such a way as to prevent free flow of water and consequent erosion – *U.S.D.A.*

8

Good Management Brings Results

DIGGING

Why Dig?

Under natural conditions, soil is neither dug nor ploughed, yet it supports a flourishing vegetation and sustains an excellent structure. Why, then, do we dig and plough the soil in which we grow crops?

The reason lies in the fact that we are opposing the natural order of things when we set out to make a garden or a farm. We have decided that the vegetation nature provides does not satisfy our requirements. So we plan to remove the plants which are growing naturally in our soil, and to replace them with others that we prefer.

Digging and ploughing are the first steps we take in putting our plans into effect. We remove a slice of surface soil and replace it upside down. In this way, we have buried the unwanted plants already growing on the soil, leaving a clean soil surface which we can break up and prepare to receive our own choice of plants. Left to itself, the soil supports the vegetation it can afford. The cover of vegetation is controlled by the environment and by the amount of plant nutrients that are released naturally into the soil. But we expect the soil to do more than this in our gardens. We have decided that it must grow a different kind of plant, and we require it to provide much greater

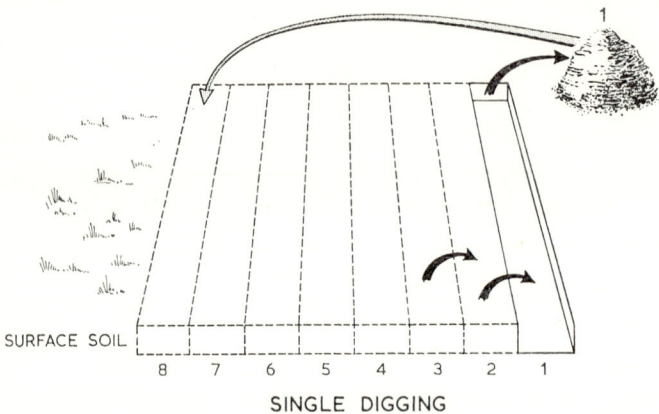

SURFACE SOIL

8 7 6 5 4 3 2 1

SINGLE DIGGING

Single Digging: (Plain Digging, Digging One Spit Deep, Ordinary Digging)

A trench is dug, (strip 1), one spit deep, and soil is heaped to one side of plot. Strip 2 is then turned into the trench, the soil being broken up and mixed with manure, compost etc. The heap of soil from strip 1 is used for filling up the last trench.

Single digging is used on land that has already been cultivated by Double Digging. It should be carried out annually, except where land is permanently planted.

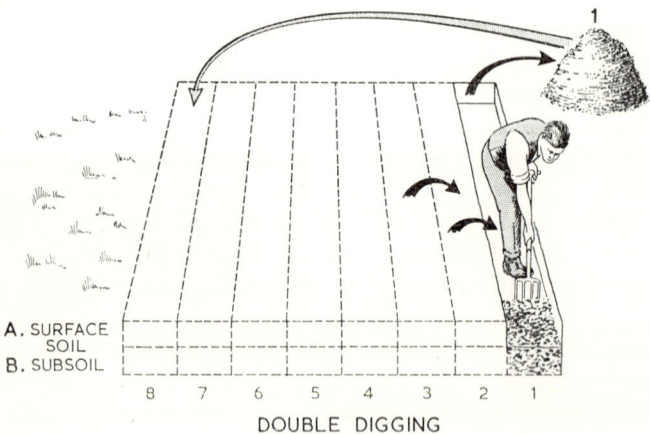

A. SURFACE SOIL
B. SUBSOIL

8 7 6 5 4 3 2 1

DOUBLE DIGGING

DIGGING

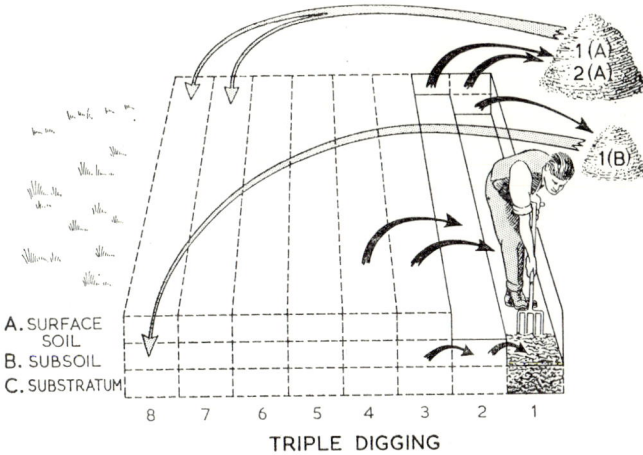

TRIPLE DIGGING

Triple Digging

A trench is dug, one spit deep and two strips in width (strips 1(A) and 2(A)). The soil is heaped to one side of the plot. A second spit of soil is removed from strip 1, and piled separately to one side of plot (strip 1(B)). The bottom of the strip 1 trench is forked over, manure and bonemeal being added as in Double Digging, and strip 2(B) is then turned onto strip 1(C), followed by the top spit from strip 3 (i.e. strip 3(A)).

The bottom of strip 2 is forked and manured in the same way, and then covered by strip 3(B) and strip 4(A). The process is repeated until the end of the plot is reached. Then the heap from 1(B) is used to fill the last second-spit trench (strip 8(B)), and the large heap from strips 1(A) and 2(A) is used to fill the trench at strips 7(A) and 8(A).

Opposite:

Double Digging: (Bastard Trenching, Half Trenching)

A trench is dug (strip 1) one spit deep, and soil is heaped to side of plot. The bottom of the trench is forked over to a depth of one spit, manure or compost and bone meal (2 oz. per yard run) being mixed into the soil. Strip 2 is then turned into the trench, and the bottom of strip 2 trench is forked and manured in the same way. Then strip 3 is turned into trench 2, and so on. The heap of soil from strip 1 is used for filling up the last trench.

returns than it did when left to its own devices. This means that we must create conditions in the soil that will increase its productivity.

To start with, we must increase the quantity of plant nutrients in the soil by adding to the supplies that nature herself makes available. We do this by adding organic manures or fertilizers. And digging gives us an opportunity of mixing these and other materials into the soil.

The very act of digging increases the rate at which the soil can release its nutrient chemicals. Digging opens up the soil, allowing air and moisture to circulate more freely. The growth of micro-organisms is stimulated, and organic matter decomposes more rapidly into nutrient chemicals. This is a useful result of digging, in that it increases the amount of plant food available. But it must be remembered too that by 'burning up' the humus we are destroying the natural cement that holds soil particles together in aggregates or crumbs.

If humus is removed too quickly, without being replaced from added organic matter, the crumb structure of the soil may be destroyed. And the results could be disastrous.

When our garden is established, we are forever at work on the soil. Weeds must be kept down, water and fertilizers applied, manure and compost spread on the surface, weed-killers and insecticides sprayed on the crops. In due course, crops are harvested and preparations must be made for the following season.

All this activity means that we are trampling on the soil day after day, and perhaps trundling heavy equipment over it. The soil is compressed, and its aggregates may be broken down. Clay is puddled, and pans of compacted soil are formed.

The rain beats down on the soil, helping to disrupt the crumbs, which are no longer protected by their cover of natural vegetation. Crusts of hard soil may seal the surface.

Weeds have become established, and the residues of

crop plants are littering the garden. By the end of the season, the soil is ready for cleaning and loosening in preparation for the following season. It must be dug or ploughed again.

The seasonal routines of digging or ploughing have become established over the centuries. These operations are accepted as necessary, but they should not be carried out indiscriminately. Too much digging or ploughing can have a disastrous effect on soil structure, and they should be indulged in with restraint.

Autumn is the best time for turning over a heavy clayey soil, and it should be left undisturbed as far as possible during spring and summer. In the case of sandy soils, ploughing and digging may with advantage be left until early spring; these soils do not form heavy clods, and do not benefit greatly from the pulverising action of winter frost and wind. They will break down easily into a fine tilth when dug or ploughed in the spring. This has the advantage of minimising loss of nitrates from the soil during winter.

Whenever soil is dug, as much organic manure as possible should be incorporated into it. This will make up for the loss of humus that takes place when the soil is aerated, and help to sustain its structure.

How to Dig

Large gardens nowadays are often ploughed with machines, or tilled with rotary cultivators. But most gardeners find that they are faced with the job of digging over their plot at least once a year. And as this age-old occupation is the basic act in tilling the soil, it is as well to do it properly.

First, you should be certain that the soil is in a proper condition before it is dug. Test the soil by moulding it into a ball in your hand. It should crumble easily after it has been tightly squeezed. If it does not, it is not in a condition

RIDGING

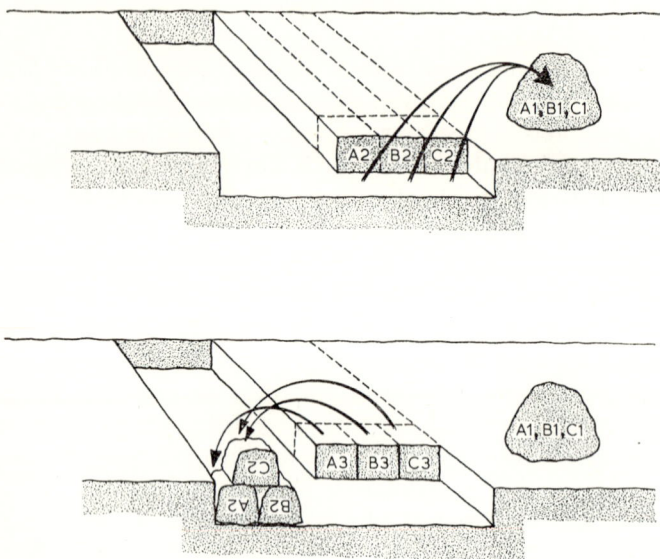

Stiff clay soils are often ridged in the autumn as shown. A trench 2 ft. wide is first dug out, as in double digging, and the soil moved to the far end of the plot, where it will be used for the last ridge. A second strip 2 ft. wide is then marked out alongside the first one, and three spadefuls of soil are dug out from one end of it (A1, B1, C1). These are piled to one side.

A second strip of three spadefuls is then dug as shown (A2, B2, C2) and these are piled in the end of the first trench to form a ridge. The operation is continued along the breadth of the plot, A1, B1 and C1 being used to make the end of the ridge. A new ridge is then started alongside the first one.

WHAT RIDGING DOES
Ridging offers the greatest amount of surface to the effects of winter weather, and enables the frost to break up the clods of clay soil. The soil drains well and is ready for tillage more quickly than usual when spring comes.

suitable for digging, and you should leave it to dry out a little longer.

If wet, sticky soils are dug, they may lose their granular structure and become massive and blocky, especially if they contain much clay and little organic matter. Once a clayey soil has been badly puddled, it may take years of careful handling to restore a good structure again.

The technique you follow when digging will depend upon the depth of the horizons you have found in the soil profile. You must be careful to dig in such a way that the horizons are not mixed. The light-coloured subsoil is a dead inactive material, and should not be mixed with the fertile, living topsoil.

Many gardeners make a fetish of digging deeply, and spoil their topsoil by diluting it with a mass of subsoil. This form of deep digging is rarely good practice except in the few soils that have deep topsoils which merge imperceptibly into the subsoil.

If your examination of the soil profile has disclosed a crumbly, porous subsoil, with plenty of root-channels and fissures running through it from top to bottom, and no sign of bad drainage, you can with advantage confine your digging to the topsoil. Follow the *Single Digging* routine as shown on page 170, to a depth of about 5 inches on dry sites and 7 to 9 inches on wetter sites. *Ridging* is a useful way of breaking down a heavy topsoil (see page 174).

If your subsoil is compact and structureless, as in most garden soils, you should make every effort to break it up and create a good structure in it. *Double Digging* should be used, the subsoil being mixed with as much organic matter as possible. Lime should be added to correct acidity, and fertilizers included to provide food for the deep roots of plants.

If there is a distinct third layer beneath the subsoil, this too may be broken up and enriched. But again, you must make sure that this layer is not mixed with either subsoil or topsoil. It should be dug over separately, following the *Triple Digging* routine.

No matter which method of digging is used, you should incorporate as much organic matter as possible into the soil. This is the most effective way of building up a granular structure in any form of soil. And by adding it to the lower layers you will create conditions which encourage plants to extend their rooting systems to great depths. In due course, the roots will themselves increase the amount of organic matter deep in the soil.

If organic matter is not available, triple digging should be followed by the planting of deep-rooted leguminous crops, such as sweet clover. When the plants have grown for a season or two, they will produce a large amount of organic matter above and below ground. They may then be dug into the soil as a green manure. This technique may delay the garden plan for a season or two, but it will prove well worth while in the long run.

OTHER TILLAGE OPERATIONS

Digging or ploughing will break up your soil in preparation for the new season, and provide you with a clean surface by burying old crop residues and weeds. But other tillage operations will be necessary to prepare the soil for seeds and plants, and to keep it in good condition through the growing season.

If you have dug your soil in autumn, it will remain rough and lumpy through the winter. Frost and wind will have worked on the clods of clayey soil, making them crumbly and readily broken into smaller particles.

Forking

You cannot sow seed properly, or plant out seedlings, in a soil with a lumpy surface, and you must break down the masses of soil left by the autumn digging. This is done by forking over the surface.

The spring forking should not be regarded as another digging operation. It is a much less drastic process, and you should restrict it to the top four inches or so of soil. The object is to break down the lumps left by digging, and to level off the surface.

It is difficult to suggest how forking should be tackled to give the best results, as almost every gardener has his own individual technique. The essentials of the process are to lift the soil and turn it over, and then to hit the lumps lightly with the prongs of the fork.

Treading or Rolling

When your soil has been forked over, it will be rough-surfaced but not lumpy, and reasonably level. Further work will now be necessary to produce the fine surface tilth that gives seedlings a really good start in life. Lumps left by forking must be broken down into smaller particles, and the surface consolidated to create a firm rooting zone.

If you have a light roller, you can run this over the forked surface. On a small plot of land, you can get the desired result by treading the soil carefully. An even pressure should be exerted by 'shuffling' over the ground, or by tying boards to your boots and tramping the soil surface.

If treading or rolling is done effectively, your soil will now have a firm but not compacted surface. Large clods will have been broken down, and the small aggregates will be pressed together so that they make good contact with each other. This will help to bring adequate supplies of moisture to seeds and seedlings, encouraging good germination and growth.

Raking

The final operation in preparing your soil will be a gentle raking. By passing the rake through the soil, you will continue the gradual breaking down of the crumbs. Your object will be to produce a tilth in the top inch or two of soil that provides an ideal home for seeds. The crumbs will be about ⅛ to ¼ inch in diameter, and the soil will be firm without being compacted.

Hoeing

The hoe is really a miniature spade. It carries a small blade at the end of a long handle, enabling you to break up and turn over the surface of the soil, and to chop through weeds and unwanted plants.

The most important function of the hoe is to destroy weeds, and so reduce the losses of moisture and plant nutrients from the soil. Hoeing also breaks up surface crusts, and maintains a loose soil mulch which absorbs rainwater more readily. Some loss of water by evaporation from the surface is prevented, but this is not now regarded as a very significant effect.

KEEP THE SOIL MOIST

Direct loss from the surface may be kept down by using mulches to protect the soil from wind and sunshine. Mulches may be in the form of organic matter that will subsequently add humus to the soil, such as straw, peat, sawdust or compost. They may also be artificial "mulches" in the form of plastic or aluminium sheets, which simply provide a protective blanket.

Loosening the soil has long been regarded as a way of cutting down direct moisture loss (see page 100), but it is now believed that this helps mainly by keeping down weeds.

When the soil becomes dry and needs watering, it is best to give it a thorough soaking. A sprinkling will wet the surface, but the water will evaporate before doing any good. A dry soil may need 2 or 3 buckets of water per square yard to wet it to a depth of 9 to 12 inches, depending on the type of soil. Watering is best done at night.

The *Dutch Hoe* has a blade which is in line with the handle. You should use this regularly throughout the growing season, destroying the weeds before they can grow to any size.

The *Draw Hoe* has its blade set at an angle to the shaft. You should use this primarily for chopping through weeds which have become established.

ORGANIC MATTER AND SOIL STRUCTURE

An essential fact to remember about the management of your soil is that you are fighting a constant battle to sustain its structure. If you have started off with a virgin grassland soil, your soil will already have a good crumb structure. But all the tillage operations you carry out from that time on will tend to destroy the structure that nature has provided.

The basis of a good soil structure is to be found in the material that is holding soil particles together into crumbs. Many factors play a part in this, depending on the texture and condition of the soil. But in almost any soil, we can find the answer to good soil structure in the humus that has come from its organic matter.

In a coarse-textured, sandy soil, the particles can be held together into aggregates if there is plenty of humus in the soil. But the humus decomposes quickly in a well-aerated sandy soil.

A loamy soil will contain a higher proportion of clay, and this helps to bind the particles together. Decomposition of humus is less rapid, and these soils retain their structure better than sandy or clayey soils.

Clayey soils are the most difficult of all. The high clay content makes them potentially fertile soils, but they are more sensitive to structure-destroying influences. They tend to be poorly-drained, and form crusts and pans under the effects of rain and pressure.

No matter what type of soil you have in your garden, you

will find that an ample supply of organic matter is the best insurance against loss of soil structure. You can add organic matter as farmyard manure or as compost, as peat or as green manure. Anything that can increase the humus-content of the soil is a contribution to the creation of a good soil structure.

With plenty of humus in your soil, you have the foundation on which to build its structure. Careful tillage will break up clods and pans in a clayey soil; a good crop cover, and the use of mulches, will prevent the surface being battered by rain; the proper use of fertilizers will encourage the soil to sustain a vigorous growth of micro-organisms and crop plants.

CONTROL YOUR SOIL MOISTURE

If tests show that water is lying too near the surface of your soil, you must take steps to reduce the level by suitable drainage. The subsoil should be broken up thoroughly by double digging, and a soakaway made at the lowest point of the garden (see page 183).

If this is not sufficient, it will be necessary to lay soil drains (see page 183). They should lead into the soakaway, or if possible into a ditch, stream or storm drain that will carry away the water.

The ideal garden soil will admit most of the water that falls on it, and will hold a large quantity in the fine pores and capillaries between the soil particles. Excess water will drain away through the large pores and channels separating the crumbs, and the water table will lie at a depth of at least 3 feet.

To achieve this ideal, you will need to create a good soil structure and ensure that your soil is properly drained.

On sloping soils, special precautions must be taken to prevent water running away unchecked across the surface. The soil should be landscaped so that little terraces trap the water, giving it time to sink into the surface. If your soil is properly drained, your plants will spread their roots deep in the soil. They will withstand periods of drought better than shallow-rooted plants growing in badly-drained soils. But there will always be times during summer when the soil will become dry, and watering is necessary.

Plants should be watered before they begin to wilt. Wilting means that some damage has already been done, and watering has been left too late.

When you *do* water, make a job of it by using enough to wet the soil thoroughly to a depth of about 15 inches. A sprinkling of water on the surface is useless, as it evaporates before reaching the plant roots.

If your soil structure and drainage are good, you cannot use too much water. Your aim should be to keep the capillary supply at full strength; excess water will drain away without waterlogging the soil.

In hot weather, it is best to water in the evening. A mulch prevents evaporation of water from the surface during the day (see page 100).

CONTROL YOUR SOIL pH

Most garden soils tend to become acid through leaching and loss of lime, and the production of carbon dioxide by animals and plants in the soil. The gardener's problem is generally to reduce the acidity, i.e. to *raise* the pH value of the soil. He does this by adding liming materials in the appropriate quantity.

The pH value is a measure of the intensity of your soil acidity, but it does not represent the total *amount* of acidity (see page 309). This varies greatly depending on the proportion of clay, the activity of the clay and the amount of organic matter. The total acidity of a soil of pH 6.0, for example, will increase with increasing amounts of clay in your soil, and with increasing activity of your clay, and with increasing amounts of organic matter.

For this reason, the quantity of lime needed to change

the pH through 1 unit, e.g. from 5.0 to 6.0, increases with the amount and activity of the clay, and the amount of organic matter in your soil.

It is difficult, therefore, to make an accurate estimate of the amount of lime needed to change the acidity of a soil from one pH value to another. The table on page 125 gives an indication of the amounts of lime to use on the average garden soil. The following table shows the amounts of finely ground limestone to use on soils of different textural classes to raise the pH through 1 unit.

Finely Ground Limestone Required to Raise the pH of a 7-inch layer of Soil, in Pounds per 1,000 Square Feet.

	pH 4.5 to 5.5	pH 5.5 to 6.5
Sands and loamy sands	15–25	20–30
Sandy loams	25–45	35–55
Loams	40–60	50–85
Silt loams	60–80	75–105
Clay loams	80–100	100–120
Muck	175–200	200–225

Note: 1. Quicklime—use half quantities. 2. If organic matter in soil is high, use higher figures. 3. If organic matter is low, use lower figures.

When you are testing your soil for pH, it is useful to measure the acidity of each horizon separately. The pHs of topsoil, subsoil and parent material are commonly different, and each layer requires a separate liming treatment to adjust the pH to the required amount.

One of the commonest errors that gardeners make is to over-lime their soils. Very small additions of lime can cause big changes of pH in some fertile soils, and the results can be disastrous. Overliming may reduce the availability of some nutrient elements, and cause deficiency symptoms in plants. For this reason it is often preferable to use finely ground limestone in preference to quicklime or slaked lime, which act more quickly.

Also, you should make sure that lime is spread evenly, and avoid leaving pockets of concentrated lime in the soil.

Dolomitic limestone is the least likely to cause damage through overliming. It becomes almost insoluble at pH 7 or higher, and the danger of overliming through uneven spreading is reduced.

There are many liming materials to choose from (see page 184), and the one you use will depend upon circumstances and requirements. Ground limestone and chalk are easy and safe to use, as they are slow-acting and will not damage plants.

Slaked or hydrated lime is more rapid in action than

SOAKAWAY

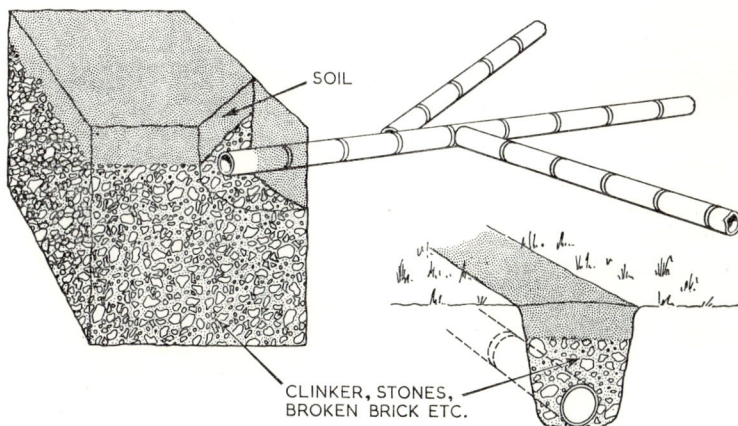

CLINKER, STONES, BROKEN BRICK ETC.

A soakaway pit is commonly about 5 – 6 feet deep, and the same in width. It is filled with clinker, stones, broken brick etc. to within about 1 ft. of the top, the remaining space being filled with soil.

MATERIALS USED IN LIMING

Chemically, "lime" means calcium oxide (CaO), which is more commonly known as burnt lime or quicklime. In agriculture, 'lime' means any calcium-containing material which is capable of correcting soil acidity, including ground limestone, quicklime, hydrated lime, chalk, marl, blast furnace slag, oyster shells, sugar mill and paper mill waste lime.

Gypsum, or land plaster, is an excellent source of calcium and sulphur for plants, but it does not correct soil acidity. It is therefore not a liming material.

GROUND LIMESTONE
Limestone rock, which may be calcium carbonate, $CaCO_3$, or a mixture of calcium carbonate with magnesium carbonate, $MgCO_3$. Both substances correct soil acidity.

Dolomite is limestone containing about as much magnesium carbonate as calcium carbonate.

Dolomitic Limestone (Magnesium Limestone) is limestone containing lesser proportions of magnesium carbonate.

Ground limestone is made simply by crushing the rock to any specified size. The speed at which it corrects soil acidity depends upon the size; the finer it is ground, the faster it works.

Dolomitic limestone acts more slowly than high-calcium limestone of equal fineness.

QUICKLIME
Calcium oxide, CaO, made by heating calcium carbonate (limestone) to high temperature. If dolomitic limestone is used, the quicklime contains magnesium oxide, MgO.

Quicklime reacts vigorously with water, which converts it to hydrated lime. It is difficult and unpleasant to handle, and may damage foliage on direct contact. It acts rapidly in neutralizing soil acidity.

HYDRATED LIME (*Slaked Lime*)
Calcium hydroxide, $Ca(OH)_2$, made by addition of water to quicklime. It is usually a very fine powder, and it acts quickly against acid in the soil. It is commonly more expensive than limestone, owing to the extra processing involved.

AIR-SLAKED LIME
A mixture of hydrated lime and limestone, made by exposing quicklime to air.

MARL
Granular or loosely-consolidated, often impure, calcium carbonate formed from the shells of marine animals, or by precipitation of calcium carbonate in the water of lakes and ponds.

The term is used for almost any earthy material rich in lime, e.g. calcareous clays. Often contains much clay, silt or organic matter. It is probably a little faster in action than limestone. It does not supply any magnesium.

(Continued opposite)

Percent Availability in 1 to 3 Years

LIMESTONE. EFFECT OF PARTICLE SIZE

The relative availability of ground limestone is influenced by its particle or mesh size.

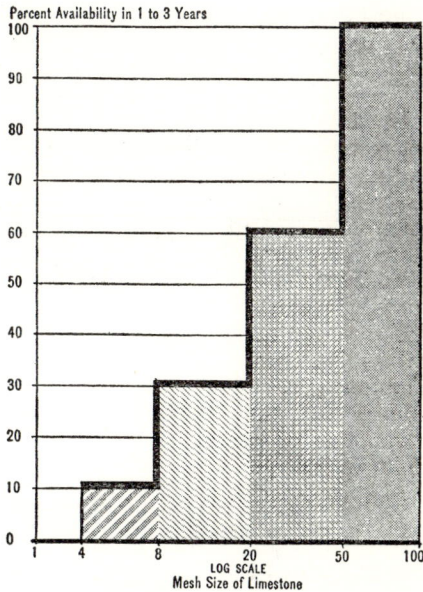

LOG SCALE
Mesh Size of Limestone

MATERIALS USED IN LIMING (Continued)

CHALK
Soft calcium carbonate rock. Ground before use, and widely used in regions where it occurs naturally.

SLAGS
Waste materials formed during smelting operations.

Blast Furnace Slag is a by-product of the iron industry. It contains calcium and magnesium as silicates, and is made in two forms:
(1) Air-cooled, which is ground before use.
(2) Water-quenched, which is granulated, and acts more quickly than (1).

Basic Slag is also produced by the iron and steel industry, but is used manily for its phosphorus content. It is of value as a liming material.

Calcium Silicate Slag is a by-product from phosphorus manufacture. It is similar in action to blast furnace slag.

SHELLS AND OTHER MATERIALS
Oyster shells and other sea shells are mostly calcium carbonate. When ground, they make useful liming materials.

Many industrial by-products contain lime, e.g. paper mill waste, tannery waste etc.

G

limestone, but its fineness sometimes makes for unpleasant handling.

Lime is usually spread on the soil after it has been dug, and may be raked into the surface. It is washed in by rain, hydrated lime dissolving more readily than limestone.

Increasing Acidity

Sometimes you will find it necessary to increase the acidity of the soil to provide for the needs of acid-loving plants.

If the soil contains free lime, it is best to remove it altogether and replace it with a naturally acid woodland soil. Rhododendrons and azaleas, for example, need an acid soil, and a layer of soil about 20 inches deep should be replaced for them.

When soils contain little or no free lime, they can be acidified by adding sulphur to them. The amounts to use are as follows:

Amount of Powdered Sulphur to Reduce pH of an 8-inch Layer of Soil.
(Pints per 100 Square Feet.)

Original pH of Soil	Sulphur required to reach pH of:									
	4.5		5.0		5.5		6.0		6.5	
	Sand	Loam	Sand	Loam	Sand	Loam	Sand	Loam	Sand	Loam
5.0	⅔	2								
5.5	1⅓	4	⅔	2						
6.0	2	5½	1⅓	4	⅔	2				
6.5	2½	8	2	5½	1⅓	4	⅔	2		
7.0	3	10	2½	8	2	5½	1⅓	4	⅔	2

If your soil is clayey, it is not really suitable for growing acid-loving plants. It is best to remove it completely and replace it with a sandy soil mixed with acid organic matter such as a leaf mould.

Aluminium sulphate may be used to increase soil acidity. About 7 pounds will achieve the same effect as 1 pound of sulphur, but aluminium sulphate should be used with great care, as large amounts may be toxic to plants.

When you use sulphur to increase soil acidity, make sure that the soil is well drained. Sulphur and organic matter in a wet soil will release hydrogen sulphide, which has an objectionable smell and is also toxic to plants.

It is best to prepare soil for acid-loving plants well in advance. The soil is kept moist during the acidification process, and watered when the pH has reached the required point. This washes out undesirable materials that may have formed.

If your plants are already established in the soil before you find that it needs acidification, you can mix sulphur into the surface soil above the roots at the rate of ½ to 1 tablespoonful per square foot.

Acid mulches, including pine needles, sawdust and acid peat will help to increase soil acidity. Ammonium sulphate fertilizer, used repeatedly, will have the same effect.

9

Stocking the Soil Larder

MANURES AND FERTILIZERS

Plants obtain carbon, oxygen and hydrogen from air and water, and we can assume that they do not go short of any of these nutrient elements. In addition, they need adequate supplies of at least 12 other elements, all of which are essential raw materials in building living matter. They obtain these elements from the soil, and you must be sure that your soil is meeting the plant's requirements if it is to grow healthy crops.

Nitrogen, phosphorus and potassium are used in substantial quantities by most plants, and these are the elements that are usually in short supply in the soil. Shortages of the other essential elements are much less common. They are used in comparatively small amounts, and most soils are able to meet the plant's needs. There are times, however, when a soil is unable to provide enough of one or more of the trace elements, and deficiency diseases will result.

Nutrient elements are absorbed by plants in the form of simple chemicals dissolved in the soil water. We can feed a plant by providing it with supplies of the necessary chemicals, or of substances which are readily converted into nutrient chemicals in the soil. We call any such substances 'fertilizers'; they increase the fertility of the soil.

In practice, we are concerned largely with providing supplies of nitrogen, phosphorus and potassium when we add nutrient materials to the soil. And the term 'fertilizer' has acquired a restricted meaning; it is commonly used to describe substances which increase the amount of one or more of these three elements.

Fertilizers may be minerals obtained from the earth's crust, like Chile Saltpetre (sodium nitrate) or phosphate rock. They may be chemicals produced synthetically, like the ammonium sulphate which is made from nitrogen of the air.

Fertilizers of this sort come from non-living sources, either natural or synthetic, and for this reason are commonly called *inorganic fertilizers.*

The nutrient chemicals provided by these fertilizers, and by natural soil processes, are used by plants as raw materials from which living matter is made. The plant itself, and the animal which eats it, become stores of the nutrient elements which were obtained from the soil. These may be incorporated into complex chemical substances, such as proteins, which form part of the living matter itself.

When plants and animals die, the materials of their bodies are returned to the soil. But nutrient elements present in the living matter are not immediately available to plants growing in the soil. They may be locked away inside the complex molecules of proteins and other materials. And they cannot be used by plants until they have been converted into simple chemicals by the processes of decay.

Material which has come from living things – vegetable or animal – is thus a source of plant nutrients. As it decays, it releases chemical raw materials for re-use by new generations of plants. And by adding supplies of animal or vegetable remains to the soil we can increase the amounts of plant nutrients that are available.

This type of soil-enriching material, which comes from a living source, is described as an *organic fertilizer.*

Organic fertilizers may consist of all manners of

In the past, before mechanization came to the farm, animal manure was the most important fertilizer available. Farms were small, and cultivation was less intensive than it is today; animal manure was plentiful, and the farmer relied upon it to return the "goodness" to his soil.

Today, the tractor has taken over from the horse, and farms are run on factory lines. Animal manure is no longer plentiful, and is quite inadequate to supply the plant foods that are needed. Even so, supplies that *are* available are seldom used to best advantage, despite the fact that the need for humus-builders is greater than it has ever been before. Less than half the potential value of manure is realized, largely because of inadequate handling and storing.

PROPER HANDLING AND STORAGE IMPROVES VALUE

The value of animal manure is conserved by

* Using enough bedding to absorb the liquid.

* Spreading as quickly as possible after rotting.

* Storing in a covered shed and compacting it so that air is excluded.

* Adding superphosphate to conserve nitrogen and increase phosphorus. Animal manures are poorly balanced in their plant food content, being low in phosphorus. The addition of superphosphate not only improves plant food balance, but helps to conserve nitrogen. Adding 2 to 2½ lb. of normal superphosphate ($18 - 20\%$ P_2O_5) per day for each horse, cow or beast is recommended practice. This prevents loss of nitrogen in storage. If it is not done, 60 to 80 lb. of normal superphosphate should be added to each ton of manure as it is placed in storage or spread on the soil.

* Allowing it to decay before use. Fresh manure should not be added to the soil, as it gives off harmful materials, and because some plant foods are not available until decay has taken place.
  Before use, the manure should be stacked under some sort of roofing, covered with a few inches of soil, and left to decay. It is ready for use when there is no longer any unpleasant smell, and the texture has become even (the straw is no longer recognizable).

WHEN TO USE MANURE

The usual time to add manure to the soil is in the autumn. It is commonly dug or ploughed in at the rate of 1 ton to every $200 - 400$ square yards (1 barrowload of ½ to 1 cwt. per 10 sq. yds.). A thin layer of well-rotted manure may also be used as a mulch around growing plants at any time of year.

MANURE

PLANT FOOD VALUE OF MANURES

The composition of various animal excrements and the average quantities produced annually are shown in the table below. It should be recognized that the composition of farm manures varies widely under different conditions and methods of handling. The average manure containing straw bedding, as applied to the soil, contains 0.6 percent N, 0.35 percent P_2O_5, and 0.5 percent K_2O.

AVERAGE ANNUAL PRODUCTION AND NUTRIENT CONTENT OF EXCREMENTS PER ANIMAL								
	Production		N		P_2O_5		K_2O	
Kind	Faeces	Urine	Faeces	Urine	Faeces	Urine	Faeces	Urine
	Tons	Tons	%	%	%	%	%	%
e	6.5	1.5	0.50	1.20	0.30	Trace	0.24	1.50
le	8.9	4.0	.32	.95	.21	.03	.16	.95
ep	.46	.27	.65	1.68	.46	.03	.23	2.10
....	1.10	.64	.60	.30	.46	.12	.44	1.00
ey	.17	......	1.31	......	.71	......	.49	......
....	.07	......	1.48	......	.96	......	.47	......

. Agr. Expt. Sta. Bul. 469.

Yearly Excrement From 1 Ton of Livestock

Animal	Actual Output (Tons)	Adjusted Output [1] (Tons)	Content of Fresh Manure				
			Organic Matter (Tons)	Plant Food			
				N (Pounds)	P_2O_5 (Pounds)	K_2O (Pounds)	Total (Pounds)
Cattle	26	12.6	4.4	260	104	182	546
Horses	18	13.3	4.7	234	90	270	594
Hogs	30	12.0	4.2	300	210	390	900
Sheep	13	12.6	4.4	273	78	247	598
Poultry	10	12.9	4.5	200	160	80	440

[1] Actual output adjusted to 65% water content.

Source: Ohio Bulletin No. 262

materials. The remains of animals and plants which have died will decompose and release nutrient elements as simple chemicals in the soil. The excrement of animals includes chemicals that have come from food; these chemicals are valuable in that they return plant nutrients to the soil from which they came.

For centuries, we have been making use of the excrement of farm animals as a fertilizer. Mixed with litter, such as straw, and allowed to undergo partial decay, the droppings of horses, cows, pigs and other animals provide us with one of the most valuable of all organic fertilizers – farmyard manure.

The term "manure" does not have any precise meaning. Some people use it to describe anything of plant or animal origin which is used as a fertilizer. Others use the term only for certain bulky materials which come from living sources, such as farmyard manure, or the decomposed vegetable material we know as compost ("artificial manure").

Used in this restricted sense, the term manure does not include materials of living origin which have a more obvious and precise composition. Dried blood, or bone meal, or hoof and horn meal, for example are not usually described as manures. They are used to meet specific soil requirements and are called organic fertilizers.

WHICH ARE BEST – INORGANIC FERTILIZERS OR MANURES?

Ever since we began using chemical nutrients on the soil, controversy has raged regarding the relative merits of inorganic fertilizers and organic manures. More often than not, the arguments result from a misunderstanding of the processes involved in plant feeding.

The plant obtains its nutrients as simple chemicals which can be absorbed through the roots. And these chemicals are exactly the same, whether they come from an inorganic fertilizer or an organic manure.

When natural organic substances decay, the elements in their molecules are re-arranged and form simpler molecules. Nitrogen, for example, may be part of a complex protein molecule in the remains of a leaf which has fallen to the ground. As such, it cannot be absorbed by a growing plant, and a plant may suffer nitrogen-deficiency even though it is growing in a soil full of undecomposed dead leaves.

As the dead material begins to decay, the nitrogen in its proteins undergoes chemical changes, and it is converted eventually into simple inorganic chemicals, including nitrates. In this form, the nitrogen may be absorbed by plant roots.

When we apply inorganic chemicals, such as ammonium sulphate or nitrates, directly to the soil, we are providing the plant with precisely the same nitrogenous chemicals that it obtains from the decay of organic matter. But we have cut out the time-absorbing processes operated by nature, and we bring the plant an immediately-available supply of food.

When we impose our will upon Nature, by creating a farm or garden, we are increasing the demands made on the soil. It must provide more nutrient chemicals if it is to grow the plants we prefer in the quantities we require.

Supplies of good quality humus-building manure are restricted, and we can rarely get enough to sustain soil structure. Some manures are deficient in one or more of the nutrient elements needed by growing crops, and, in any case, organic manures will not release nutrient elements fast enough to meet the demands of crops growing "under pressure".

Most authorities now agree that organic manures and inorganic fertilizers both have a vital role to play in maintaining soil fertility. We cannot do without either if we are to encourage the soil to grow the plants we need.

Organic manures are of vital importance in that they
G*

COMPOST

All plant and animal matter contains supplies of nutrient elements which were drawn originally from the soil. These nutrients may be used again by new generations of plants if they are made available as simple chemicals.

Waste vegetable matter may be converted into useful "manure substitute" by the process of controlled decay known as *composting*. Organic matter is composted by storing it under such conditions that decay bacteria are encouraged to use it as food, and break down the complex chemicals. Essential elements are released as simple plant food chemicals, as in the rotting of stable and farmyard manure.

When farmyard manure is allowed to rot, bacteria are able to draw on supplies of nutrients available in the manure itself. Using these materials as essential food constituents, they attack the organic matter and bring about its decomposition. But in a mass of vegetable matter there are insufficient nutrient chemicals—especially nitrogenous chemicals—to provide for the needs of bacteria. It is necessary to add supplies of simple chemicals that the bacteria can use. This is done by mixing the vegetable matter with suitable chemicals, and storing it in such a way that bacteria are supplied with adequate moisture and oxygen.

Under these conditions, the vegetable matter decays to form a useful substitute for stable manure, providing nutrient chemicals formed during decay, and a supply of humus.

MATERIALS THAT ARE SUITABLE

Almost any form of vegetable material may be used in making compost, provided it is not diseased or contaminated, including grass clippings, soft vegetable and flower stems, leaves, straw, crushed cabbage stalks, annual weeds, wood ashes, bracken, peat, soft hedge clippings and household refuse such as tea leaves and peelings.

MATERIALS THAT ARE NOT SUITABLE

Diseased plants, twigs, tough weeds, and grass clippings from the first cut after using a weed killer should not be used for making compost.

MAKING THE HEAP

1. Dig a shallow pit 3 ft. wide and of any convenient length in a sheltered spot away from the house. Keep the topsoil on one side.

2. Put down a bottom layer (3 to 4 inches thick) of coarse material such as smashed-up cabbage stalks. This will help drainage and aeration.

3. Sprinkle a suitable composting mixture over the top of the layer, (*see below*) using about a handful to every barrow load of greenstuff. On top of this place a 1 inch layer of top-soil.

4. Build up the heap by repeating the following sandwich – a 6 inch layer of mixed vegetable refuse, followed by a thin layer of fertilizer, and then a 1 inch layer of soil.   (*Continued opposite*)

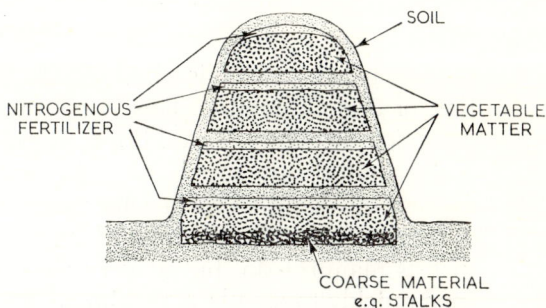

SOIL

NITROGENOUS FERTILIZER

VEGETABLE MATTER

COARSE MATERIAL
e.g. STALKS

MAKING THE HEAP (Continued)

5. When the heap is about 3 ft. high finish it off with a 1 to 2 inch casing of soil. Flatten the top of the heap.

6. When the heap is 1 month old, see if any part of it has dried out. If it has, drive a rod into several places and pour water down the holes.

7. There is no need to turn the heap once it is made. After about 2 months in warm weather or 3 months in cold weather, the compost is ready for use. It is used in exactly the same way as well-rotted animal manure.

MATERIAL TO ADD IN MAKING COMPOST
(Cups per tightly-packed bushel)

Material	*Cups*
1. For General Purpose Compost, including acid-loving shrubs.	
Combination A:	
Ammonium sulphate	1
Superphosphate (20%)	½
Epsom salt	$\frac{1}{16}$
Combination B:	
Mixed Fertilizer 10–6–4	1½
Mixed Fertilizer 5–10–5	2½
2. For Kitchen Garden or Flowers not requiring an acid soil.	
Combination C:	
Ammonium sulphate	1
Superphosphate (20%)	½
Ground dolomitic limestone – or wood ashes	⅔
Combination D:	
Like B, above, plus ground dolomitic limestone or wood ashes	⅓

provide humus, which is a half-way stage in the decomposition of organic matter. This is essential in maintaining a good soil structure. In addition, organic manures release a slow but steady supply of plant nutrients into the soil, and go on doing so for a long time.

Inorganic fertilizers provide plant nutrient chemicals, just as manures do, but at very short notice. They bring food quickly to the plant, making up the deficiencies which would result if the soil had to feed our plants from its own resources.

ORGANIC FERTILIZERS AND MANURES

Almost every form of dead vegetable or animal material, and the excrement of a great variety of animals, has been used as a source of plant food for the soil. These fertilizers contain elements that came originally from the soil, and the process of decay releases them again for use by new generations of plants.

Fertilizers formed from the whole animal or plant body will generally provide a supply of most of the essential elements. But those consisting of specific parts of the body, like bone meal, or of mixtures of animal droppings and straw litter, like farmyard manure, do not necessarily supply all the essential nutrients. Also, batches of the same type of manure may vary greatly among themselves.

When we use organic manures, we rarely know exactly what we are adding to the soil in terms of nutrient elements. It is difficult, therefore, to estimate the amounts that are necessary to release a desired quantity of nutrient elements in the soil.

In fact, this problem often solves itself. Good bulky organic manures, such as horse manure, are generally in short supply, and gardeners seldom have enough. Organic manures of this type are invaluable as a source of humus, and are used as much for sustaining soil structure as in providing plants with food.

GREEN MANURE

Organic matter may be returned to the soil by growing a crop which is ploughed in. This is a green manure.

The organic matter of the plant is constructed very largely from carbon which is absorbed through the leaves. Only about one twentieth of the dry matter of the plant consists of nutrients drawn from the soil. A green manure thus provides the soil with much more material than was taken out of it, and this is converted into humus.

Fast growing crops are commonly used as green manures, including clover, rape, and mustard. Leguminous crops are especially valuable, as they also enrich the soil with nitrogen fixed by bacteria in the root nodules.

NITROGEN IN GREEN MANURES
(Percentage – dry basis)

Alfalfa	3.0 – 4.0
Austrian Winter Peas	3.0 – 3.8
Clover, Red	2.8 – 3.2
Clover, Crimson	3.0 – 3.3
Cowpeas	2.5 – 3.0
Lespedeza, Common	2.2 – 2.5
Lespedeza, Sericea	2.1 – 2.4
Lupin, Blue	2.0 – 2.5
Vetch, Hairy	3.0 – 4.0
Oats	1.3 – 1.4
Rye	1.2 – 1.3
Ryegrass	1.2 – 1.3

If you have a source of farmyard manure, compost or other bulky organic material at your disposal, add as much as you can to your soil, no matter what sort of plants you aim to grow. You will seldom create difficulties for yourself by using too much manure in this way, provided you prepare it properly before it is mixed into your soil (see page 190).

LET MANURES DECAY

Many plant residues, such as straw or sawdust, contain only a relatively small amount of nitrogen. They are correspondingly high in carbon and hydrogen, in the form of carbohydrates such as cellulose.

If organic materials of this sort are mixed into the soil, they undergo decay. But the attacking micro-organisms need supplies of nitrogen to sustain them as they feed on the carbohydrates, and they take their nitrogen from the resources around them in the soil.

This is the reason for the bad effect on crops when straw stubble or fresh manure is dug or ploughed into the soil. Microbes are competing with the crops for available nitrogen.

The effect can be prevented by adding extra nitrogen to materials of this sort, and allowing them to undergo a partial decay before they are mixed into the soil. The microbes feed on the added nitrogen, and decomposition has approached the stage where it is releasing nutrients from the decaying material by the time it enters the soil.

Farmyard manure contains nitrogenous substances in the urine and droppings mixed with the straw litter, and it is unnecessary to add an extra quantity. Well-composted farmyard manure is an excellent organic fertilizer.

When "artificial manure" is made by composting leaves and other vegetable material, on the other hand, it is necessary to add a source of readily-available nitrogen to provide for the needs of decay bacteria. Decomposition proceeds in the compost heap, and the composted material is a balanced fertilizer material when it is added to the soil. Nitrogen used by microbes growing on the carbohydrates and other materials in the vegetable matter has come from the nitrogenous material added to the heap. It becomes part of the body-material of the microbes, and is released as simple nitrogenous nutrients when the microbes die.

This need for nitrogen on the part of decay micro-organisms is an important point to remember. Bulky vegetable materials and litter, which consist essentially of tough cellulosic residues such as straw, fibrous leaves, stalks and roots, sawdust and the like, must be provided with readily-available nitrogen if they are to decay. And the decomposition must, if possible, take place before the material is dug into the soil. It will then be a rich, balanced manure, on its way to becoming humus. And it will make an invaluable contribution to soil fertility.

If you dig coarse, undecomposed vegetable litter into your ground, on the other hand, you are encouraging decay microbes to draw on the soil's resources of nitrogen, and your crops may go short of nitrogen. This is a temporary setback, as the nitrogen will be released again when the microbes die and decay. But it may cause serious damage to growing crops.

If you *do* mix uncomposted litter or stubble into your soil, always add nitrogenous fertilizer to provide the extra nitrogen needed by the micro-organisms.

INORGANIC FERTILIZERS

When we apply inorganic fertilizers to the soil, we are providing nutrients that are immediately available to the plant, or nearly so. Inorganic fertilizers are chemicals which contain one or more of the essential elements needed by plants. We know precisely how much of each element is present in any weight of pure chemical used as fertilizer, and we can calculate how much fertilizer to apply to the soil to provide a desired quantity of any particular nutrient element.

This knowledge of the chemical make-up of a fertilizer adds precision to our plant feeding routines. It enables us to control the amount and balance of nutrients that we give to individual types of plant.

On the other hand, an inorganic fertilizer provides plant

* Balanced quantities of all necessary nutrients, water and oxygen must be available to plant roots for maximum yields.

* Irregular distribution of fertilizer lowers efficiency.

* Soluble salts go into solution in the soil moisture and move with it, up during dry spells, down during heavy rains.

* Leaching of nitrogen or potash can be excessive. With equal rainfall, it is much greater from bare soils than from cropped soils.

* A concentration above 1% of salt in the soil solution prevents germination of most seeds and injures or kills plants.

* When a soil dries out the soil solution is concentrated.

* Fixation of phosphate in insoluble forms decreases efficiency.

* Potash is fixed to a much lesser degree.

* Ammonia is usualy fixed by soil colloids temporarily, but this generally does not reduce efficiency because the soil micro-organisms change it (NH_4) to nitrates (NO_3). Nitrates are not fixed in the soil.

* Strongly acid soils fix phosphates more than slightly acid or neutral soils.

* Copper, iron, manganese and zinc are likely to be unavailable in heavily limed soils, or in calcareous soil. Molybdenum behaves in the opposite manner.

* Since phosphates do not ordinarily move in the soil, they should be placed where roots from germinating seed will promptly reach them.

* Band placement of fertilizer from 1 to 2 inches to the side of the seed and from 1 to 2 inches lower in the soil minimizes leaching and fixation losses, makes nutrients available to the roots as soon as they start to grow, and does not encourage weeds between the rows.

* Broadcasting most of the fertilizer is necessary under most conditions because only a small portion of the crop's needs can usually be applied in the row or starter fertilizers.

* The same principles apply to the use of liquid fertilizers and to the non-pressure nitrogen solutions as apply to the use of solid fertilizers.

* Anhydrous ammonia and the low pressure nitrogen solutions must be placed under the soil surface.

* Some nutrients are used immediately by the plant when applied to the foliage.

ABOUT FERTILIZERS

FERTILIZER FOR SOILS OF VARIOUS TEXTURES
(Amounts to apply in pounds per 1000 square feet)

General Soil Class		Nutrients		
Texture	Fertility Level	Nitrogen (N)	Phosphoric Acid (P_2O_5)	Potash (K_2O)
Sandy soils	Low	1 − 4	2 − 5	1 − 4
	High	0 − 2	0 − 3	$\frac{1}{2}$ − 3
Loamy soils	Low	1 − 4	2 − 5	1 − 4
	High	0 − 2	0 − 3	0 − 2
Clayey soils	Low	1 − 4	3 − 6	2 − 5
	High	0 − 2	0 − 3	0 − 3
Muck soils	Low	$\frac{1}{2}$ − 3	3 − 6	1 − 7
	High	0 − 2	1 − 4	0 − 3

SOME FERTILIZER "DONT'S"

Don't use more than the amount recommended on the label, no matter how small it is. If you do not have a scale handy, use a standard matchbox (2 in. × 1⅓ in. × ⅖ in.) as a measure. The approximate weight of a matchboxful (level with the top of the box) of various fertilizers is as follows:

Bone Meal	¾ oz.
Sulphate of Ammonia	¾ oz.
Sulphate of Potash	1 oz.
Superphosphate of Lime	½ oz.
"Growmore" 7: 7: 7	¾ oz.
Flower Fertilizer 8.2: 5.9: 12	¾ oz.
Tomato Fertilizer 5: 8.1: 10	¾ oz.
Rose Fertilizer 5.2: 9: 6	¾ oz.

Don't allow fertilizers to touch leaves or flowers – they may scorch. If rain seems unlikely, water fertilizers into the soil.

Don't store fertilizers in a damp place, and always keep the bags off the floor.

Don't put fertilizers in too deeply. Slow-acting fertilizers should be forked into the top spit. Quick-acting kinds should be worked into the top 1 − 2 inches with a hoe, rake or fork.

Don't apply liquid fertilizers to dry soil. Always water first.

nutrients in a concentrated form, and we need to take special care in using them. It is much easier to use inorganic fertilizers wrongly than it is to misuse organic manures.

Inorganic fertilizers may be bought as single chemical types, such as ammonium sulphate, muriate of potash, or superphosphate. The amount of a particular nutrient element in a fertilizer of this type is a fixed percentage (assuming it is pure) which may be worked out from its chemical formula (see page 226).

Many types of compound fertilizer are now produced, in which chemicals are mixed to provide the three major nutrients in specified amounts.

As the requirements of plants vary, and different conditions create different needs, the proportions of the ingredients will be chosen to meet particular circumstances. Most manufacturers make up a range of compound fertilizers to cater for all normal requirements. The analysis or grade (see page 206) is always quoted on the package, indicating the percentages of the three nutrients that are present.

Mix them Yourself

You can make up compound fertilizers for yourself by mixing nutrient chemicals in appropriate amounts. A useful mixture may be made from ammonium sulphate, superphosphate and potassium sulphate. For normal use, such as the preparation of the ground for sowing or planting, the amounts should be adjusted to give roughly equal percentages of the three nutrients. This may be achieved, for example, by mixing 10 lb. ammonium sulphate, 10 lb. superphosphate and 4 lb. potassium sulphate.

A popular compound fertilizer, made by most manufacturers, is the 7:7:7 grade sold in Britain as National Growmore fertilizer. It meets most of the general purpose needs of the gardener.

HOW MUCH FERTILIZER TO USE

1. *General Guide*

Every plant responds best to a particular balance of plant nutrients, but the following table gives a rough guide to the fertility requirements for broad groups of plants. These are indicated as high, low or medium, and refer to the three basic nutrients, nitrogen, phosphorus and potassium.

It must be realized that individual plants within the groups vary considerably in their requirements.

Vegetables	High
Herbs	Medium to low
Lawn grasses	Medium to high
Fruits	Medium
Annual flowers	Medium
Perennial flowers	Medium to low
Shrubs, deciduous	Medium to low
Shrubs, evergreen	Low
Shade trees, deciduous	Medium to low
Shade trees, evergreen	Low

The table on page 201 shows roughly the amounts of nitrogen, phosphorus and potassium to use on garden soils of various textures, and of low and high fertility as indicated by present growth or soil tests.

The high part of the range is for plants responding to high levels of fertility for the element, and the low range is for plants needing only low amounts of the element.

Example: Suppose your garden soil is a loam of high fertility, which you plan to use for vegetables. You would need about 2 pounds of nitrogen, 3 pounds of phosphoric oxide and 2 pounds of potash per 1,000 square feet. This would be provided, for example, by 20 pounds of a 10-15-10 mixed fertilizer per 1,000 square feet containing 10 percent of nitrogen (i.e. 2 pounds), 15 percent of phosphoric oxide (i.e. 3 pounds) and 10 percent of potash (i.e. 2 pounds).

Alternatively, you could use 40 pounds of a 5-10-5 fertilizer, which would provide the amount of nitrogen and potassium needed, with a little extra phosphorus (i.e. 4 pounds instead of 3 pounds).

2. *Accurate Assessment*

In estimating with greater accuracy the amounts of fertilizer to apply, you will need to know three things:

(1) the nutrient requirements of the crop you will be growing

(2) the quantities of available nutrients already in the soil

(3) the amounts of nutrients in the manures and fertilizers you are going to use.

GUIDE TO COMMON FERTILIZERS

Nutrient Added	Fertilizer	Plants which Benefit	Amount (oz. per sq. yd.)	When to use
Nitrogen	Sulphate of Ammonia (quick-acting) 20·6% nitrogen	'Leafy' vegetables	1	When plants are growing
	Dried Blood (quick-acting) 12–13% nitrogen	'Leafy' vegetables	1–2	Rake in at sowing or planting time, and when plants are growing.
Phosphates	Superphosphate of Lime (quick-acting) 18% phosphates	Flowers, fruit, vegetables and shrubs	2–3 2	Rake in at sowing or planting time. When plants are growing spring or early summer.
	Bonemeal (slow-acting) 20·5% phosphates. 3·7% nitrogen	Flowers, fruit, vegetables, shrubs	2–4	Dig into top spit during autumn or winter. Top dressing around tree and shrubs.
Potash	Sulphate of Potash (quick-acting) 48·6% potash	Flowers, fruit, vegetables (especially tomatoes)	1–2	Rake in at sowing or planting time. Any time year for established plants.
	Wood Ashes (quick-acting) 1·7% potash	Flowers, fruit, vegetables (especially tomatoes)	8	Rake in any time of year.

Requirements of the Crop

The quantities of the three major plant nutrients required by various crops are shown in the table on page 220. This table lists the amounts of nitrogen, phosphoric acid (P_2O_5) and potash (K_2O) in the above-ground portions of the crop.

If we take, as an example, a crop of wheat yielding 40 bushels to the acre, we find that the grain and straw contain 70 pounds of nitrogen, 30 pounds of phosphoric acid and 50 pounds of potash per acre. Adding a further quantity of one third to allow for the roots, we find that the total quantities of nutrients per acre in the crop are as follows:

Nitrogen (N)	93 lb.
Phosphoric acid (P_2O_5)	40 lb.
Potash (K_2O)	67 lb.

These figures represent the amounts of the three nutrients that the plants must take from the soil if they are to grow properly. And it is our job to make sure that these nutrients are available in the soil in the necessary quantities.

To do this, we must know how much of each nutrient is already available in the soil, and then work out how much must be added in the form of manure or fertilizer to make up any deficiencies.

How much Plant Food is Available?

A chemical test is the only way of assessing accurately the amounts of the various nutrients already in the soil. The test will indicate the amounts that are available, e.g. in pounds per acre, and this represents your capital resources in terms of plant foods.

Although these quantities show the amounts of nutrients available to the plant, they do not represent the amounts that the crop will actually absorb. Only a proportion of the

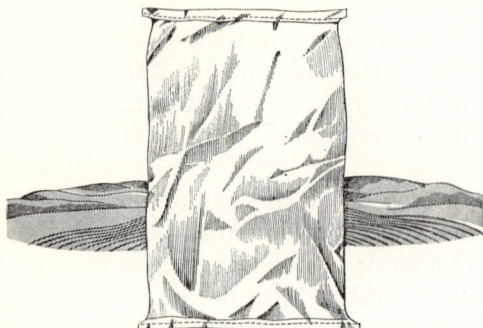

WHAT'S IN YOUR FERTILIZER?

Commercial fertilizers are usually intended to supply the major essential elements nitrogen, phosphorus and potassium to the soil. These elements are not present as the pure elements themselves – the plant cannot absorb its plant foods in this form. The ingredients of a fertilizer are always chemicals in which the essential elements are constituents; they are united with other elements to form chemical compounds.

When we buy a bag of fertilizer, we want to know how much of every essential element it contains, and this information is given in the *analysis* or *grade* provided with the fertilizer. In its simplest form, the analysis states the fertilizer grade in three numerals representing the percentage of nitrogen, available phosphorus (as P_2O_5) and potassium (soluble potash) (as K_2O) in the material. A fertilizer of 8 : 16 : 16 grade, for example, contains 8% nitrogen, 16% P_2O_5 and 16% K_2O. This does not mean that it contains the three elements in these forms; it means that it contains *the equivalent* of the three elements expressed as nitrogen, phosphoric oxide (P_2O_5) and potassium oxide (K_2O).

All three elements are combined with other elements in the constituents of the fertilizer – nitrogen, for example, may be present as ammonium sulphate, phosphorus as calcium phosphate and potassium as potassium sulphate. The percentages of the elements as expressed in the grade figures will not, therefore, add up to 100. They may not even add up to more than 20 – 30% of the total, as many fertilizers contain other ingredients which do not contain any of the three essential elements. These may be of little value as plant foods, but are harmless materials that would be costly to remove in making the fertilizer. Or they may be ingredients which supply valuable secondary or micro elements; when soils are very acid, or magnesium is deficient, for example, dolomitic limestone may be added to the fertilizer.

available nutrients will be used by the first crop; this is commonly assessed as 40 per cent (see table on page 230).

Suppose, for example, a soil test has shown that your soil contains the following amounts of available nutrients:

N	20 lb. per acre
P_2O_5	30 lb. per acre
K_2O	20 lb. per acre.

The amounts which a first crop absorbs would be

N	$20 \times 40/100 = 8$ lb. per acre
P_2O_5	$30 \times 40/100 = 12$ lb. per acre
K_2O	$20 \times 40/100 = 8$ lb. per acre.

If you are planning to grow a 40 bushel per acre wheat crop, therefore, you will need to provide the crop with extra nutrients in the following amounts:

N	$93 - 8 = 85$ lb. per acre
P_2O_5	$40 - 12 = 28$ lb. per acre
K_2O	$67 - 8 = 59$ lb. per acre.

These extra supplies of nutrients must come from manures and/or fertilizers.

How much Manure and Fertilizer to Use?

MANURE If you add manure or compost to the soil, this will provide a supply of nutrients. The quantities will vary considerably, depending on the type and quality of the material (see table on page 191). An average figure for a farmyard manure containing bedding litter is as follows:

N	0.6%
P_2O_5	0.35%
K_2O	0.5%

A ton (2240 lb.) of manure will therefore provide the following amounts of available nutrients:

$$\text{N} \qquad 2240 \times \frac{0.6}{100} = 13.44 \text{ lb.}$$

$$\text{P}_2\text{O}_5 \qquad 2240 \times \frac{0.35}{100} = 7.84 \text{ lb.}$$

$$\text{K}_2\text{O} \qquad 2240 \times \frac{0.5}{100} = 11.2 \text{ lb.}$$

The first crop will take only a proportion of the available nutrients from this source (see table on page 230), i.e. 30 per cent of N, 30 per cent of P_2O_5, and 50 per cent of K_2O. From a ton of manure, therefore, a crop will obtain the following quantities of nutrients:

N	$13.44 \times 30/100 = 4.032$ lb.
P_2O_5	$7.84 \times 30/100 = 2.352$ lb.
K_2O	$11.2 \ \times 50/100 = 5.6$ lb.

If you are adding manure at the rate of, say, 10 tons to the acre, you will provide the crop with the following quantities of nutrients (approx.):

N	40 lb.
P_2O_5	23 lb.
K_2O	56 lb.

This means that your wheat crop will still need the following amounts of nutrients:

N	$85 - 40 = 45$ lb.
P_2O_5	$28 - 23 = 5$ lb.
K_2O	$59 - 56 = 3$ lb.

These remaining quantities represent the amounts of nutrients that you must provide from other sources, e.g. inorganic fertilizers.

FERTILIZERS In estimating the amounts of fertilizer needed to make up the remaining requirements of the crop, it is necessary again to allow for the fact that only a proportion will be taken up by the first crop (see table on page 230). The proportions are as follows:

N	60%
P_2O_5	30%
K_2O	50%

This means that, in the example we have used, we must provide the following amounts of nutrients per acre from fertilizers:

$$N \qquad 45 \times \frac{100}{60} = 75 \text{ lb.}$$

$$P_2O_5 \qquad 5 \times \frac{100}{30} = 17 \text{ lb.}$$

$$K_2O \qquad 3 \times \frac{100}{50} = 6 \text{ lb.}$$

CALCULATING FERTILIZER REQUIREMENTS

In the example above, we have worked out the amounts of the three major nutrients that must be provided to meet the needs of a 40 bushel per acre wheat crop, bearing in mind the nutrients available in the soil, and the nutrients provided in manure. We must now work out the amounts of fertilizers to be used to provide the nutrients that are needed.

A. *Individual Fertilizers* Fertilizers in the form of individual chemicals contain nutrient elements in a percentage which is known and fixed. It is a simple matter to calculate the amount of fertilizer needed to give a required amount of a nutrient.

METHODS OF APPLYING FERTILIZER

There are many ways of applying fertilizer, each of which has its advantages. The method to be used depends upon the crops, soil, climate, date and rate of application, kinds of fertilizer and equipment available. The aim should be to get the proper amount of fertilizer into the soil where it will do most good.

Years ago, when crop yields were much lower than they are today, most of the plant food was applied in or along the row at planting. Today, much larger quantities of fertilizer are commonly used to get top yields. This means that all the fertilizer can no longer be put on at planting, and most of the total annual application must go on at some other time. For most crops, this means a broadcast application in advance of planting. Then, at planting, all the farmer has to do is to put on the recommended amount of a starter fertilizer, banded below and to the side of the seed row.

BANDING ALONG THE ROW
Banding fertilizer 1 to 2 inches to the side of the row, and 1 to 2 inches below seed level, is the recommended method for starter fertilizer for row crops.

BROADCASTING
Spreading fertilizer uniformly over the soil is the most convenient method of applying the greater part of the plant food needs. Under some conditions it is done cheaply, quickly and effectively by aircraft.

Liquid and granular fertilizers are advantageously applied by aircraft to rough pastures, trees, fish ponds and land too wet to work, such as rice fields.

DEEP DRILLING
Placing fertilizer in bands at desired depths. Anhydrous ammonia must be placed 4 to 6 inches deep.

PLOUGHSOLE OR DEEP FURROW
Under some conditions, fertilizer on the bottom of each furrow is helpful to the plant when the surface of the soil becomes dry during the growing season.

DRILLING WITH SEED
Applying fertilizer in the row when the seed is drilled or planted. This method should be used only when very light rates of application are used.

FOLIAR APPLICATION
Copper, manganese, iron and zinc deficiencies are often corrected quickly by spraying dilute solutions of salts of these metals on the leaves of plants. (Continued opposite)

SIDE DRESSING
Putting fertilizer along the row after plants have started growing. Often used where additional amounts of readily available fertilizer, such as nitrogen, are needed for top yields.

BEDDING
Applying fertilizer in the bottom of the furrow, then bedding or covering before planting.

STARTER SOLUTIONS
Dissolving fertilizer in water and applying at the time of transplanting various crops is a common practice. Solutions of fertilizer are applied also as preplanting applications and as side dressings or top dressings for growing crops. Young plants are easily injured by highly concentrated fertilizer solutions, and care should be taken when applying the fertilizer in solution form.

TOP DRESSING
Applying fertilizer on the surface of the soil for pasture, grassland, small grains and other crops.

IRRIGATION
Adding soluble fertilizers to irrigation water, either in ditches or to the water supply being pumped through sprinklers. When a fertilizer solution is sprayed on growing plants, it should be followed with water to wash the fertilizer into the soil.

VARIATIONS
Variations and combinations of these methods are often used. Part of the fertilizer is sometimes placed on fields by broadcasting, the remainder drilled along the row at planting. Some may be ploughed under, the rest broadcast after ploughing.

An important development is the direct application of anhydrous ammonia or nitrogen solutions. Both methods require special equipment. Solid fertilizers or nitrogen solutions containing herbicides are applied to grass or cereal crops, combining the provision of plant nutrients with the killing of weeds. Combinations with pesticides are also used.

Nitrogen, for example, may be provided by urea (45 per cent N), ammonium nitrate (33.5 per cent N), or ammonium sulphate (20.5 per cent N).

In the example used, the 75 lb. per acre of nitrogen needed would be obtained from the following quantities of these fertilizers:

Urea $\qquad$ $75 \times \dfrac{100}{45} = 167$ lb. per acre

Ammonium nitrate $\qquad$ $75 \times \dfrac{100}{33.5} = 224$ lb. per acre

Ammonium sulphate $\qquad$ $75 \times \dfrac{100}{20.5} = 366$ lb. per acre.

The 17 lb. per acre of phosphoric acid (P_2O_5) could be obtained from normal superphosphate (20 per cent P_2O_5), used at the following rate:

$$17 \times \dfrac{100}{20} = 85 \text{ lb. per acre.}$$

The 6 lb. per acre of potash could be obtained from potassium sulphate (50 per cent K_2O) used at the following rate:

$$6 \times \dfrac{100}{50} = 12 \text{ lb. per acre.}$$

B. *Compound Fertilizers* Compound fertilizers will commonly provide all three major nutrients at once, in proportions depending on the grade of the fertilizer (see page 206). Thus, a fertilizer graded as $7:7:7$ will contain the equivalent of 7 per cent of N, 7 per cent of P_2O_5 and 7 per cent of K_2O.

In the example we have used, the three nutrients are required in the following amounts per acre:

N	75 lb.
P_2O_5	17 lb.
K_2O	6 lb.

Suppose that we have available a supply of compound fertilizer of grade 20:10:10. This means that 100 lb. of the fertilizer contains 20 lb. of N, 10 lb. of P_2O_5, and 10 lb. of K_2O. If we take the smallest of the nutrient requirements – 6 lb. per acre of K_2O – we can provide this by using $100 \times \dfrac{6}{10}$ lb. of the compound fertilizer, i.e. 60 lb. to the acre.

This amount of fertilizer would also provide 6 lb. of P_2O_5 and 12 lb. of N per acre. We would thus be left with a deficiency of $75 - 12 = 63$ lb. of N, and $18 - 6 = 12$ lb. of P_2O_5.

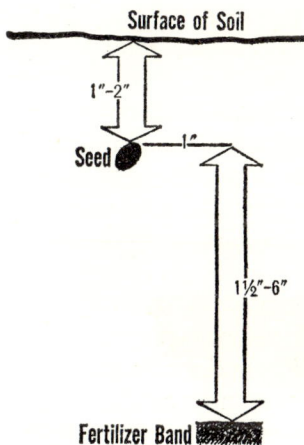

FERTILIZER
PLACEMENT

Fertilizer is often most effective when placed 1½ to 6 inches below, and 1 inch to the side of seeds such as beans, corn, sugar beet and many vegetable crops.

These shortages could be made up by adding the necessary quantities of individual fertilizers, calculated as described, to the mixture. Urea, for example, could provide the nitrogen, and superphosphate the P_2O_5.

In this way, we can work out how to use any fertilizer, individual or compound, to provide the nutrients that are needed by specific crops growing in particular soil conditions.

APPLYING THE FERTILIZER

When you are preparing the soil for your plants, the fertilizer may be broadcast before sowing or planting. You should make sure that it is hoed or raked into the surface. Once your soil fertility has been built up, apply the fertilizer so that plant roots will reach it effectively. It may be placed in bands about 1½ inches to the side and below the soil surface. You can do this most readily by making a V-shaped trench alongside the guide line to be used in planting the seeds. When the fertilizer has been put into the trench, fill it in and then sow the seeds in a shallow trench directly along the guide line. Fertilizers may also be placed in this way alongside rows and around individual plants.

When fertilizers have been used, they should be watered in to carry their nutrients in solution to the plant roots. They must not be allowed to come into direct contact with the plant leaves, unless they are special solutions to be used for foliar application.

LIQUID FERTILIZERS

For many purposes, liquids are more easily applied than solids, and many concentrated solutions of nutrient chemicals are now available. They are often simpler and safer to use than solid chemicals, giving more even distribution and acting more rapidly.

FOLIAR APPLICATION

Plants can absorb nutrient chemicals through their leaves, and by spraying them with dilute solutions it is possible to provide supplies of nutrients which could not be obtained successfully in other ways. The nutrients make their way quickly into the sap, where they may be detected a few minutes after application.

This technique is especially useful when the soil has become very dry, or when plants have suffered root damage that prevents them obtaining nutrients from the soil in adequate amounts.

TRACE ELEMENTS

If you are able to give your garden plenty of bulky manure or compost, it is unlikely that you will find your soil deficient in any of the trace elements. But some soils lack even the very small amounts of one or more of these elements required by plants, and you will have to add the necessary nutrient chemicals to correct the deficiency.

MAGNESIUM

Magnesium may be supplied by using dolomitic limestone. If you are growing acid-loving plants, and do not wish to use a limestone, you can supply the necessary magnesium by applying Epsom Salt at the rate of ½ cupful per 100 square feet for sandy soils, and twice this amount on clayey soils.

IRON

You can spray your plants directly with solutions containing 1-2 percent of ferrous sulphate. Woody plants will need a spraying every year to prevent chlorosis if the soil pH is too high, or if it contains free lime.

Special iron-containing fertilizers are available, in which the iron is present as a chelate. These may be applied in

FERTILIZERS IN THE GARDEN

Detailed chemical analysis of the soil in a garden is not always a practical proposition. It is good practice to dig in as much manure and compost as available to provide a background supply of nutrients, and to ensure that the soil builds up the crumb or aggregated structure that is so important to fertility.

Extra nutrients are commonly supplied by applying compound fertilizers, in which there is a balanced supply of nutrients, including all three major plant foods. The amount of the three primary nutrients is indicated by the number system commonly used, e.g. 6:9:7, which means that the fertilizer contains percentages of nitrogen, phosphorus (as P_2O_5) and potassium (as K_2O) in that order.

"Growmore" fertilizer, made to the specification of the U.K. Ministry of Agriculture, is a 7:7:7 balanced fertilizer for general use. Most manufacturers make other compound fertilizers for use with special plants or under special circumstances. The proportions of the three major nutrients will be indicated on the packages, and instructions are commonly given for their use. These should be followed carefully.

Examples of typical compound fertilizers for special use are as follows:

Tomato Fertilizer	5:8.1:10
Flower Fertilizer	8.2:5.9:12
Rose Fertilizer	5.2:9:6

FEEDING VEGETABLES

The base dressing commonly used on a vegetable plot is "Growmore", i.e. 7:7:7.

Before Sowing or Planting: Apply 2 oz. per square yard and rake into the soil surface, just before sowing or planting. After setting out potatoes in drills, scatter a little soil over them and apply an extra 1 oz. per square yard on top. The drills can then be filled in.

When Plants are Growing: After vegetables have been thinned or transplanted, they should be given a top dressing of balanced liquid fertilizer, such as 6:6:7.

A top dressing of ammonium sulphate may be used if the growth of leafy vegetables is slow during summer.

FEEDING TOMATOES

Correct tomato feeding provides sufficient phosphates and potash to produce stocky plants bearing full trusses of top-quality fruit. A balanced fertilizer of 5:8.1:10 composition is satisfactory for this purpose.

Before Planting: Under Glass: Fork in 3 oz. per square yard, about 1 week before planting. Water in.

Outdoors: Fork in 4 oz. per square yard about 1 week before planting. Water in.

After Planting: Do not begin feeding until the first truss has set. Then sprinkle 2 oz. per square yard around the plants every 10 – 14 days until the final truss has set.

Water before and after feeding.

For pots, use 1 teaspoonful per plant.

Alternatively, use 6:6:7 liquid fertilizer.

FERTILIZERS IN
THE GARDEN (*Continued*)

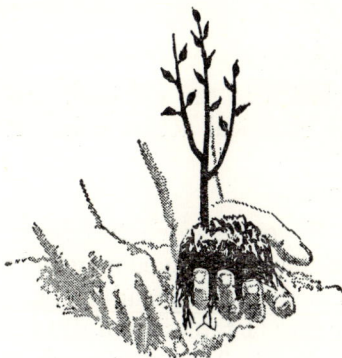

FEEDING FRUIT TREES AND BUSHES

The appearance of the tree or bush should be used as a guide. If it is making a lot of leaf, but very few flowers, apply a dressing of bonemeal and sulphate of potash. If, on the other hand, the plant is stunted, apply sulphate of ammonia instead.

FEEDING BULBS

A good flower fertilizer, e.g. 8.2:5.9:12, should be forked into the top-soil, 4 oz. per square yard, before planting. When the flower buds appear, 6:6:7 liquid fertilizer should be used.

FEEDING FLOWERS

A high-potash flower fertilizer should be used, e.g. 8.2: 5.9: 12.
Herbaceous Borders and Flowering Shrubs:
Before planting, work bonemeal into the soil. With established plants, sprinkle 4 oz. of flower fertilizer per square yard around the plants in the spring, and fork into the top soil. Feed in the summer with 6:6:7 liquid fertilizer.
Bedding Plants, Chrysanthemums and Dahlias:
Before planting, fork 2 oz. per square yard of flower fertilizer into the soil. When the plants are established, feed with liquid fertilizer, 6:6:7.

FEEDING ROSES

Compound rose fertilizers often contain both quick-acting and slow-acting (organic) constituents, giving an analysis of, for example, 5.2:9:6.
Before Planting Fork 4 oz. per square yard into the top soil, 1 to 2 weeks prior to planting.
After Planting Sprinkle 4 oz. per square yard around the bushes or trees in April. Carefully rake in, and water the soil if dry.

Apply 2 oz. per square yard around the plants every month throughout the flowering season, beginning when the flower buds first appear. Alternatively, use liquid fertilizer, e.g. 6:6:7.

H

solution to the soil itself; the iron will not be "locked up"
by chemical action before it reaches the plant roots.

BORON

If your garden has been made from a soil that was
originally acid, you may find that it lacks boron. This can be
remedied by spreading borax on the soil at the rate of 5
ounces (1 tablespoonful) to 100 square feet for sandy soils,
and up to 3 times as much on clayey soils.

Spreading of such a small quantity is easier if the borax
is first mixed with bulkier fertilizers, or with sand.

If your garden tends to be deficient in boron, you should
give it a light borax application every 2 or 3 years.

Celery, cauliflower, apples, beets and tomatoes are
especially sensitive to a deficiency of boron. Beans are easily
damaged by an excess of this element.

MANGANESE

For manganese deficiency, apply manganese sulphate at
the rate of 1 tablespoonful per 100 square feet. If plants are
already suffering chlorosis from manganese deficiency, a
1- or 2-percent solution of manganese sulphate may be
sprayed onto them.

ZINC

Zinc deficiency is rare. Where it does occur, you can
cure it by applying zinc sulphate to the soil at the rate of 1
tablespoonful per 100 square feet.

COPPER

Newly-developed peat soils and old, highly-leached
sandy soils are likely to be deficient in copper. You should
apply copper sulphate at the rate of 1½ teaspoonsful on
sandy soil and up to 4 tablespoonsful on peat soil per 100
square feet.

MOLYBDENUM

Old, leached soils may contain insufficient molybdenum for growing clover. You should correct this by applying ½ teaspoonful of sodium molybdate per 100 square feet. Be careful not to use excessive amounts, which may be toxic.

SULPHUR

This is unlikely to be in short supply if your soil is near a town or city area, as sulphuric acid is formed in air from the sulphur dioxide released in smoke. In country areas, however, the soil may be deficient in sulphur.

Normal superphosphate fertilizer will usually contain sufficient sulphur to correct the deficiency, and no further treatment will be needed if this is used. When necessary, powdered sulphur may be spread on the soil at the rate of 1 cupful per 100 square feet.

Fertilizer Requirements for Soils of Various Textures, with Low and High Fertility.
(Pounds per 1,000 Square Feet.)

General Soil Class		Nutrients		
Texture	Fertility Level	Nitrogen (N)	Phosphoric Oxide (P$_2$O$_5$)	Potash (K$_2$O)
Sandy	Low	1–4	2–5	1–4
	High	0–2	0–3	½–3
Loamy	Low	1–4	2–5	1–4
	High	0–2	0–3	0–2
Clayey	Low	1–4	3–6	2–5
	High	0–2	0–3	0–3
Muck	Low	½–3	3–6	1–7
	High	0–2	1–4	0–3

Note: With high applications of compost or manure, these quantities should be reduced by about half.

APPROXIMATE POUNDS PER ACRE OF NUTRIENTS

THESE FIGURES MAY VARY WITH SOIL

CROP	ACRE YIELD	NITROGEN	PHOSPHORUS AS P_2O_5
GRAINS			
Barley (Grain)	40 bu.	35	15
Barley (Straw)	1 ton	15	5
Corn (Grain)	150 bu.	135	53
Corn (Stover)	4.5 tons	100	37
Oats (Grain)	80 bu.	50	20
Oats (Straw)	2 tons	25	15
Rice (Rough)	80 bu.	50	20
Rice (Straw)	2.5 tons	30	10
Rye (Grain)	30 bu.	35	10
Rye (Straw)	1.5 tons	15	8
Sorghum (Grain)	60 bu.	50	25
Sorghum (Stover)	3 tons	65	20
Wheat (Grain)	40 bu.	50	25
Wheat (Straw)	1.5 tons	20	5
HAY			
*Alfalfa	4 tons	180	40
Bluegrass	2 tons	60	20
Coastal Bermuda	8 tons	185	70
*Cowpea	2 tons	120	25
*Peanut	2.25 tons	105	25
*Red Clover	2.5 tons	100	25
*Soybean	2 tons	90	20
Timothy	2.5 tons	60	25
FRUITS AND VEGETABLES			
Apples	500 bu.	30	10
Beans, Dry	30 bu.	75	25
Cabbage	20 tons	130	35
Onions	7.5 tons	45	20
Oranges (70 Pound Boxes)	800 boxes	85	30
Peaches	600 bu.	35	20
Potatoes (Tubers)	400 bu.	80	30
Spinach	5 tons	50	15
Sweet Potatoes (Roots)	300 bu.	45	15
Tomatoes (Fruit)	20 tons	120	40
Turnips (Roots)	10 tons	45	20
OTHER CROPS			
Cotton (Seed and Lint)	1500 lbs.	40	20
Cotton (Stalks, Leaves & Burs)	2000 lbs.	35	10
*Peanuts (Nuts)	1.25 tons	90	10
*Soybeans (Grain)	40 bu.	150	35
Sugar Beets (Roots)	15 tons	60	20
Sugarcane	30 tons	96	54
Tobacco (Leaves)	2000 lbs.	75	15
Tobacco (Stalks)	—	35	15

*Legumes normally get the greater part of their nitrogen from the air.

Calculated from plant composition data of Beeson in USDA Misc. Pub. 369, Morrison in the 21st ed. of "Feeds and Feeding", Lowe in a Special USDA report and the American Potash Institute. The data on trace elements in tobacco are from USDA Tech.

CONTAINED IN PORTION OF CROP OF THE SIZE SHOWN
TYPE, SEASON, AND FERTILITY OF SOIL

POTASSIUM AS K_2O	CALCIUM	MAGNESIUM	SULPHUR	COPPER	MANGANESE	ZINC
10	1	2	3	0.03	0.03	0.06
30	8	2	4	0.01	0.32	0.05
40	16	20	14	0.06	0.09	0.15
145	28	17	10	0.05	1.50	0.30
15	2	3	5	0.03	0.12	0.05
80	8	8	9	0.03	....	0.29
10	3	4	3	0.01	0.08	0.07
70	9	5	....	....	1.58	....
10	2	3	7	0.02	0.22	0.03
25	8	2	3	0.01	0.14	0.07
15	4	5	5	0.01	0.04	0.04
95	29	18	....	....	....	....
15	1	6	3	0.03	0.09	0.14
35	6	3	5	0.01	0.16	0.05
180	112	21	19	0.06	0.44	0.42
60	16	7	5	0.02	0.30	0.08
270	59	24	....	0.21	....	....
80	55	15	13	....	0.65	....
95	45	17	16	....	0.23	....
100	69	17	7	0.04	0.54	0.36
50	40	18	10	0.04	0.46	0.15
95	18	6	5	0.03	0.31	0.20
45	8	5	10	0.03	0.03	0.03
25	2	2	5	0.02	0.03	0.06
130	20	8	44	0.04	0.10	0.08
40	11	2	18	0.03	0.08	0.31
140	33	12	9	0.20	0.06	0.24
65	4	8	2	....	....	0.01
150	3	6	6	0.04	0.09	0.05
30	12	5	4	0.02	0.10	0.10
75	4	9	6	0.03	0.06	0.03
160	7	11	14	0.07	0.13	0.16
90	12	6	....	....	....	....
15	2	4	2	0.06	0.11	0.32
35	28	8	....	....	....	....
15	1	3	6	0.02	0.01	....
55	7	7	4	0.04	0.05	0.04
50	33	24	10	0.03	0.75	....
270	28	24	24	....	....	....
120	75	18	14	0.03	0.55	0.07
50	....	....	....	....	....	....

Bul. 1009. Data for Boron are: alfalfa hay, 0.06; cowpea hay, 0.21; red clover hay, 0.05; soybean hay, 0.01; apples, 0.01; cabbage, 0.09; oranges, 0.14; peaches, 0.05; potatoes, 0.05; tomatoes, 0.14; and tobacco, 0.05 lbs. per acre.

1000 lbs. each of milk and beef (live weight) contain: N, 6 and 27; P_2O_5, 2 and 17; K_2O, 2 and 2; and Ca, 1 and 13 lbs., respectively.

GIVE YOUR PLANTS THE SOILS THEY PREFER

In general, climatic conditions are more important than the state of your soil in deciding how well a particular plant will grow. Or if it will grow at all. But if a plant *does* grow in your district, you can give it every encouragement by making sure that it has the soil that suits it.

Annual Flowers

Most annuals are shallow-rooted, and good drainage is less essential to them than it is for bulbs and perennials. Annuals will often grow quite well in a soil that has a high water table, and may become waterlogged in winter.

The best soil for annuals is a sandy soil, or a loam, but most of them will make do with almost any type of soil. They are the least exacting of ornamental plants in this respect. The length of growing season and air temperatures are more important factors in their lives than soil conditions.

Herbaceous Perennials

Perennials will occupy your soil space for several years, and it is important that you get the soil into a satisfactory state before the plants are put in.

Most perennials will grow well in a wide range of soil types, but it is essential that the soil is well drained. The plants will die if the soil remains waterlogged through the winter.

Sandy loams, loams and silt loams are usually the best types of soil for herbaceous perennials. Sands are also satisfactory, but plants in coarse textured soils will need frequent watering, especially if the soil lacks humus.

In general, perennials will grow best in a rich, fertile soil containing plenty of organic matter. Most of them prefer slightly acid conditions.

Flowering Bulbs

Bulbs grow well in a friable, fertile and well-drained soil, especially in sandy loams, loams and even well-drained clay loams. They need a rich soil, but too much nitrogenous material (especially organic manure) encourages fungus attack, and should be avoided.

Drainage is important. Many lilies (e.g. testaceum, candidum and auratum) will not tolerate poor drainage. Others (including pardalinum, parryi and canadense) do well in wet soils where the water is not stagnant, such as the edge of a running stream or on the slope near a spring.

In general, bulbs seem to prefer slightly acid soils.

Ornamental Shrubs

Most shrubs do well in a deep, friable, well-drained sandy loam that contains plenty of organic matter. But many will thrive on poorer soils.

Some shrubs are fairly exacting in the preference for a particular type of soil, especially with regard to acidity.

1. SHRUBS THAT REQUIRE AN ACID SOIL include the following:

> Rhododendron, Azalea (*Rhododendron* species)
> Serviceberry (*Amelanchier* species)
> Strawberry-tree (*Arbutus unedo*)
> Heather (*Calluna* species)
> Summersweet (*Clethra* species)
> Broom (*Cytisus* species)
> Heath (*Erica* species)
> Wintergreen (*Gaultheria procumbens*)
> Hollies (*Ilex* species)
> Common Juniper (*Juniperus communis* and varieties)
> Laurel (*Kalmia* species)
> Box Sandmyrtle (*Leiophyllum buxifolium*)
> Leucothoe (*Leucothoe* species)
> Bayberry (*Myrica* species)
> Blueberry (*Vaccinium* species)
> Hobblebush (*Viburnum alnifolium*)

Azaleas may be taken as typical of this group of plants. They grow best at pH 4.5 to 5.5, in well-drained sandy loam that is rich in organic matter including partly-rotted oak leaves, twigs, peat and old sawdust.

Soil structure is most important, and must permit ample aeration in the root region, with high water-holding capacity. (Some shrubs in this group, including juniper and bayberry, require an acid soil but will tolerate dry sites).

A mulch of peat moss or oak leaves 2-3 inches deep should be maintained throughout the year. This keeps the soil acid, provides nutrients and maintains iron availability.

The chief nutrient required by shrubs of this type is nitrogen, which may come from organic sources, or from ammonium sulphate.

Chlorosis, caused by iron-deficiency, is common in shrubs of this group. It results in a yellowing of the leaves, and may be due to root injury, lack of acidity, application of too much lime or phosphate, poor drainage and certain nutrient deficiencies. It can be corrected temporarily by spraying the plants with ferrous sulphate or by applying chelated iron into the soil (see page 215).

2. SHRUBS THAT REQUIRE A NEUTRAL OR SLIGHTLY ALKALINE SOIL include barberry, daphne and lilac. They will grow well, however, in slightly acid soils too. They are influenced more by light, fertility level and water than by soil reaction.

Shade and Ornamental Trees

Within their climatic limitations, most trees grow best in fertile, well-drained loam, but will tolerate a wide variety of soil conditions.

Inadequate drainage and consequent poor aeration is bad for most trees, but certain kinds will grow on wet sites.

The following lists include examples of kinds of trees that require special types of soil for good growth or that will grow in certain types of soil.

1. TREES THAT NEED AN ACID SOIL :

> Pin Oak (*Quercus palustris*)
> Strawberry-tree (*Arbutus unedo*)

2. TREES THAT WILL GROW ON RELATIVELY DRY SOILS :

> Velvet Ash (*Fraxinus velutina*)
> Acacia (most species)
> Tree-of-Heaven (*Ailanthus altissima*)
> Boxelder (*Acer negundo*)
> Chinaberry (*Melia azedarach*)
> Smooth Arizona Cypress (*Cupressus arizonica bonita*)
> Carob (*Ceratona siliqua*)
> Giant Evergreen Chinquapin (*Castanopsis chryso-phylla*)
> California Peppertree (*Schinus molle*)
> Eucalyptus (most species)
> Green Ash (*Fraxinus pennsylvanica lanceolata*)
> Hop Hornbeam (*Ostrya virginiana*)
> Pignut Hickory (*Carya glabra*)
> American Hornbeam (*Carpinus caroliniana*)
> Eastern Redcedar (*Juniperus virginiana*)
> Jujube (*Zizyphus jujube*)
> Pacific Madrone (*Arbutus menziesi*)
> Mimosa (*Albizzia julibrissin*)
> Chestnut Oak (*Quercus montana*)
> Oregon White Oak (*Quercus garryana*)
> White Poplar (*Populus alba*)
> Fremont Cottonwood (*Populus fremonti*)
> Jerusalem-thorn (*Parkinsonia aculeata*)
> Blue Paloverde (*Cercidium floridum*)
> Ponderosa Pine (*Pinus ponderosa*)
> Brazil Peppertree, Christmas-berry Tree (*Schinus terebinthifolius*)
> Torrey Pine (*Pinus torreyana*)
> Virginia Pine, Scrub Pine (*Pinus virginiana*)
> Pitch Pine (*Pinus rigida*)
> Russian Olive (*Elaeagnus angustifolia*)
> Sassafras (*Sassafras albidum officinale*)

H[*]

Composition of

Material	Nitrogen %	Phosphorus as available P_2O_5 %	Potassium as soluble K_2O %	Calcium %	Magnesium %
Ammonia anhydrous	82				
Ammonia, aqua	16–25				
Ammonia nitrate	33.5				
Ammonium nitrate-limestone mixtures	20.5			7.3	4.4
Ammonium phosphate (mono)	11	48	.2	1.1	.3
Ammonium phosphate (am. phosphate-sulphate)	13–16	20–39	.2	.3	.1
Ammonium phosphate (di)	16–21	48–53			
Ammonium sulphate	20.5–21.0			.3	
Ammonium sulphate-nitrate	26.0				
Ammoniated superphosphate	3–6	18–20		17.2	
Basic slag, Open-hearth		(3) 8–12		29	3.4
Bone meal	2–4.5	(4) 22–28	.2	22–25	.4
Borax					
Calcium cyanamide	21			38.5	.06
Calcium nitrate	15			19.4	1.5
Castor pomace	5.2	1.8	1.1	.4	.3
Copper oxide					
Copper sulphate					
Cotton hull ashes		4–7	22–30	6.8	3.1
Cottonseed meal	6	2.6	1.4	.2	.4
Fish scrap	6–10	7	.8	6.0	.2
Gypsum (land plaster)			.5	22.5	.4
Magnesium oxide				1.1	56.1
Manganese sulphate				6.6	1.9
Nitric phosphates	14–22	10–22	.1–16	8–10	.1
Nitrogen solutions	21–49				
Phosphoric acid (liquid)		52–54			
Potassium chloride (muriate of potash)			60–62		.1
Potassium-magnesium sulphate			22		11.2
Potassium nitrate	14		44–46	.4	.2
Potassium sulphate			50–53	.5	.7
Rock phosphate		(5)		33.2	.2
Sewage sludge, Activated	5–6	2.9	.6	1.3	.7
Sewage sludge, Digested	2	1.4	.8	2.1	.5
Sodium nitrate	16		.2	.1	.05
Superphosphate, Normal		18–20	.2	20.4	.2
Superphosphate, Concentrated		42–50	.4	13.6	.3
Tankage, Animal	6–9	6–15	.4	8–11	.2
Tankage, Process	7–9	1	.1	.8	.01
Tobacco stems	2	.7	6.0	3.6	.4
Urea	42–46			0–1.5	.7
Urea-formaldehyde	36–40				
Zinc oxide					
Zinc sulphate					.06

1. Most of the percentages larger than one of N, P_2O_5 and K_2O are the usual guarantees. Where more than one grade is commonly sold, the range is indicated by two numbers separated by a dash. The rest of the percentages are averages compiled by A. L. Mehring, USDA chemist, from many published analyses.

2. Ind. Eng. Chem. Anal. Ed. 5, 229-34 and other sources. A minus sign indicates the number of pounds of calcium carbonate needed to neutralize acid formed when one ton of the material is applied to the soil. A plus sign indicates basic materials, and a zero physiologically neutral materials.

Fertilizer Materials[1]

Sulphur %	Chlorine %	Copper %	Manganese %	Zinc %	Boron %	Approx. Calcium Carbonate equivalent[2] lbs. per ton
						−2,960
						−720 to −1,080
				.01		−1,200
.4	.4					0
2.2	.1	.02	.03	.03	.02	−1,300
15.4	.1	.02	.2	.02	.03	−1,520 to −2,260
						−2,240
23.7	.5	.03		.01		−2,200
15.1						−1,700
12					.02	− 140
.3			2.2			+1,000
1	.2			.02		+ 500
					11.6	+1,260
.3	.2	.02	.04			+1,245
.02	.2					+ 320
.04	.3		.04	.05	.01	− 100
		75				
12.8		24.9		.55		
1.0	1.9	.04	.06	.07		
.3	.06			.02		− 200
.2	.4					− 100
16.8	.3					
.2	.5					+4,600
14.5		.05	25.1	.08	.3	
.2–3.6	0.1–12.0	.02	.2	.02	.03	−300 to −580
						−1,000 to −1,400
.1	47.0				.03	0
22.7	1.5					0
.3	1.1				.09	+ 520
17.6	2.1					0
.3	.1		.03			+ 200
.5	.6	.07	.07	.1		
.1	.2	.3	.3	.4		
.07	.4	.07			.01	+ 585
11.9	.3			.01		0
1.4		.01	.01		.01	0
.5	.8			.02		+ 240
.9	.8				.03	− 320
.4	1.2	.01	.03		.02	+
.02	.2			.02		−1,500
				77.2		
13.6		.02		27.8		

3. By the 2-% citric acid method.

4. Total P_2O_5. All of the phosporus in natural organics is considered available.

5. 30–36% total P_2O_5, which is relatively unavailable in many soils.

Commercial sodium molybdate contains about 38% molybdenum. Two forms of iron sulphate are used in agriculture. Hydrated ferrous sulphate contains 19.7% iron, and white copperas has 34.4% iron.

3. TREES THAT WILL GROW ON WET SOILS:

> Alders (several species)
> Baldcypress (*Taxodium distichum*)
> Cajeput Tree (*Melaleuca leucadendron*)
> Dahoon (*Ilex cassine*)
> Eastern Larch, or Tamarack (*Larix laricina*)
> Poplars (*Populus*)—most species will grow on wet soils
> Whitecedar Falsecypress (*Chamaecyparis thyoides*)
> Red Maple (*Acer rubrum*)
> Pin Oak (*Quercus palustris*)
> Water-elm (*Planera aquatica*)
> Sweetbay Magnolia (*Magnolia virginiana*)
> American Sweetgum (*Liquidambar styraciflua*)
> Willow (*Salix*) (most species)

4. TREES THAT WILL GROW ON GRAVELLY SOILS:

> Tree-of-Heaven (*Ailanthus altissima*)
> Dahurian Birch (*Betula davurica*)
> Common Honeylocust (*Gleditsia triacanthos*)
> Nordmann Fir (*Abies nordmanniana*)—will grow on gravelly hardpan.
> Mimosa (*Albizzia julibrissin*)
> Oregon White Oak (*Quercus garryana*)
> Mugho Pine, or Swiss Mountain Pine (*Pinus mugo*)
> Common Paper-mulberry (*Broussonetia papyrifera*)
> Common Sassafras (*Sassafras albidum* (*officinale*))

5. TREES THAT WILL GROW ON DRY, ALKALINE SOIL:

> Fremont Cottonwood (*Populus fremonti*)
> Jujube (*Zizyphus jujube*)
> Velvet Ash (*Fraxinus velutina*)
> Eastern Redcedar (*Juniperus virginiana*)
> Franklinia (*Franklinia alatamaha*)—prefers slightly alkaline, moist but well-drained soil
> Beech (*Fagus*)

6. TREES THAT WILL GROW ON VERY SANDY SOIL:

> Australian Tea-tree (*Leptospermum laevigatum*)
> Ailanthus (*Ailanthus altissima*)
> Smooth Arizona Cypress (*Cupressus arizonica bonita*)
> Pfitzer Juniper (*Juniperus chinensis pfitzeriana*)
> Savin Juniper (*Juniperus sabina*)
> Creeping Juniper (*Juniperus horizontalis*)
> Shore Juniper (*Juniperus compacta*)—on sandy shores
> Jerusalem-thorn (*Parkinsonia aculeata*)
> Mimosa (*Albizzia julibrissin*)
> Silk-oak Grevillea (*Grevillea robusta*)
> Pitch Pine (*Pinus rigida*)
> Scotch Pine (*Pinus sylvestris*)

Vegetables

Most vegetables require well-drained, fertile soils, with plenty of moisture throughout the growing season. These conditions may be met by proper management and cultivation, using organic manures and inorganic fertilizers as necessary to bring the soil to its required state of fertility.

On mineral soils, most vegetables respond well to additions of organic matter and to inorganic fertilizers containing nitrogen, phosphorus and potassium in the ratio $1 - 1.5 - 1$ to $1 - 2 - 1$, with judicious top dressings of readily-available nitrogen through the growing season.

Leafy crops, in particular, need plenty of nitrogen. Fruit, seed, root and tuber vegetables need moderate amounts of nitrogen.

Vegetables growing on muck soils need less nitrogen and more potassium than those growing on mineral soils.

Field Crops

Crop plants with fine fibrous roots, including wheat, oats and barley, are best suited to medium or heavy soils. Plants with thicker roots, such as corn, alfalfa and sugar beets, do

HOW MUCH FERTILIZER TO USE?

The amounts of various elements contained in different crops are shown on page 220. You can estimate from the table the quantities of the essential elements that a crop is going to need. And if you know the amounts that are available in your soil you can estimate how much of each must be added to make up any deficiencies.

Only a proportion of the elements available from any source will be used by the first crop, and the following table gives a guide on which an estimate may be based:

Source of Nutrients	Proportion of Nutrient Obtainable by First Crop Grown (per cent)		
	N	P_2O_5	K_2O
Soil	40	40	40
Manure	30	30	50
Fertilizer	60	30	50

If the quantities of available nitrogen, phosphate and potash in the soil, and the amounts of manure added to the soil (see page 190) are known, the total nutrients that the crop will obtain from these sources may be calculated. The difference between these quantities and the amounts required indicate how much is required from added fertilizers.

As indicated in the table above, only a proportion of the nutrients available in the fertilizers will be taken up by the first crop grown, so an excess must be used. Also, the roots and other unharvested parts of the crop must be catered for, even though these will be returned when the crop residues decay. As a rough guide, the roots will commonly need about one third of the amounts required by the rest of the plant.

In most soils, there will be sufficient secondary and micro nutrients for the crops, but a watch must be kept to ensure that deficiencies do not occur. Inadequate supplies of any single nutrient may cause a crop to fail, even though it is lavishly supplied with all other nutrients. (See examples of calculations on page 209.)

well on sandy loam soils, but will also grow satisfactorily on heavy soils.

Soils rich in nitrogen are often unsuitable for small grains, as too much nitrogen encourages lodging and the development of rust, and delays maturity. These adverse effects, which seldom occur in other crops, can be avoided to some extent in small grains by applying phosphorus and potash.

Abundance of moisture and nitrogen are often the main soil factors in deciding which variety of a crop should be grown. Quick maturing varieties having small plants may be best suited to rolling uplands, and larger and later varieties to rich bottom lands.

Grasses

Climatic factors will often influence the responses of grasses to different soil conditions. It is not easy, therefore, to suggest optimum soil requirements for different species and varieties of grasses.

Legumes

Leguminous crops obtain their nitrogen requirements from soil air, so long as adequate numbers of nitrogen-fixing bacteria of the right type are available. These may be present in the soil, or they may be provided by inoculating the plants.

Supplies of calcium, phosphorus and potassium should be maintained by adding appropriate fertilizers. And trace elements may be needed in certain regions.

Usually, legumes do best in slightly acid to neutral soils.

Orchard Trees and Fruits

Orchard trees may remain in one place in the soil for 50 years or more. During their lifetime, the trees will grow extensive root systems that will forage downwards and outwards for considerable distances if the soil is open and well drained.

The ideal soil for orchard trees is deep and well-drained, and free of impervious layers that would restrict root development. It will hold water well, and have a slightly acid reaction in the region of pH 5.5 to 6.5.

Sites for orchards are chosen to afford as much protection from spring frosts as possible. They are usually near large bodies of water, which help to keep the air warm, or on hillsides, so that cold air will drain away into the valley below.

Sloping sites will seldom have a good deep soil, and erosion problems may be serious. Trees should be planted on the contour, and the soil surface protected by a cover crop where possible.

NOTE:

Details of the soil requirements of individual plants are given on page 401.

WIND EROSION.

PLATE 13

Above : Whirlwinds picking up dust on a field where intensive cultivation has broken up the soil into fine particles which blow easily.

Below : The damage done by wind erosion on a well-developed farm. Some fields have been blown out to a depth of four feet, and the resultant drift has ruined the remaining portion – *U.S.D.A.*

PLATE 14

SOIL PROFILE

The dark, deep layer of topsoil is the product of centuries of weathering, accumulation of plant and animal remains, and the work of many living organisms. The less fertile subsoil, which is lighter in colour has little or no organic matter.

Below : The profile on the left shows soil which has been subjected to poor treatment ; the profile on right is from land cultivated under an excellent cropping system. The poorly-treated soil has a formless structure, and is low in organic matter. The well-treated soil has a good structure, and is high in organic matter – *U.S.D.A.*

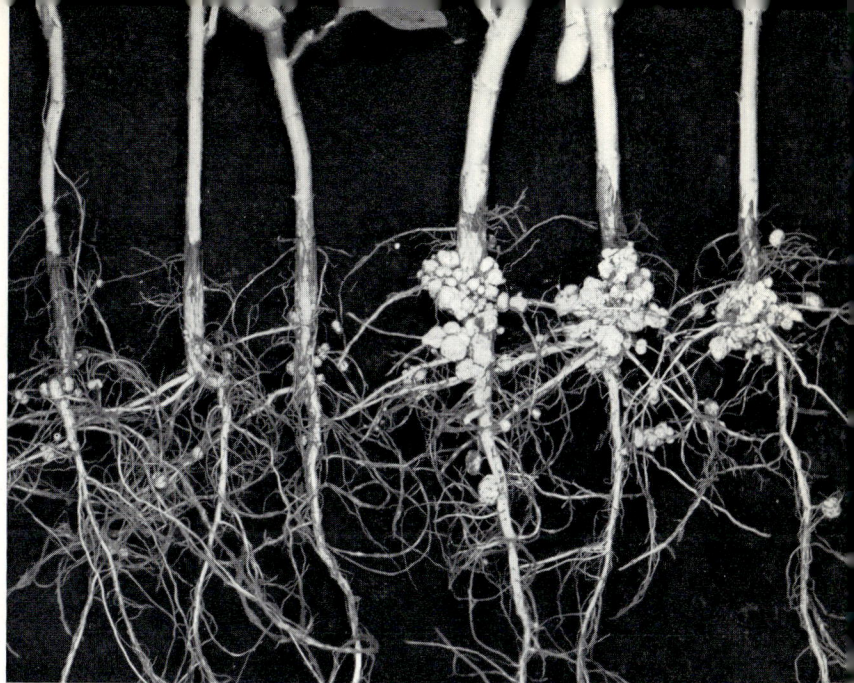

NODULE BACTERIA AND FERTILITY

It has been known since Biblical times that leguminous plants, including for example clover, peas and beans, will enrich the soil in which they are grown. During the 19th century, scientists discovered that this was due to the fixation of atmospheric nitrogen by bacteria living in nodules on the plant roots.

These bacteria belong to the genus *Rhizobium*, and they include several species, each of which has its own preferred leguminous plants as hosts. The bacteria invade the root hairs of the host, causing damage which results in the formation of a nodule. The bacteria multiply inside the nodule, feeding on minerals, sugars and other dissolved materials which they take from the host plant. The nitrogenous chemicals they need are manufactured from nitrogen in the soil air, and the nitrogen fixed in this way is incorporated in the living matter of the bacterium.

When bacteria die, their bodies decompose like other plant remains. The complex chemicals of their body-matter are changed into simple chemicals which dissolve in soil water and are available to other plants as food. The nitrogen fixed by the bacteria is thus released into the soil in the form of nutrient chemicals. These are used by the legume itself, and by crops which follow them later.

Soils do not necessarily contain a flourishing population of the species of *Rhizobium* appropriate to a particular leguminous crop that is to be grown. Remarkable results are obtained by inoculating soil with the bacteria required when the crop is sown. The picture above, for example, shows the roots of soybeans (*left*) grown in non-inoculated soil, and (*right*) in inoculated soil – *Nitragin Co. Inc.*

PLATE 15

Above left : Soil taken from a virgin fence row, showing excellent tilth. This is what the black prairie soils of the U.S. looked like when they were first broken by the early settlers. They were fertile and highly permeable to water.

Above right : A sample of this soil was placed in a bottle with water, shaken up 50 times, and poured onto a piece of paper. Note how the soil has kept its shape, remaining porous and open.

Above left : This soil came from a field that had been cropped strenuously for many years. The tilth is poor, and the soil is dense, heavy and only slowly permeable to water.

Above right : A sample of this soil was shaken 50 times with water in the same way as the soil above. When poured onto paper, it ran together into a plastic mass. This is what happens in the field during heavy rains, resulting in crusts on the soil surface – *U.S.D.A.*

PLATE 16

PART 3

SCIENCE AND THE SOIL

10

Soil Development

WHAT SOIL IS

The mantle of loose material that covers the hard rock crust of the earth is a complex mixture of substances. Some have been formed by the weathering of parent rocks, and some by the decay of plant and animal remains.

The processes that have produced this layer we call the soil are always active, and soil is not a static, lifeless mass. Any soil is in a state of constant development and change, and the assessment of the character of a soil is made with this in mind. Mineral fragments are breaking down into smaller and smaller particles, and new materials are formed by chemical action. Organic substances from the bodies of plants and animals are decaying and decomposing, releasing simple chemicals into the soil.

Substances produced by the continuous physical and chemical changes in the soil are moved from place to place in many ways. Animals burrow in the soil, mixing and churning the materials through which they move. Plant roots thrust down into the soil, absorbing substances that are needed by the plant as food.

Rainwater flows through the soil, carrying with it soluble chemicals and fine particles of suspended matter. These substances may be carried away by drainage water until eventually they reach the sea. Or they may be deposited at a lower level in the soil as a result of chemical or physical action.

As water flows over the surface of the land, it may erode vast quantities of soil and deposit them hundreds of miles away. Soil is carried in similar fashion by wind, and is scraped from the surface of the land by moving glaciers.

When we consider the range of sources from which the soil materials may come, and the many influences that are always playing upon them, it is apparent that there must be an infinite variety of soils lying on the earth's surface. Any farmer knows that the soil of one field may be entirely different from that of a neighbouring field, even though the basic materials from which the mineral particles have been formed may be the same. The effects of past cultivation, and of differences in environment and "lie of the land" have resulted in soils of varying character.

This infinite variety in the nature of soils from different regions, and the "living" character of every individual soil, makes classification an apparently impossible task. Until quite recent times, the progress of soil science was restricted by the difficulty experienced in relating one soil to another.

Towards the end of the 19th Century, Russian scientists led by K. D. Dokuchaiev began a study of soils which was to lay the foundation of modern systems of classification. The Russian scientists recognized soils as independent natural bodies each of which resulted from a unique combination of climate, living matter, parent rock materials, relief and time. They recognized similarities in the characteristics of different soils, and were able to bring together soils into groups which formed the basis of a classification system.

In the last half-century, soil classification has linked with the steady development of soil science in many countries. Various systems of classification have been proposed and modified, and none can yet be regarded as a universally accepted system.

The first step in attempting the classification of anything is always to define what is to be classified, and this is a difficult matter in the case of soil. The word "soil" means all manner of different things to different people. Most people think of soil as the stuff that plants grow in on the earth's surface. Scientists who are studying the soil, however, must include much more than this in their definition of a soil; they consider all the layers of unconsolidated material that lie upon the hard rock of the earth's crust. In this sense, soil extends into the partly-weathered material that lies immediately above the solid rock.

It is only by considering the entire layer in this way that the true personality of any soil may be assessed, and soils with recognizable, similar characteristics may be brought together into groups.

SOIL PROFILE

All gardeners realise that the nature of a soil changes as we dig deeper into the ground. There is a "topsoil" in which most of the cultivation procedures are carried out. And beneath this there is the "subsoil" which can be recognized quite clearly as being different in appearance, texture and structure from the soil in the surface layer.

These differences in the nature of a soil at varying depths must all be taken into account in assessing the character of a soil, and in the scientific study of soils it is necessary to examine the properties of the soil throughout its entire depth, from surface to bedrock. For this purpose, the scientist studies a vertical section taken through the soil, which is called a *profile*.

If a pit is dug, the vertical sides will show the profile of the soil, and examination of such a profile will commonly show that it forms a number of recognizable layers. These may differ one from another in colour and texture, in structure and porosity. They are described as *horizons,* and they reflect the progress of soil development at different depths. The horizons forming the profile of a soil provide us with a record of its origin and history, through periods that may extend over thousands of years.

The profile of a soil examined at any point on the earth's surface will be different from that at any other place. Every soil profile is as unique and characteristic as the profile of every human being on earth. No two are ever entirely alike.

The horizons in the soil profile may be likened to the features on the human face; all faces are different, but they all have features in common. They have noses and mouths, eyes and chins, and we can compare and contrast human faces by considering each feature in turn.

In the scientific study of soils, profiles are considered in a similar way, and for this purpose it is convenient to compare similarly-situated horizons in soils generally. These can be regarded as identifiable features making up the soil profile as a whole.

In this way we can recognise similarities between the profiles of various soils, just as we can see general racial characteristics in the features of human beings. Some human beings form recognizable groups because they have a characteristic colour of skin, or almond-shaped eyes, or noses of a particular shape. This does not mean that all the individuals in a group are alike; far from it—they are all different. But they have features in common which enable us to bring them together into groups.

In the case of soils, we have an infinite diversity of personalities between individual profiles, but we can bring together soils into broad groups by comparing them on the basis of the horizons that make up complete profiles.

This analogy between a soil profile and the profile of a human being must not be carried too far. Every human being is an individual, but there are no individual soils. The earth's layer of soil is a mass of material that lies on the land surface. Its character changes continuously, and we describe "a soil" by fixing arbitrary limits to an area of ground. We speak of "the soil in our garden", or "the soil in the lower field", but this does not mean that all the soil in the specified area is the same, or even similar. The profile we obtain by digging a pit at any point, or by using an auger to bore out a core of earth, is the profile only of a particular section of soil in that particular place. If we take another profile immediately alongside the first, it will be different.

Despite these infinite variations, there is usually a general similarity in soil which has derived from common sources in a particular environment, and by examining profiles at intervals it is possible to assess the general character of an area of soil as a whole.

SOIL HORIZONS

The recognizable layers in a soil – the horizons – may be of almost any depth. Some are only a fraction of an inch thick; others may extend to depths of several feet.

In some soils, the boundaries between the horizons are sharp and clear. More often, they are less distinct, one horizon merging gradually into another.

In most soils, three main horizons may be recognized, which are commonly identified by the letters A, B and C. These master horizons may in turn be sub-divided, and the sub-divisions are identified by adding a subscript number to the horizon letter, e.g., A_1, A_2, B_1, B_2. In the scientific study of soil, the nature of these sub-divisions provides important information on the processes of soil formation which are in operation, and the way in which the soil may best be managed.

1. "A" Horizon

This is the surface layer of the soil, in which the remnants of plants and animals are being incorporated into a mass of weathered material derived from parent rocks.

A HORIZON — Organic debris lodged on the soil, usually absent on soils developed from grasses.	Aoo	Loose leaves and organic debris, largely undecomposed.
	Ao	Organic debris partially decomposed or matted.
Horizons of maximum biological activity, of eluviation (removal of materials dissolved or suspended in water), or both.	A1	A dark-coloured horizon with a high content of organic matter mixed with mineral matter.
	A2	A light-coloured horizon of maximum eluviation. Prominent in Podzolic soils; faintly developed or absent in Chernozemic soils.
	A3	Transitional to B, but more like A than B. Sometimes absent.
B HORIZON — Horizons of illuviation (of accumulation of suspended material from A) or of maximum clay accumulation, or of blocky or prismatic structure, or both.	B1	Transitional to B, but more like B than A. Sometimes absent.
	B2	Maximum accumulation of silicate clay minerals or of iron and organic matter; maximum development of blocky or prismatic structure; or both.
	B3	Transitional to C.
C HORIZON — The weathered parent material. Occasionally absent i.e., soil building may follow weathering such that no weathered material that is not included in the solum is found between B and D.	G · Cca · C · Ccs	Horizon G for intensely gleyed layers, as in hydromorphic soils. Horizons Cca and Ccs are layers of accumulated calcium carbonate and calcium sulphate found in some soils.
D HORIZON — Any stratum underneath the soil, such as hard rock or layers of clay or sand, that are not parent material but which may have significance to the overlying soil.	D	

SOIL PROFILE. A hypothetical soil profile that has all the principal horizons. Not all of these horizons are present in any profile, but every profile has some of them.

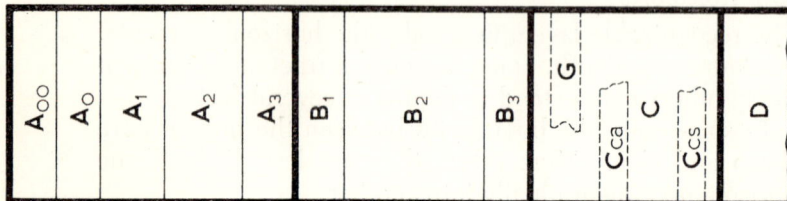

It may range in thickness from a fraction of an inch to several feet.

The A horizon is the gardener's topsoil. It is the upper layer of the soil in which organic matter is decomposed, releasing simple substances, including nitrogen compounds, which provide food for the growing plant. In this layer too, the mineral particles are undergoing intensive weathering; they continue to break down in size, and undergo chemical changes which may release supplies of phosphorus, potassium and other elements in the form of soluble compounds.

The A horizon supports most of the life of the soil; plant roots seek out the water and air, and the soluble chemicals they need as food; bacteria, fungi, viruses and other microorganisms live and die in their countless millions; insects and small animals burrow into the surface layer in which they make their homes.

As rain falls on this busy, bustling surface layer of the soil, it soaks into the porous mass and flows downwards towards the layers below. Inevitably, the water dissolves some of the soluble substances which have been released by intense biological, chemical and physical activity within the A horizon. It also sweeps along fine particles of humus, clay and materials such as oxides of iron and aluminium, which have been released as the parent rocks have weathered.

These soluble materials and fine particles are carried away by the flowing water, and may be deposited in a lower layer of the soil, or may be swept along in streams and rivers until eventually they reach the sea.

An A horizon rich in organic matter and weathered minerals is commonly dark in colour, with a brown or grey-brown hue. If the washing or "leaching" by rainwater has been heavy, much of the organic matter and the red-brown iron oxides will have been carried away, and the surface soil will have a greyish tinge. This is an indication that the A horizon has been severely leached, and a soil of this type may be expected to have lost much of its iron and aluminium salts, its soluble plant foods, its clay and silt and its humus as well.

In a well-developed soil, the effects of weathering and other influences will commonly result in a number of clearly-defined sub-divisions of the A horizon as follows:

A_{00} The uppermost layer, consisting of organic matter, such as leaves and twigs, which have fallen on the soil but have not yet started to decompose.

A_0 The next layer, consisting of organic debris which has started to decompose.

A_1 The layer in which decaying organic matter is becoming mixed with mineral particles derived from parent rocks. This layer is commonly darker in colour, as a result of the organic matter it contains.

A_2 A lighter-coloured layer, from which rainwater flowing through the soil has carried away much of the soluble material and fine particles.

2. "B" Horizon

Beneath the A horizon is a layer which supports much less life than the surface layers. This is the B horizon, which the gardener knows as the subsoil.

The B horizon is usually much firmer and more compact than the A horizon. It often contains more clay which makes it hard when dry, and sticky when wet. It holds much of the material washed from the soil above, and sub-divisions of the B horizon may be distinguished where substances have been deposited to different degrees.

Iron compounds washed from the A horizon will often give their characteristic colour to the B horizon, which may be orange, red or brown. Humus compounds will darken the layer where they accumulate, and fine particles of clay or silt may settle into a recognizable layer.

3. "C" Horizon

Beneath the B horizon lies a layer of material consisting largely of partly-weathered rock. This is usually the source of the mineral matter in the soil above, and the C horizon is the parent material of the soil.

The material of the C horizon may have been formed by the weathering of rocks on which it lies, or it may have been carried from elsewhere by water, wind or moving ice.

The C horizon is essentially a dead region of the soil, containing little living matter. Its humus-content is low, and its colour is commonly lighter than that of the humus-rich surface layers.

4. "D" Horizon

Beneath the C horizon lies the hard rock of the earth's crust. This is sometimes described as the D horizon, although it is not really part of the soil at all.

In many soils, the horizons cannot be distinguished clearly one from another. Often, one or other of the horizons may be missing altogether. Some soils, for example, do not have any B horizon, and are described as AC profiles. When wind erosion has taken place, the entire A horizon may have been swept away as a cloud of dust; even the B horizon may be washed away by water, leaving the lifeless C horizon where once the earth was covered with a rich, living topsoil.

The recognition of horizons in the soil profile has been of the greatest value in the scientific study of the soil. No soil on earth contains all the horizons and sub-horizons recognized by soil scientists, but every soil includes one or more horizon. By studying the nature and arrangement of the horizons, we can understand the history and development of a soil, and examine the way in which the various soil-forming processes have brought it to its present state.

HOW THE PROFILE IS FORMED

The rocks of the earth's crust provide a store of aluminium and silicon, iron and oxygen, calcium, sodium, potassium and other elements united in a great variety of chemical compounds. These are the original source of the mineral matter that now makes up much of our soil.

The disintegration of solid rock takes place slowly and inexorably under the attack of the weather. Sunshine and frost, rain and wind all play their part, their combined assault on the rock serving to weaken it surface structure.

Under the effects of heat and cold, the surface of the rock expands and contracts much more than the layers of rock beneath. Small cracks and fissures appear, and water seeps in. As the water freezes, it expands, and ice pushes open the crack until eventually a portion of the rock surface flakes away (see page 69).

These physical attacks are joined by chemical attacks. Rainwater absorbs carbon dioxide gas as it falls through the air, forming an acid solution that gnaws steadily at the rock. Oxygen in the air takes part too, and chemical changes take place in the exposed rock surfaces. New substances are formed, resulting in additional stresses and strains which contribute to the breakdown of the rock.

As weathering crumbles away the outer layers of rock, fresh surfaces are exposed; these in turn, are attacked until they too disintegrate. In this way, the earth's rocky crust is undergoing a slow but steady disintegration under the attack of the atmosphere, producing a litter of mineral matter that now blankets the solid crust.

This disintegrated rock is the soil parent material. Some of it consists of lumps of the rock itself; the rest is secondary material resulting from rock which has undergone chemical change under the attack of air and water. This mass of material forms the C horizon that we recognize in soils today.

When pieces of rock have been broken away from the

parent mass, they continue to be attacked by weathering forces. Gradually, they are broken into smaller and smaller pieces. Some of the rock constituents undergo chemical change to form new materials; other constituents resist such change, and appear eventually as tiny particles of resistant matter like the grains of quartz in sand.

The process of rock-weathering is always at work in the soil, generating a continuous supply of mineral particles and soluble substances within the soil. In the millions of years that have passed since the earth's crust formed, vast quantities of unconsolidated mineral matter have been created in this way. Sometimes, it lies where it was formed above the parent rock; often, it has been moved from its place of origin by wind or water or ice (see page 60).

The blanket of weathered rock that we find on the earth's surface today may have sustained virtually any degree of weathering, depending on circumstances. In Alaska, for example, recent glacial deposits consist almost entirely of rocks which have undergone only a slight amount of weathering. In the jungle regions of the Amazon forest, on the other hand, weathering has often been so intense that the soil contains little more than the most highly resistant minerals; everything that could be attacked by the atmospheric forces *has* been attacked.

Organic Matter

The weathering of parent rocks is only the beginning of the formation of a soil. It is followed by the addition of organic matter, which comes from all the living things that make their homes in and on the soil. Often, lichens and other simple plants will begin to grow on the parent rock, even before it has disintegrated. As the weathered rock accumulates, bacteria and fungi settle down among the particles, soon to be joined by more complex plants, which send their roots probing into the young soil. No sooner have plants established themselves than the animals arrive, living on plant materials or on other animals. And so we have all the ingredients needed for the making of a living soil.

The presence of plants and animals brings about a fundamental change. As living things die, the material of their bodies decays, adding soluble and insoluble chemicals, including humus, to the surface layer. The layer darkens, and its character changes so that it differs from the lower layers. The addition of organic matter has begun the creation of an A horizon.

The formation of an A horizon begins as soon as living things make their home in the soil, and establishment of the horizon runs concurrently with continued weathering of the rock. In a young soil, the A horizon may be thin and indistinct, but it will be there. As time passes, the A horizon becomes thicker and more clearly seen as organic matter accumulates in the surface layer. It will lie immediately above the weathered rock that forms the C horizon, and an AC profile is typical of many young soils.

Within the A horizon, organic matter may decay rapidly, and weathering of the mineral particles continues. Soluble chemicals are formed, and fine particles of insoluble material may be released from the disintegrating rock. As rain falls on the soil, leaching carries these substances in solution, or in suspension, into the lower layers of the soil, and profile formation thus reaches a further stage – the creation of a B horizon.

In many soils, the B horizon makes its appearance almost as soon as the A horizon begins to form. In other soils, the A horizon may become thick and distinct before any sign of a B horizon is to be seen.

As time goes on, the profile of the soil develops, and acquires a character of its own. By analysing and studying the profile, we can follow the history of the soil, and assess the part that has been played by each of the factors that contribute to its formation.

FACTORS IN SOIL FORMATION

There are five major factors in soil formation:

1. Climate
2. Parent material
3. Topography or Relief
4. Living organisms (flora and fauna)
5. Time.

These factors are often closely related, and between them they control the chemical, physical and biological changes which result in the weathering of rocks, the decay of organic substances and the movement of materials from one place to another. Together they create the profile of any soil.

1. Climate

This is the most important of all the factors that control the development of a soil. Temperature influences the rate at which weathering takes place, stimulating rapid weathering in hot regions, and slowing it down in colder regions.

The alternation of hot and cold spells, and the effect of frost, combine to break up the rock into finer and finer particles.

Rainfall plays its part in the weathering of rocks and the decomposition of organic matter. Water flowing through the soil delineates the horizons by carrying materials from one layer to another, or by removing them altogether. Heavy rain may even wash away surface layers to expose a B or C horizon lying beneath.

In addition to its direct effects on the soil, climate acts indirectly by controlling vegetation and animal life. In humid climates, lush forests will grow on the soil; in arid regions, vegetation will be sparse and thin. The nature of the vegetation, and the animal life it supports, have an important influence on the character of the soil.

The importance of climate as a factor in soil formation

is reflected in the distribution of broad soil regions of the world, which follows a general climatic pattern. This is not a precise relationship, however, as the other four factors also influence soil development within a climatic zone.

2. Parent Materials

The mineral particles in the soil have come from parent rock which has disintegrated as a result of weathering. The elements which make up the mineral particles were present in the substances of the parent rock; they consist of compounds which existed in the rock itself, or new compounds resulting from chemical changes which formed part of the weathering process.

All manner of materials are to be found in the earth's rock crust, which is a storehouse of the ninety-odd elements from which our world is built. As rocks decay, they release an immense variety of compounds into the soil, and the chemical structure of a soil is thus controlled by the chemical constitution of the parent rocks from which it comes.

The geologist sub-divides his rocks into three main groups: igneous, sedimentary and metamorphic rocks.

IGNEOUS ROCKS

These are rocks formed by the cooling of molten matter. The crust that formed when the young earth cooled consisted of igneous rocks. These rocks are still being formed today as molten lava seeps from volcanoes, or solidifies deep in the earth's crust.

The chemical structure of igneous rock varies greatly. Granite, rhyolites, syenites, diorites and basalts are all igneous rocks; they disintegrate in their own individual ways under the attack of the weather.

Igneous rocks are usually hard, but they often decay rapidly when weathered. Some form gravel and sand; others release silt and clay.

Igneous rocks are rich in silicates, formed by union of the elements silicon and oxygen with aluminium, calcium, iron and other elements. When silicates are weathered, they commonly unite with water, becoming hydrated, and fine particles of hydrated silicate are the basis of most clays.

Basalt is almost entirely a mixture of silicates, and long continued weathering will produce a clayey residue.

Granite, however, contains quartz which is highly resistant to weathering. As granite decays, the silicates produce silt and clay, while the unattacked quartz grains are released (see page 56).

SEDIMENTARY ROCKS

Throughout the millions of years that have passed since the earth's crust cooled, the layer of loose material on its surface has been moved from place to place. Carried along by wind and water, or by moving ice, masses of fine particles have been left far from the parent rocks that released them as they weathered.

Some of the particles were swept along by rivers and streams, ultimately to be deposited on the floor of a lake, or on the ocean bed. Layers of sediment might collect in this way for thousands of years, increasing in thickness slowly but steadily as century followed century. Gradually, the mass of particles became compressed into a layer of rock that lay like a blanket on the earth's crust.

Rocks formed in this way are sedimentary rocks. In the course of time, great movements of the earth's crust have taken place, and sedimentary rocks formed on the sea-floor have been lifted above sea level to become dry land. So we find sedimentary rocks forming mountains and valleys in every continent. The origin of these rocks is to be seen in the fossils embedded in them; imprints of the bodies of sea-creatures are found in sedimentary rocks thousands of feet above the sea.

I

The chemical structure of sedimentary rocks varies widely, depending upon the source from which the deposits came. Sandstones, for example, have been created from particles of quartz and other materials released by weathered igneous and other rocks.

Limestones are sedimentary rocks derived from the shells of microscopic marine creatures that flourished millions of years ago. As they died, the tiny organisms left calcareous shells which settled slowly to the bottom of the sea. Over thousands of years, a thick layer of sediment was formed which became consolidated into a limestone rock.

The chemical composition of limestone varies considerably, depending on its origin and development. The major constituents are calcium and magnesium carbonates; some limestones, such as those which are quarried in Derbyshire, are almost pure calcium carbonate.

Shale is a sedimentary rock formed by the deposition of fine clay particles, or of silt.

METAMORPHIC ROCKS

In the course of time, igneous and sedimentary rocks may be subjected to heat and pressure which cause changes in chemical or physical structure. Rocks modified in this way are called metamorphic rocks. They include, for example, marble, which is a modified form of limestone, and gneiss, a laminated rock of granite-like constitution.

ORGANIC MATERIAL

Plants and animals have been living and dying on the earth's surface since life appeared, and their remains have been incorporated into the soil. This once-living matter is a parent material which has a major influence on the structure of the soil.

The complex chemical substances that make up living matter are based on the element carbon. Carbon atoms have a unique ability to link together into a limitless variety of molecules, and the chemistry of carbon is virtually synonymous with the chemistry of life. In the plant and animal body, carbon atoms provide the backbone structure of innumerable molecules which take part in the endless interplay of chemical activity making up life itself.

A few elements, including hydrogen, oxygen, phosphorus, nitrogen, calcium and sulphur, are linked with carbon in significant quantities in the chemical compounds of living matter. Many other elements play an essential role but are present only in very small amounts.

When plants and animals die, the organic matter of their bodies is attacked by micro-organisms in the soil. Chemical changes occur which break down the complex materials, forming simpler substances. Nitrogen from the once-living matter, for example, is released into the soil as soluble chemicals which provide growing plants with supplies of the nitrogen they need.

The amount and nature of its organic matter plays a vital role in the development of a soil. In a fertile soil, decay takes place rapidly, the organic material decomposing much faster than the mineral particles disintegrate by weathering. Much of the organic matter falling on the soil in one growing season may have decomposed by the end of the following season.

Under normal conditions, the decomposition of organic matter results in the formation of humus. This helps to sustain a desirable structure in the soil. It acts as a store of organic matter, decaying steadily to release its constituent elements into the soil.

If organic matter falls on a waterlogged soil, the lack of air will restrict decomposition, and a mass of partly-decayed material may accumulate. *Peat* is the result of such accumulation in boggy land; it is a residue that has formed under conditions of oxygen shortage.

3. Topography or Relief

The development of a soil is influenced greatly by the slope of the land surface. This affects the movement of water across and through the soil, and the nature of the profile that is formed.

On a steep hillside, water will tend to flow rapidly across the surface, carrying away more soil than water that flows gently down a shallow slope. The horizons in the profile of a hillside soil are often shallow and indistinct.

Water flowing steadily through the soil of flat or level ground will tend to form horizons that are thicker and more clearly developed than those on steeply-sloping ground. The humus content is commonly higher in the soil, and vegetation is more prolific.

The effect of the sustained water-flow through soils on level sites may be seen in a greyish tint of the surface soil, indicating removal of iron oxides, humus and other highly-coloured material by leaching.

If the topography is such as to keep water standing at the surface, lack of oxygen will restrict decomposition of organic matter, and peat will be formed.

Aspect has an important influence too upon the warmth that reaches the soil from sunshine. A slope in the northern hemisphere that faces south will receive more radiation to the acre than a slope that faces north; the reverse is true in the southern hemisphere. Topography thus affects the temperature of the soil, and influences the rates of weathering and decay (see page 107).

4. Living Organisms

Plants and animals are important factors in soil development, providing organic matter that is so vital a constituent of any soil. Organic materials from plant and animal remains are incorporated into the A horizon. Bacteria and fungi attack the organic materials, converting complex substances into simpler chemicals which the plant is able to use as food. The bodies of bacteria and fungi are themselves an important part of humus.

Nitrogen chemicals are released into the soil in this way, some plants providing additional supplies by supporting nitrogen-fixing bacteria which live in nodules on the plant roots. When the plant dies, extra fixed nitrogen is released into the soil (see page 80).

Plants play a much more important role than animals in the development of a soil. They determine the kind of organic material that is incorporated in the A horizon, and the form in which it reaches the soil – as twigs and leaves, flowers and fruit, or as roots.

The chemistry of the soil is affected by plants in other ways too. The roots of plants may reach down into the B and C horizons, where they absorb solutions of substances which have been washed from the surface layers, or formed through weathering. Calcium, phosphorus, potassium and other elements obtained in this way are incorporated into the body material of the plant, and when it dies they are returned to the A horizon of the soil. Thus, the plant tends to reverse the leaching process, carrying materials upwards through the soil.

Plants are often very effective in this respect. Shadscale, for example – a desert shrub – will create a strongly alkaline soil in its immediate vicinity by bringing up sodium salts from the subsoil.

Plants and animals also exert a direct effect on the physical structure of the soil. Insects, earthworms and other animals tunnel through the soil, churning and mixing it as they go. The roots of plants help to prevent erosion by gripping the soil, holding it against the insidious attack of wind and water. As trees and other large plants fall over, they bring up masses of soil from lower horizons. The roots decay, releasing the soil onto the surface.

5. Time

The weathering of rock is a slow process when we measure it against the span of the human life. A hundred years will make only a modest contribution to the amount of weathered material that forms above a parent rock. But a hundred years is merely an instant in the time that has passed since the earth's crust cooled. The mineral matter that forms the basis of our soil today is a mass of weathered rock which has accumulated over thousands of millions of years.

The development of a soil profile is, by comparison, a much more rapid process. If the soil remained in place above its parent rock, it would acquire a profile that marked out its history since the parent rock was formed. But the soil material has been moved and mixed so often in the past that many soils are the latest of several that have formed in any particular region in the past.

Infinite Variation

Every one of the five factors in soil formation is capable of wide variation, and none of them is uniform over the earth's surface. At any place the combination of these factors differs from the combination at any other place, and the soils that result from them are correspondingly diverse. The soil profile we examine by digging a pit at any point is quite unique; it will not be repeated exactly anywhere else in the world.

11

Classification of Soils

In the early days of soil science, which were not so very long ago, attempts were made to classify soils according to their geological origins, or the vegetation they supported, or their response to cultivation techniques, or to the climate. Today, the soil scientist approaches the problem in a different way. He bases his attempts at classification upon the characteristics of the soil itself, rather than upon its origin or its behaviour.

In the scientific study of soils, a careful assessment is made of the entire soil profile. The number and relative positions of the horizons are recorded, together with the colour, texture, structure and thickness of each horizon. A chemical examination and analysis of each horizon is made, and the geological origin of the soil material is determined.

By considering soils in this way, the scientist obtains detailed information which enables him to compare one soil with another. He can discover relationships between different soils, and bring together into groups those soils which have features in common. The groups may then be aligned with others into groups of a higher category, and in due course a system of classification may be built up.

Classification systems of this type, based upon the observed characteristics of individual soils, have been developed by soil scientists of many nationalities in the last century or so. But the infinite variations in the soils of the earth, and the lack of information about the majority of soils, have made the establishment of a satisfactory classification system a very difficult task.

BALDWIN SYSTEM

In 1938, American scientists M. Baldwin, C. E. Kellogg and J. Thorp devised a classification system which has been widely accepted in many countries. It was revised in 1949, and the higher categories of the system are shown in the diagram on page 258.

1. Orders

All soils are considered initially as belonging to one of three basic categories, or *orders*, called Zonal Soils, Intrazonal Soils and Azonal Soils.

ZONAL SOILS are those with well-developed characteristics which reflect the dominating influences of climate and vegetation. Other soil-forming factors have not been of such an extreme nature as to outweigh the effects of climate and vegetation.

Zonal Soils are commonly developed on the gentler slopes of well-drained uplands, from parent materials that are not of an unusual texture or chemical composition. The soils will have been developing for a time sufficient to enable them to acquire a mature profile.

INTRAZONAL SOILS are soils with more or less well-developed characteristics that reflect the dominating influence of some local factor of relief, parent material or age over the normal effect of climate and vegetation.

AZONAL SOILS are soils which do not possess well-developed soil characteristics, possibly due to lack of time, or to conditions of parent material or relief.

2. Suborders

The three Orders are sub-divided into *suborders*, of

which there are six in the Zonal Order, three in the Intrazonal Order and none in the Azonal Order.

3. Great Soil Groups

The third category in the classification system consists
of the sub-divisions of the suborders, known as *Great Soil
Groups.*

The Great Soil Groups represent broad groupings of
soils with certain characteristics in common. Every member of a Great Soil Group has the same number and kind
of horizons, although they may appear to different degrees
in different soils.

4. Series

The further sub-divisions of Great Soil Groups may be
continued through categories of increasing numerical size.
For most practical purposes, however, it is usual to consider the category called the *series.*

Within a series are included soils which are similar in
every feature *other than the texture of the surface soil.* The
series is usually named after a place, such as Miami, Cisne
or Muscatine, and the series category is such that it identifies a soil precisely, apart from the texture of the surface
layer.

5. Types

The final identification of an individual soil is achieved
by adding a description of the surface texture to the series
name. Thus, Miami silt loam is the name given to a soil
of Miami series with a silt loam surface layer.

This is, in practice, the final and lowest category of
classification, and it is called the *type.* It represents an individual soil "species", and a number of soils of the same
type can be regarded as similar in all their characteristics.

6. Phases

Within an individual soil type, there may be minor
I*

SOIL CLASSIFICATION*

Order	Suborder	Great Soil Groups
ZONAL SOILS	1. Tundra Soils Soils of cold zone	Tundra soils
	2. Desertic Soils Light coloured soils of arid regions	Desert, Red Desert, Sierozem, Brown, Red- dish-Brown soils
	3. Chernozemic Soils Dark coloured soils of semi-arid, sub- humid and humid grasslands	Chestnut, Reddish- Chestnut, Chernozem, Prairie, Reddish Prairie soils
	4. Forest - Grassland Transition Soils	Degraded Chernozem, Non-calcic Brown or Shantung Brown soils
	5. Podzolic Soils Light coloured pod- zolized soils of once timbered regions	Podzol, Gray wooded, or Gray Podzolic, Brown Podzolic, Gray- Brown Podzolic, Red- Yellow Podzolic soils
	6. Latosolic Soils Lateritic soils of forested warm-tem- perate and tropical regions	Reddish-Brown Later- itic, Yellowish-Brown Lateritic, Laterite soils
INTRAZONAL SOILS	1. Halomorphic Soils Saline and alkali soils of imperfectly drained arid regions and littoral deposits	Solonchak, or Saline, Solonetz, Soloth soils
	2. Hydromorphic Soils Soils of marshes, swamps, seep areas and flats	Humic Gley (includes Weisenboden), Alpine Meadow, Bog, Half-Bog, Low-Humic Gley, Planosols Ground-Water Podzol, Ground-Water Laterite soils
	3. Calcimorphic Soils	Brown Forest (Braun- erde), Rendzina soils
AZONAL SOILS		Lithosols, Regosols (in- cludes Dry Sands), Alluvial soils

* Based on system of Baldwin, M., Kellogg, C. E., and Thorp, J., as revised
by Thorp, J. and Smith, G. D. in 1949.

variations which are not sufficient in themselves to warrant recognition of a new type. These variants are called *phases.*

The information about a phase is provided by adding a descriptive term after the type name, e.g. Muscatine silt loam, stony phase.

SUBORDERS AND THEIR GREAT SOIL GROUPS

The classification system brings together Great Soil Groups into suborders which are recognized by descriptive names familiar to soil scientists everywhere.

A. Zonal Soil Suborders

TUNDRA SOILS

These are the soils to be found in the cold latitudes. Biological activity is restricted and vegetation – mostly shrubs and mosses – is sparse. In Arctic regions, the soil may be permanently frozen beneath the surface layers.

The surface horizon is commonly dark in colour, containing a high proportion of organic material. The B horizon may be gray or brown.

In well-drained tundra soils, the profile may be similar to those of Podzolic soils, with narrower and less distinct horizons.

DESERTIC SOILS

In the arid regions of the world – which may be in cold or hot climates -- soils have formed beneath a sparse cover of grass or shrubby vegetation. These are the Desertic Soils, which are commonly associated with the great deserts of Africa, Asia and Australia, and the desert regions of North and South America. They include the following Great Soil Groups: Desert Soils, Red Desert Soils, Sierozem, Brown Soils and Reddish-Brown Soils.

The limited rainfall in these regions restricts weathering, and there is little leaching of the surface layers. The cover of vegetation is skimpy, and the A horizon of the soil is low in organic matter. The soil may be comparatively rich in most plant nutrients, but is commonly low in nitrogen.

The small amount of water flowing through a Desertic Soil results in shallow horizons, which are often faint and indistinct. Fine clay particles are carried down from the A horizon, which is light in colour, and are deposited in the B horizon. This horizon, too, contains little organic matter.

Under carefully-planned cultivation, some Desertic Soils are very productive; others remain poor growing soils under almost all conditions. The sparse vegetation and spasmodic rainfall tend to encourage erosion. The topsoil may be carried away in vast duststorms, leaving a stony residue.

CHERNOZEMIC SOILS

In the humid to semi-arid regions of the world's temperate zones, soils are formed beneath a grassy vegetation. These are Chernozemic Soils, which extend also into the tropical regions.

The following Great Soil Groups are included in this suborder: Chernozemic, Brunizems (Prairie Soils), Reddish Prairie Soils, Chestnut Soils and Reddish Chestnut Soils. In tropical regions, the suborder includes Black Cotton Soils, Grumusols, Regurs and Dark Clays.

Chernozemic soils are rich in humus, which accumulates to form dark A_1 horizons reaching depths of several feet. The A_1 horizon is a prominent feature of a Chernozemic soil, with its high content of organic matter and a plentiful supply of nitrogen. These may be reduced in tropical or sub-tropical regions, owing to excessive leaching. The B horizon is usually indistinct, and may have a layer of calcium sulphate and carbonate.

In temperate zones, the A horizon is not heavily leached,

and the removal of clay, oxides, humus and soluble matter is on a modest scale. The grass vegetation absorbs calcium and magnesium from the B horizon, and these are brought back to the surface in the dead leaves and other plant materials that fall to the ground. Chernozemic soils, in consequence, are seldom acid.

In temperate zones, these soils are fertile, with good water-holding characteristics. The surface forms a crumb-structure which is ideal for plant growth, and Chernozemic soils form the basis of many of the world's great grain belts.

FOREST-GRASSLAND TRANSITION SOILS

This suborder forms a link between Chernozemic and Podzolic Soils. It may be regarded as a transition sub-order containing Great Soil Groups with characteristics intermediate between the two.

PODZOLIC SOILS

In the higher latitudes of the northern hemisphere, in-cluding northern regions of U.S.A., Canada, northern Europe and Asia, and in some regions of the southern hemisphere, vast areas of the earth were covered by forest vegetation growing in Podzolic soils. The name of these soils comes from the Russian words meaning "ash beneath", referring to a characteristic bleached A_2 horizon.

The suborder of Podzolic soils includes the following Great Soil Groups: Podzols, Brown Podzolic Soils, Grey Brown Podzolic Soils, Grey Wooded Soils, and Red-Yellow Podzolic Soils.

Podzolic soils are found usually in humid, temperate climates, and they are strongly leached, acid soils. Calcium and magnesium compounds are leached from the A hori-zon, and the resinous leaves which fall to the ground do not return these elements as rapidly as they are lost from the surface soil. The calcium content of Podzolic soil is commonly low, and the soil has an acid reaction.

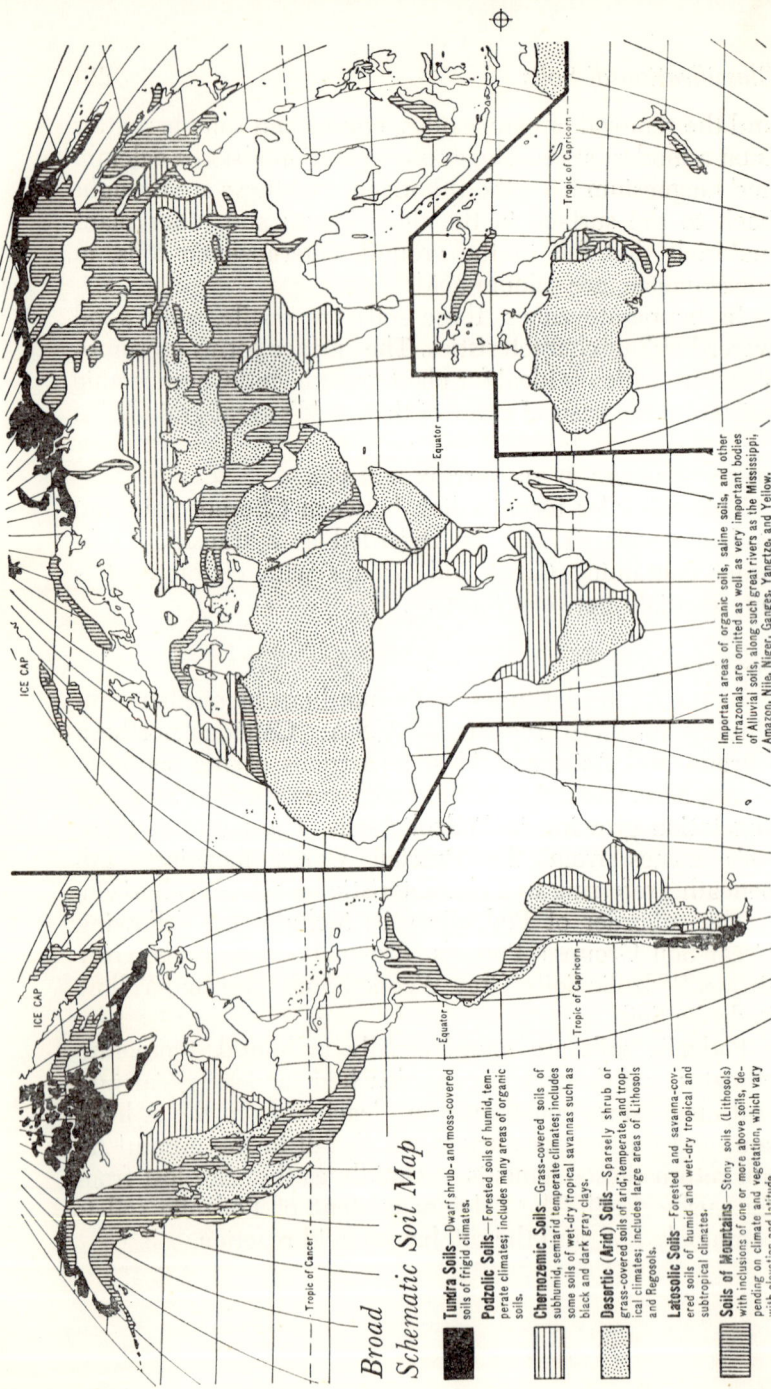

Broad Schematic Soil Map

■ **Tundra Soils**—Dwarf shrub-and moss-covered soils of frigid climates.

Podzolic Soils—Forested soils of humid, temperate climates; includes many areas of organic soils.

Chernozemic Soils—Grass-covered soils of subhumid, semiarid temperate climates; includes some soils of wet-dry tropical savannas such as black and dark gray clays.

Desertic (Arid) Soils—Sparsely shrub or grass-covered soils of arid, temperate, and tropical climates; includes large areas of Lithosols and Regosols.

Latosolic Soils—Forested and savanna-covered soils of humid and wet-dry tropical and subtropical climates.

Soils of Mountains (Lithosols)—Stony soils with inclusions of one or more above soils, depending on climate and vegetation, which vary with elevation and latitude.

Important areas of organic soils, saline soils, and other intrazonals are omitted as well as very important bodies of Alluvial soils, along such great rivers as the Mississippi, Amazon, Nile, Niger, Ganges, Yangtze, and Yellow.

WORLD SOIL ZONES. This map of the world shows six broad soil zones. Each zone generally has similar processes of horizon differentiation prevailing over it. These are reflected in the character of the well-drained soils with undulating to rolling topography. Many kinds of soils

Organic matter decomposes slowly in a Podzolic soil, fungi often playing a more important role than bacteria. The decomposition products, together with fine particles of clay and iron oxides released by weathering are carried to the B horizon where they may accumulate.

The strongly-leached A_2 horizon is a characteristic of Podzolic soils. It is usually grey, and its ash-like appearance gave these soils their name.

The B horizon may be rich in humus, oxides of iron or aluminium, or clay which have been leached from the A horizon. The proportions vary considerably, depending on local conditions; some Podzolic soils have a B horizon that is heavily impregnated with clay.

The level of fertility in a heavily-leached Podzolic soil tends to be low, but these soils respond well to scientific cultivation.

LATOSOLIC SOILS

This suborder consists of soils which have formed beneath forest and savannah vegetation in tropical and sub-tropical climates, under humid to moderately-dry conditions. They are found in the equatorial forest belts of the world, including South America, Africa, South-East Asia and the East Indies, south-east of U.S.A., north-east Australia and the islands of the Pacific.

Latosolic soils include the following Great Soil Groups: Laterites, Reddish-Brown Lateritic and Yellowish-Brown Lateritic. (Red-yellow Podzolic soils are commonly included in the Latosolic suborder. These soils have features common to both Podzolic and Latosolic soils, but some authorities regard them as tending more towards the Latosolic. They differ from other Latosolic Soils, however, in having the distinct A_2 horizon which is characteristic of a Podzolic soil. They do not absorb water so readily as a Latosolic soil, and may be more subject to erosion.)

Latosolic soils are heavily leached, often to great depths,

and are the most highly weathered soils in the world. The A_1 horizon is dark and rich in organic matter, but supplies of plant nutrients are commonly low. The soil is porous, and water flows readily through the A and B horizons, which are penetrated by innumerable tiny channels.

The B horizon is often indistinct, consisting of reddish or reddish-yellow material coloured by iron oxide washed from the A horizon. It may extend to considerable depths, and tree roots will reach down through the B horizon to fifty feet or more.

Latosolic soils are highly absorbent, but are often of low productivity. They may respond well to careful cultivation, and do not erode readily.

B. Intrazonal Soil Suborders

HALOMORPHIC SOILS

These are soils containing excessive concentrations of salts, e.g. common salt or alkali.

The suborder includes the following Great Soil Groups: Solonchak or Saline Soils, Solonetz Soils, and Soloth Soils.

HYDROMORPHIC SOILS

These are soils in which water has accumulated to such an extent as to stifle the normal soil development processes.

The suborder includes the following Great Soil Groups: Humic Gley Soils (including Wiesenboden), Alpine Meadow Soils, Bog Soils, Half-Bog Soils, Low Humic Gley Soils, Planosols, Ground-Water Podzol Soils, Ground-Water Laterite Soils.

These soils are formed in poorly-drained regions of high humidity. Lack of oxygen restricts the decay of organic matter, and peaty deposits may result. The extent of accumulation depends upon the drainage conditions. Bog soils, for example, are formed when water lies on the surface. Humic gley soils, or Alpine Meadow soils may result when some degree of drainage exists.

SOIL ORDERS AND APPROXIMATE EQUIVALENTS IN REVISED BALDWIN CLASSIFICATION *

Order	Approximate Equivalents
1. Entisols	Azonal soils, and some Low Humic Gley soils
2. Vertisols	Grumusols
3. Inceptisols	Ando, Sol Brun Acide, some Brown Forest, Low-Humic Gley, and Humic Gley soils
4. Aridisols	Desert, Reddish Desert, Sierozem, Solonchak, some Brown and Reddish Brown soils, and associated Solonetz
5. Mollisols	Chestnut, Chernozem, Brunizem (Prairie), Rendzinas, some Brown, Brown Forest and associated Solonetz and Humic Gley soils
6. Spodosols	Podzols, Brown Podzolic soils, and Ground-Water Podzols
7. Alfisols	Gray-Brown Podzolic, Gray Wooded soils, Noncalcic Brown soils, Degraded Chernozem, and associated Planosols and some Half-Bog soils
8. Ultisols	Red-Yellow Podzolic soils, Reddish-Brown Lateritic soils of the U.S., and associated Planosols and Half-Bog soils
9. Oxisols	Laterite soils, Latosols
10. Histosols	Bog soils

* Based on system proposed by Soil Conservation Service, U.S. Dept of Agriculture, 1960.

Planosols are created on flat ground, where water run-off is almost non-existent. Water flows through the A horizon, which is in consequence heavily leached; this surface horizon becomes pale-coloured and acid. The B horizon acquires a layer of silt or clay leached from the A horizon. Planosols seldom suffer from water erosion, but if erosion does take place it may expose the hard infertile clay pan of the B horizon.

CALCIMORPHIC SOILS

These are soils produced by the weathering of limestone. The suborder includes two Great Soil Groups, the Brown Forest Soils, and the Rendzina Soils.

No matter how much leaching may take place, these soils do not become acid. They are generally black or brown, and are commonly covered by a grassy vegetation.

C. Azonal Soils

This order is not generally sub-divided into suborders, consisting as it does of soils which have suffered restricted development for one reason or another. It includes three Great Soil Groups, Lithosols, Regosols (including Dry Sands) and Alluvial Soils.

LITHOSOLS are masses of rock particles which may have undergone little or no weathering. They are commonly found on steep hillsides, where material produced by weathering is quickly washed away. They are useless for cultivation purposes.

REGOSOLS are soils consisting of sands containing little or no clay, humus or soluble salts. The particles are highly resistant to weathering, and there is no development of horizons to form a recognizable profile.

ALLUVIAL SOILS are created from material which has been carried along by rivers. The suspended matter is deposited on deltas and flood plains, as in the Nile valley, and is often the basis of a flourishing agriculture. In time, soil-forming processes may create a profile with discernible horizons in soil that has been deposited in this way.

MODERN DEVELOPMENTS

In recent years, the Soil Conservation Service of the U.S. Department of Agriculture has put forward proposals on which a new classification system could be based. This is a much more detailed and comprehensive system than that already described, which is based on the system originally proposed by Baldwin and his colleagues.

In place of the three orders – Zonal, Intrazonal and Azonal – of the earlier system, the new U.S. classification establishes ten orders. The table on page 265 shows how the Great Soil Groups of the earlier system are classified in the new arrangement.

The range of categories in the new system begins with Order (the highest category) and passes through Sub-orders, Great Groups, Sub-groups, Families and Series.

The earlier concept of soil type as the lowest category depended only upon the single characteristic of the texture of the surface soil to distinguish one type from another in the same series. The texture, however, is subject to constant modification, e.g. by wind or water erosion, and the type could thus vary from season to season depending on conditions. Under such conditions, the type name can become virtually meaningless, and it is now proposed that *Series* should be the lowest category in the classification.

A series is regarded as a collection of soil individuals essentially uniform in characteristics. Variation within a series may include slope, stoniness, erosion effects, nature of horizons within the normal depth of ploughing, depth to bedrock, and depth to a lithological discontinuity.

These variations are less than sufficient to modify the kind, arrangement, thickness of horizons or other factors in such a way as to change the series of a particular soil. The A_1 and A_2 horizons could be affected, for example, by ploughing or other treatment, but the essential series profile would remain undisturbed below the A horizon.

12

Texture, Structure and
other Characteristics

In assessing a soil for classification purposes, the nature of
the soil profile as a whole is considered. The physical and
chemical characteristics of individual horizons are examined, and the part played by each horizon in the soil profile is studied.

Some of the characteristics are a matter of careful observation and measurement, such as the colour, thickness,
shape and relative arrangement of the horizons. But soil
is a complex mixture of materials of all shapes, sizes and
compositions, and many of its characteristics are very difficult to assess. Properties such as texture, structure, consistence and chemical constitution are not easily determined or defined. And yet they are of immense practical
importance, especially with respect to the surface layer of
soil in which the growth of plants largely takes place.

SOIL TEXTURE

Every soil consists of four components: inorganic materials, organic matter, air and water. All are essential to the
growth of plants in the soil, and the balance created and
maintained between these components determines how
fertile and productive a soil will be.

Inorganic and organic materials together make up the

solid matter of the soil, the inorganic material being in the form of mineral particles. Water and air fill the pores and channels that separate the particles from each other, moving to and fro in response to changing atmospheric conditions.

In a healthy soil, the particles of solid matter are in a form that allows air and water to bring to plant roots the oxygen and nutrient chemicals they need. Yet the particles must not be in a state that allows water to drain away too freely, or the soil could become too dry. Nor must the particles be packed so tight that excess water is unable to escape from the soil, or the roots of plants would be denied the oxygen they need.

In addition to these requirements, the soil must be of such a form as to permit effective cultivation. It must resist being washed away by water or blown away by wind. And it must provide a firm roothold for the growing plant.

These vitally important characteristics of a good soil are influenced by the size and arrangement of the soil particles.

The amount of water and air in a soil may fluctuate widely from season to season, from day to day, and even from hour to hour. A heavy rainstorm will fill the pores between the particles with water, driving out the air in the process. Then, as water drains away, air will be drawn into the soil again.

The nature and quantity of the organic matter, too, are in a state of constant change. Life in the soil is always on the move, and fresh supplies of dead plant and animal materials are always being added to the soil. Organic matter decays comparatively quickly, and the status of the organic content of a soil is never the same from day to day.

The mineral matter of the soil, on the other hand, may remain virtually unchanged over long periods of time. Inorganic particles account for about half the total volume of most surface soils. They include particles of material released by weathering of the parent rock. These may consist of pieces of the rock itself, which are subjected to further weathering and breakdown into smaller and smaller particles. Or they may be grains of highly-resistant material, like quartz, which have been left unchanged as other substances of the rock have decomposed.

In addition to these primary materials, which formed part of the original parent rock, there are particles of secondary inorganic materials formed as a result of chemical changes wrought by weathering of the parent rock. Clay particles, for example, are created by the weathering of granite and other igneous rocks. They consist of new material formed by chemical modification of the parent mineral.

The particles of inorganic matter in a soil vary greatly in size and shape, ranging from boulders and stones too heavy to lift, to particles so small that they may be seen only with the help of the electron microscope. The effects of weathering are slow, and the breakdown of the mineral particles of a soil takes place almost imperceptibly. The individual particles may show little change in size over long periods of time. Cultivation, tillage and management may affect other features of a soil very quickly; but they will seldom bring significant changes in the sizes of the inorganic particles.

Particle Size Distribution

The sizes of the grains of mineral matter, and the proportions in which they are present, have an important influence on the character of a soil. They control the *soil texture.*

To the farmer and the gardener, the texture of a soil is a familiar quality that is not easy to define. The experienced farmer judges texture by examining a soil visually, and by rubbing a sample between his fingers. He describes the texture in terms that have been used for genera-

SIZE LIMITS OF SOIL SEPARATES

U.S. Dept. of Agriculture Scheme		International Scheme	
Name of separate	Diameter (range) mm	Fraction	Diameter (range) mm
Very coarse sand*	2·0 – 1·0		
Coarse sand	1·0 – 0·5	I	2·0 – 0·2
Medium sand	0·5 – 0·25		
Fine sand	0·25 – 0·10	II	0·2 – 0·02
Very fine sand	0·10 – 0·05		
Silt	0·05 – 0·002	III	0·02 – 0·002
Clay	Below 0·002	IV	Below 0·002

*Note: Prior to 1947 this separate was called fine gravel. Now, fine gravel is used for coarse fragments from 2mm. to $\frac{1}{2}$ inch in diameter.

tions, like "sandy", "loamy" or "clayey". In this way, he is assessing how the soil will behave in terms of practical cultivation.

With the development of soil science, it became necessary to establish a more precise definition of texture. And in modern scientific terms, soil texture refers to the relative proportions of various size groups of individual soil grains in a mass of soil. Specifically, it refers to the proportions of three size ranges of inorganic soil particles, known as clay, silt and sand.

In these terms, soil texture becomes a property with a precise meaning. It relates only to the size-distribution of inorganic particles, and this can be measured accurately.

This modern concept of texture in terms of particle-size distribution is a simple one, but its application in practice has created difficulties. The old agricultural terms, like loam, sand and clay, describe much more complex characteristics of the soil than the same terms used in describing soil texture today. They include an assessment of soil structure and consistence, both of which are now regarded as separate and distinct features of a soil. Confusion may arise when these terms are used as modern definitions of texture, and are related to old-established understandings of the physical make-up of a soil.

In the older sense, for example, clay soils are generally supposed to be sticky and easily puddled, sandy soils are regarded as loose, structureless and droughty. When we use these terms today in their modern scientific connotations, as referring to texture in terms of size distribution, we must avoid relating them to their older meanings. Among some soil groups, for example, clay soils are indeed sticky and easily puddled; but among other soil groups, they are not. Also, many sandy soils are loose, structureless and droughty; but some are not.

In the same way, texture alone – in the modern sense – has no direct relationship with soil fertility or productivity. It is only one of many features that contribute to the full character and productivity of the soil.

Soil Separates

In assessing soil texture, only those particles of less than 2 mm. diameter are considered. The particles are classified according to their sizes, and are brought together into groups within definite size ranges. These size groups are called *soil separates*.

Two systems of classifying soil into its separates are in common use, (1) the International System and (2) the U.S. Department of Agriculture System. The two systems are essentially similar, but the U.S. System makes more separations, as shown on page 271. In practice, the separates are regarded as three major groups, each including a particular diameter range, as follows:

Sand ... 2.0 to 0.05 mm. diameter
Silt ... 0.05 to 0.002 mm. diameter
Clay ... Less than 0.002 mm. diameter.

Textural Classes

The texture of a soil, in modern terms, is determined solely on the basis of the proportions of the three soil separates – sand, silt and clay – that it contains. To assess the texture of any soil, these proportions must be found by carrying out a mechanical analysis of the soil. First, all stones, roots, twigs, leaves and other constituents of diameter greater than 2 mm. are removed by sieving a prepared sample. The organic matter, including humus, is then destroyed, for example by treatment with hydrogen peroxide. This leaves virtually nothing but grains of mineral matter of less than 2 mm. diameter.

The soil sample is carefully dispersed to make sure that small aggregates are broken down into their primary particles. Then a particle size distribution analysis is made, commonly by assessing the rates at which the soil particles settle after being dispersed in water. The results of this analysis show the proportions of sand, silt and clay (as defined above) forming the inorganic particles in the soil. These proportions define the texture of the soil.

When the proportions are known, the texture may be found by reference to a texture chart as shown on page 274. This is a simple guide to major textural classes, and it enables the textural name of a soil to be found quite easily when the proportions of the three separates are known.

Suppose, for example, a soil sample is found to contain :

Sand ... 50 per cent
Silt ... 30 per cent
Clay ... 20 per cent

To find the textural name for this soil, we find the sand percentage figure – 50 – on the bottom of the triangle, and then follow the heavy line upwards to the left. All points on this line represent a soil containing 50 per cent sand.

Next, we seek the silt percentage figure – 30 – on the right hand side of the triangle. We then follow the line

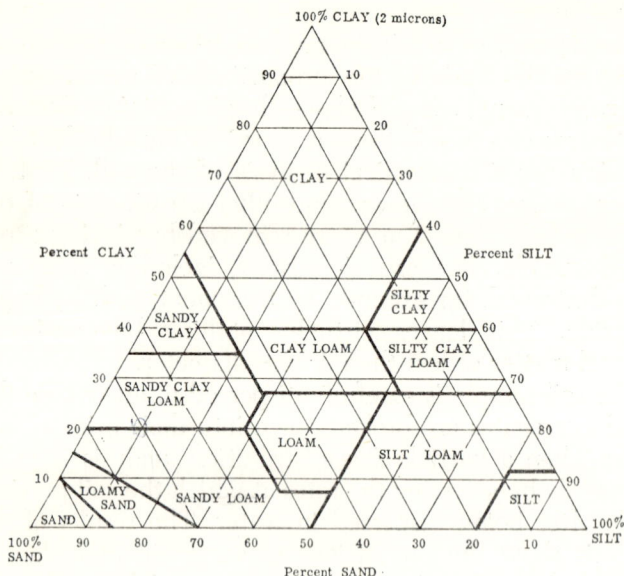

SOIL TEXTURE DIAGRAM

running down and to the left until it meets the 50 per cent sand line. The point at which they meet will coincide with the 20 per cent clay line on the left of the triangle (which serves as a check). We find that the point of intersection of the three lines is in the area of the triangle corresponding to the loam textural class.

By this means, we can assign a textural class name to any soil, once we know the percentages of separates it contains. The triangular chart as shown is adequate to indicate the major classes, but it is too small to show sub-divisions of textural classes needed for more accurate definition of soil texture. These sub-divisions, which may be shown on a larger, more detailed chart, are given in descriptive terms as follows:

SANDS – Soil material that contains 85 per cent or more of sand; percentage of silt, plus 1½ times the percentage of clay, shall not exceed 15.

Coarse sand: 25 per cent or more very coarse and coarse sand, and less than 50 per cent any other one grade of sand.

Sand: 25 per cent or more very coarse, coarse, and medium sand, and less than 50 per cent fine or very fine sand.

Fine Sand: 50 per cent or more fine sand (or) less than 25 per cent very coarse, coarse, and medium sand and less than 50 per cent very fine sand.

Very fine sand: 50 per cent or more very fine sand.

LOAMY SANDS – Soil material that contains at the upper limit 85 to 90 per cent sand, and the percentage of silt plus 1½ times the percentage of clay is not less than 15; at the lower limit it contains not less than 70 to 85 per cent sand, and the percentage of silt plus twice the percentage of clay does not exceed 30.

Loamy coarse sand: 25 per cent or more very coarse and coarse sand, and less than 50 per cent any other one grade of sand.

Loamy sand: 25 per cent or more very coarse, coarse, and medium sand, and less than 50 per cent fine or very fine sand.

Loamy fine sand: 50 per cent or more fine sand (or) less than 25 per cent very coarse, coarse, and medium sand and less than 50 per cent very fine sand.

Loamy very fine sand: 50 per cent or more very fine sand.

SANDY LOAMS – Soil material that contains either 20 per cent clay or less, and the percentage of silt plus twice the percentage of clay exceeds 30, and 52 per cent or more sand; or less than 7 per cent clay, less than 50 per cent silt, and between 43 per cent and 52 per cent sand.

Coarse sandy loam: 25 per cent or more very coarse and coarse sand and less than 50 per cent any other one grade sand.

Sandy loam: 30 per cent or more very coarse, coarse, and medium sand, but less than 25 per cent very coarse sand, and less than 30 per cent very fine sand.

Fine sandy loam: 30 per cent or more fine sand and less than 30 per cent very fine sand (or) between 15 and 30 per cent very coarse, coarse and medium sand.

Very fine sandy loam: 30 per cent or more very fine sand (or) more than 40 per cent fine and very fine sand, at least half of which is very fine, sand and less than 15 per cent very coarse, coarse, and medium sand.

LOAM – Soil material that contains 7 to 27 per cent clay, 28 to 50 per cent silt, and less than 52 per cent sand.

SILT LOAM – Soil material that contains 50 per cent or more silt and 12 to 27 per cent clay (or) 50 to 80 per cent silt and less than 12 per cent clay.

SILT – Soil material that contains 80 per cent or more silt and less than 12 per cent clay.

SANDY CLAY LOAM – Soil material that contains 20 to 35 per cent clay, less than 28 per cent silt, and 45 per cent or more sand.

CLAY LOAM – Soil material that contains 27 to 40 per cent clay and 20 to 45 per cent sand.

SILTY CLAY LOAM – Soil material that contains 27 to 40 per cent clay, and less than 20 per cent sand.

SANDY CLAY – Soil material that contains 40 per cent or more clay and 40 per cent or more silt.

SILTY CLAY – Soil material that contains 40 per cent or more clay and 40 per cent or more silt.

CLAY – Soil material that contains 40 per cent or more clay, less than 45 per cent sand, and less than 40 per cent silt.

The mineral particles of any soil may consist of the three major soil separates combined in virtually any proportions. Any one of the three may be present in an amount ranging from less than one to almost 100 per cent. By making use of the textural class system, however, it is possible to consider soil texture on a rational basis, bringing together into groups those soils with textural characteristics in common.

Modifications of Textural Classes

When the textural class of a soil has been established, it is often useful to extend the class description to include features which modify the texture in one way or another. Special terms are used for this purpose.

ORGANIC SOILS

Some soils consist largely or entirely of organic matter, and the normal textural class names cannot be applied to them. They are described as *peat, muck, mucky peat* and *peaty muck*.

Peat is raw, undecomposed material; *muck* is well-decomposed material; *mucky peat* and *peaty muck* are intermediate materials. (Earlier definitions distinguished between peat and muck in terms of mineral content; peat contained less mineral matter than muck. This distinction is now regarded as irrelevant, as the mineral content of either may vary widely).

The term *mucky* is used as an adjective attached to the textural class name when describing horizons which contain a high proportion—e.g. 15 per cent – of partially-decomposed organic matter. Horizons described as "mucky loam" or "mucky silt loam" are intergrades between muck and the soil textural class

COARSE FRAGMENTS

The selection of size-ranges used in assessing soil texture was made on the basis of practical experience, and includes the particles known to exert a major influence on this aspect of soil properties. But the size limits are entirely arbitrary, and particles larger than the 2 mm. upper limit must be taken into account if a useful description of soil texture is to be made. This is done by adding appropriate adjectives to the textural class names.

Coarse fragments in the form of rounded particles of diameter greater than 2 mm. and less than 10 inches (or 15 inches along the longer axis, if flat) are regarded as a part of the soil mass. They influence moisture storage, infiltration and run-off; they affect root growth, especially by diluting the active mass of the soil; they protect the fine particles from being washed or blown away, and they are moved with the rest of the soil in tillage.

The presence of significant proportions of coarse fragments in a soil is indicated by modifying the textural class name. A soil whose scientific description is a *sandy loam*, for example, may be described as a *gravelly sandy loam* to indicate the presence of about 20 per cent or more of gravel in the whole soil mass. Adjectives added to the textural class name in this way become a part of the name, but it must be remembered that the basic soil textural name is determined from the size distribution of material below 2 mm. in diameter. The determination of the name is done *after* removal of material of greater diameter from the soil sample.

The accepted adjectives used in modifying textural class names are given in the table below. The adjectives listed in the third and fourth columns of the table are included in the textural class name when the soil contains significant proportions of the fragments, above 15 to 20 per cent by volume, depending on the other soil characteristics. These class names become parts of soil-type names.

When the coarse fragments make up 90 per cent or more of the soil mass in the upper 8 inches, the land is classified in the appropriate miscellaneous land type. If necessary, another sub-division can be made of the coarse fragments at about 50 per cent to give, for example, *gravelly loam* (20 to 50 per cent gravel) and *very gravelly loam*

NAMES USED FOR COARSE FRAGMENTS

Shape	Kind of fragment	Size and name of fragments		
Rounded and Subrounded	All kinds	Up to 3 inches diameter	3 to 10 inches diameter	More than 10 inches diameter
		Gravelly	Cobbly	Stony (or Bouldery)
Irregular, Angular	Chert	Cherty	Coarse	Stony
	Other than Chert	Angular Gravelly	Angular Cobbly	Stony
Thin, Flat		Up to 6 inches in length	6 – 15 inches in length	More than 15 inches in length
	Sandstone, Limestone, Schist	Channery	Flaggy	Stony
	Slate	Slaty	Flaggy	Stony
	Shale	Shaly	Flaggy	Stony

(50 to 90 per cent gravel). The other defined fragments may be described similarly.

The recommended terms to apply to soil containing above 15 to 20 per cent coarse fragments smaller than stones, and less than 90 per cent, are defined as follows:

CHANNERY: Soils contain fragments of thin, flat sandstone, limestone, or schist up to 6 inches along the longer axis. A single piece is a *fragment*.

CHERTY: Soils have angular fragments that are less than 3 inches in diameter, more than 75 per cent of which are chert: *coarse cherty* soils have fragments of 3 to 10 inches. Unless the size distinction is significant to the use capability of the soil, the *cherty* soil includes the whole range up to 10 inches. Most cherty soils are developed from weathered cherty limestone. A single piece is a *chert fragment*.

COBBLY: Soils have rounded or partially rounded fragments of rock ranging from 3 to 10 inches in diameter. *Angular cobbly*, formerly included as stony, is similar to cobbly except that fragments are not rounded. A single piece of either is a *cobblestone* or *small stone*.

FLAGGY: Soils contain relatively thin fragments 6 to 15 inches long of sandstone, limestone, slate, or shale, or, rarely, of schist. A single piece is a *flagstone*.

GRAVELLY: Soils have rounded or angular fragments, not prominently flattened, up to 3 inches in diameter. If 75 per cent or more of the fragments is chert, the soils are called *cherty*. In descriptions, soils with pebbles mostly over 2 inches in diameter may be called *coarsely gravelly* soils, and those with pebbles mostly under one-half inch in diameter may be called *finely gravelly* soils. An individual piece is a *pebble*. The term "gravel" refers to a mass of pebbles.

SHALY: Soils have flattened fragments of shale less than 6 inches along the longer axis. A single piece is a *shale fragment*.

RAINDROP BOMB.

PLATE 17

When raindrops fall on bare soil, they break up small clods and granules into small particles that are thrown into the air like the debris from a tiny bomb. These particles are easily carried along, even by slow-moving water.

Rain may move as much as 100 tons per acre in this way during a single storm; soil particles are lifted to a height of 2 feet, and may be thrown for distances of 5 feet or more.

Below : A heavy rainstorm beating on this field carried away about $\frac{5}{8}$ inch of topsoil. The little stone in the picture protected the soil underneath it from the raindrop blast – *U.S.D.A.*

SURFACE CRUSTS.

When rain falls on the surface of the soil, it separates the fine particles which accumulate and fill the spaces between larger particles and granules. This results in a crust on the surface which tends to prevent water from soaking readily into the soil. If the soil is sloping, the water will run off, causing erosion.

By covering the soil with a mulch of straw, grass, wood shavings or other material of this sort, the surface is protected from the impact of raindrops, and water is able to soak into the soil more effectively.

This can be shown by the simple experiment above. The vessel on the left contains soil with an unprotected surface, and the vessel on the right contains the same soil covered by a thin layer of a straw mulch. Water is poured onto the two vessels from a sprinkler, and it flows more readily through the protected soil than through the bare soil.

Right : Crusts more than an inch thick are not un-common – *U.S.D.A.*

PLATE 18

SLATY: Soils contain fragments of slate less than 6 inches along the longer axis. A single piece is a *slate fragment*.

STONY: Soils contain rock fragments larger than 10 inches in diameter, if rounded, and longer than 15 inches along the longer axis, if flat.

STONINESS AND ROCKINESS

Stones larger than 10 inches in diameter, and rock outcrops, are not regarded as part of the soil mass as defined by soil textural classes. They have an important bearing on soil use, however, because of their interference with the use of agricultural machinery and their dilution of the soil mass. Often, soils which could respond well to management will remain unused because stoniness renders them difficult to cultivate.

Stoniness and rockiness are described by modifying the soil *type* name, distinctions within a soil type being *phases* which may be indicated by a descriptive term. Gloucester loam with a preponderance of stones, for example, will become Gloucester loam, stony phase, or Gloucester loam, very stony phase. In practice, an adjectival description is used to streamline the terms, e.g. Gloucester stony loam, or Gloucester very stony loam respectively.

Stoniness refers to the relative proportion of stones over 10 inches in diameter in or on the soil.

Classes of stoniness are outlined as follows:

Class 0: No stones or too few to interfere with tillage. Stones cover less than 0.01 per cent of the area.

Class 1: Sufficient stones to interfere with tillage but not to make intertilled crops impracticable. (If stones are 1 foot in diameter and about 30 to 100 feet apart they occupy about 0.01 to 0.1 per cent of the surface, and there are about 0.15 to 1.5 cubic yards per acre-foot.)

Class 2: Sufficient stones to make tillage of intertilled

K

crops impracticable, but the soil can be worked for hay crops or improved pasture if other soil characteristics are favourable. (If stones are 1 foot in diameter and about 5 to 30 feet apart, they occupy about 0.1 to 3 per cent of the surface, and there are about 1.5 to 50 cubic yards per acre-foot.)

Class 3: Sufficient stones to make all use of machinery impracticable, except for very light machinery or hand tools where other soil characteristics are especially favourable for improved pasture. Soils with this class of stoniness may have some use for wild pasture or forests, depending on other soil characteristics. (If stones are 1 foot in diameter and about 2.5 to 5 feet apart, they occupy about 3 to 15 per cent of the surface, and there are about 50 to 240 yards per acre-foot.)

Class 4: Sufficient stones to make all use of machinery impracticable; the land may have some value for poor pasture or for forestry. (If stones are 1 foot in diameter and are about 2.5 feet or less apart, they occupy 15 to 90 per cent of the surface, and there are more than about 240 cubic yards per acre-foot.)

Class 5: Land essentially paved with stones that occupy more than 90 per cent of the exposed surface (Rubble).

Rockiness refers to the relative proportion of bedrock exposures, either rock outcrops or patches of soil too thin over bedrock for use. Classes of rockiness are as follows:

Class 0: No bedrock exposures or too few to interfere with tillage. Less than 2 per cent bedrock exposed.

Class 1: Sufficient bedrock exposures to interfere with tillage but not to make intertilled crops impracticable. Depending upon how the pattern affects tillage, rock exposures are roughly 100 to 300 feet apart and cover about 2 to 10 per cent of the surface.

Class 2: Sufficient bedrock exposures to make tillage

of intertilled crops impracticable, but soil can be worked for hay crops or improved pasture if the other soil characteristics are favourable. Rock exposures are roughly 30 to 100 feet apart and cover about 10 to 25 per cent of the surface, depending upon the pattern.

Class 3: Sufficient rock outcrop to make all use of machinery impracticable, except for light machinery where other soil characteristics are especially favourable for improved pasture. May have some use for wild pasture or forests, depending on the other soil characteristics. Rock exposures, or patches of soil too thin over rock for use, are roughly 10 to 30 feet apart and cover about 25 to 50 per cent of the surface, depending upon the pattern.

Class 4: Sufficient rock outcrop (or of very thin soil over rock) to make all use of machinery impracticable. The land may have some value for poor pasture of for forestry. Rock outcrops are about 10 feet apart or less and cover some 50 to 90 per cent of the area.

Class 5: Land for which over 90 per cent of the surface is exposed bedrock (Rock outcrop).

SOIL STRUCTURE

Soil *texture* is determined by the proportion of individual particles of differing size-ranges in a soil; soil *structure* is the manner in which the individual particles are held together into aggregates.

If the individual particles of a soil did not hold together in clusters or aggregates, the soil would be a formless powdery mass, like sand on the seashore. In most soils, however, the particles form aggregates of recognizable size, shape and strength, and the nature of these aggregates is of immense importance in determining the productivity of a soil.

The ability of any soil to produce crops efficiently depends at least as much on its structure as on its nutrients. Soils with aggregates of spheroidal shape, for example, have more pore space between individual aggregates; they are more permeable, and are more productive than soils of comparable fertility that have a massive structure.

Sometimes, soils are overgranulated. The well-developed spheroidal aggregates of latosols, for example, may result in a low water-holding capacity. The contacts between roots and soil are too few, and the soils – though rich in plant nutrients – may be unproductive.

The ideal structure in a soil, for most purposes, is the crumb-like structure that is typical of an old well-culti-vated garden. The individual particles are held together in stable crumbs that have sufficient strength and stability to withstand digging, ploughing and other cultivation tech-niques. Soils with this crumb-like structure are easy to work, permeable and yet moisture-retaining. They provide an excellent medium for the growing plant, which can thrust its roots into the soil without difficulty, and sustain ample contacts with the soil particles from which it obtains so much of its nutrients. The crumbs in this type of soil are large enough to avoid being whisked away in the wind, and are not readily carried off by running water.

Natural and Artificial Aggregates

Individual soil particles may be held together as aggre-gates in a number of ways, some natural and others artificial.

PED. Natural aggregates of soil particles are called *peds*. Each individual crumb in a fertile garden soil, for example, is a ped. It is sufficiently stable to resist disin-tegrating readily in water.

CLOD. This is an aggregate that is created artificially, for example by ploughing or digging. The soil is moulded by pressure into a transient mass that usually

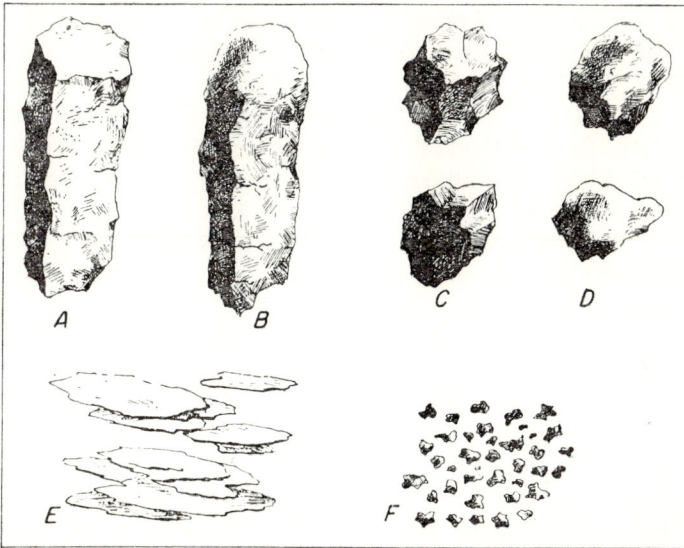

Soil Structure. These drawings illustrate some of the types of soil structure: A, prismatic; B, columnar; C, angular blocky; D, subangular blocky; E, platy; F, granular.

disintegrates easily in water. Clay soils form clods if they are dug when wet.

FRAGMENT. When a ped breaks, a *fragment* is formed.

CONCRETION. This is an aggregate formed by salts which have been deposited in the soil, cementing particles together.

Terms used in Soil Structure

In describing the structure of a soil, three features are considered:

(1) *Type.* The shape and arrangement of the peds.
(2) *Class.* The size of the peds.
(3) *Grade.* The distinctness and durability of the peds.

TYPE. (Shape and Arrangement of Peds.)

There are four primary types of structure:

(1) *Platy.* The peds are flat and plate-like.

(2) *Prismlike.* The peds are in the form of columns with flat vertical sides. There are two sub types: *prismatic,* without rounded ends, and *columnar,* with rounded caps.

(3) *Blocklike* (Polyhedral). The peds are nutlike, with flat or rounded surfaces shaped by pressure with adjoining peds.

There are two sub types: *angular blocky,* bounded by planes intersecting at sharp angles, and *subangular blocky,* having mixed rounded and plane faces with vertices mostly rounded.

(4) *Spheroidal* (Polyhedral). The peds are roughly spheroidal, with irregular surfaces that are not shaped by pressure with adjoining peds. There are two sub types: *granular,* which is relatively nonporous, and *crumb,* very porous.

Note: The following terms are sometimes used in describing a type of soil structure:

> *Nut.*　　　Blocklike peds.
> *Nuciform.*　Subangular blocky.

CLASS. (Size of Peds)

Five size classes are recognized in each of the primary types. The size limits vary with the four types, as shown on page 289. They are described generally as:

1. Very fine or very thin.
2. Fine or Thin.
3. Medium.
4. Coarse or thick.
5. Very coarse or very thick.

GRADE. (Degree of Distinctness and Durability).

Terms used for grade of structure are as follows:

0. *Structureless.* There is no aggregation to be seen, and consequently no peds. This grade may include free-running sand (small grain), or plastic clay (massive).

1. *Weak.* Peds are poorly formed – they break easily when disturbed, forming much unaggregated material.

2. *Moderate.* Peds are fairly well formed and moderately durable. Soil breaks readily into entire peds, with little unaggregated material.

Examples: loam A horizons of typical Chestnut soils in the granular type, and clayey B horizons of such Red-Yellow Podzolic soils as the Boswell in the blocky type.

3. *Strong.* Well-formed, durable peds which adhere weakly to one another, and withstand displacement to become separated when soil disturbed. Few broken peds and little or no unaggregated material may be subdivided into *moderately strong* and *very strong.*

Examples: granular-type A horizons of the typical Chernozem, and columnar-type B horizons of the typical solodized-Solonetz.

NOMENCLATURE

When a soil structure is being named, the sequence followed is (1) grade (2) class, and (3) type. A soil structure in which, for example, the peds are loosely packed, roundish but not very porous, between 1 and 2 mm. diameter, and quite distinct would be described as *strong fine granular.*

Many soils have a compound structure in which small peds are held together as larger peds. They are described accordingly, e.g. *compound moderate very coarse prismatic and moderate medium granular.*

SOIL CONSISTENCE

This is a combination of soil properties that determines the soil's resistance to crushing, and its ability to be moulded or changed in shape. It depends mainly on the forces of attraction between soil particles.

Consistence is described with reference to three standard moisture contents (dry, moist and wet). The terms used are as follows:

1. **Consistence when Wet**

Determined at or slightly above field capacity.

A. STICKINESS. This is the quality of adhesion to other objects. The soil is pressed between thumb and finger, and its adherence noted. Degrees of stickiness are described as follows:

0. *Nonsticky.* After release of pressure, practically no soil material adheres to thumb or fingers.

1. *Slightly Sticky.* After pressure, soil material adheres to both thumb and finger, but comes off one or the other rather cleanly. It is not appreciably stretched when the digits are separated.

2. *Sticky.* After pressure, soil material adheres to both thumb and finger, and tends to stretch somewhat and pull apart rather than pulling free from either digit.

3. *Very Sticky.* After pressure, soil material adheres strongly to both thumb and forefinger, and is decidedly stretched when they are separated.

B. PLASTICITY. This is the ability to change shape continuously under the influence of an applied stress, and to retain the impressed shape on removal of the stress. The soil material is rolled between thumb and finger, to note whether or not a wire or thin rod of soil can be formed. The following terms are used to describe the degree of plasticity:

0. *Nonplastic.* No wire is formable.

1. *Slightly Plastic.* Wire formable but soil mass easily deformable.

2. *Plastic.* Wire formable and moderate pressure required for deformation of soil mass.

TYPES AND CLASSES OF SOIL STRUCTURE

Class	TYPE (Shape and arrangement of peds)						
	Platelike with one dimension (the vertical) limited and greatly less than the other two; arranged around a horizontal plane; faces mostly horizontal.	Prismlike with two dimensions (the horizontal) limited and considerably less than the vertical; arranged around a vertical line; vertical faces well defined; vertices angular.		Blocklike; polyhedronlike, or spheroidal, with three dimensions of the same order of magnitude, arranged around a point.			
				Blocklike; blocks or polyhedrons having plane or curved surfaces that are casts of the molds formed by the faces of the surrounding peds.		Spheroids or polyhedrons having plane or curved surfaces which have slight or no accommodation to the faces of surrounding peds.	
		Without rounded caps.	With rounded caps.	Faces flattened; most vertices sharply angular.	Mixed rounded and flattened faces with many rounded vertices.	Relatively non-porous peds.	Porous peds.
	Platy	Prismatic	Columnar	(Angular) Blocky [1]	Subangular blocky [2]	Granular	Crumb
y fine or ery thin.	Very thin platy; <1 mm.	Very fine prismatic; <10 mm.	Very fine columnar; <10 mm.	Very fine angular blocky; <5 mm.	Very fine subangular blocky; <5 mm.	Very fine granular; <1 mm.	Very fine crumb; <1 mm.
e or thin.	Thin platy; 1 to 2 mm.	Fine prismatic; 10 to 20 mm.	Fine columnar; 10 to 20 mm.	Fine angular blocky; 5 to 10 mm.	Fine subangular blocky; 5 to 10 mm.	Fine granular; 1 to 2 mm.	Fine crumb; 1 to 2 mm.
dium.	Medium platy; 2 to 5 mm.	Medium prismatic; 20 to 50 mm.	Medium columnar; 20 to 50 mm.	Medium angular blocky; 10 to 20 mm.	Medium subangular blocky; 10 to 20 mm.	Medium granular; 2 to 5 mm.	Medium crumb; 2 to 5 mm.
rse or thick.	Thick platy; 5 to 10 mm.	Coarse prismatic; 50 to 100 mm.	Coarse columnar; 50 to 100 mm.	Coarse angular blocky; 20 to 50 mm.	Coarse subangular blocky; 20 to 50 mm.	Coarse granular; 5 to 10 mm.	
y coarse or ery thick.	Very thick platy; >10 mm.	Very coarse prismatic; >100 mm.	Very coarse columnar; >100 mm.	Very coarse angular blocky; >50 mm.	Very coarse subangular blocky; >50 mm.	Very coarse granular; >10 mm.	

[1] (a) Sometimes called nut. (b) The word "angular" in the name can ordinarily be omitted.
[2] Sometimes called nuciform, nut, or rubangular nut. Fince the size connotation of these terms is a source of great confusion to many, they are not recommended.

3. *Very Plastic.* Wire formable and much pressure required for deformation of soil mass.

2. Consistence when Moist

Determined at moisture content approximately midway between air dry and field capacity. A mass of soil is selected which appears slightly moist, and it is crushed in the hand. The following terms are used:

0. *Loose.* Noncoherent.

1. *Very Friable.* Soil material crushes under very gentle pressure but coheres when pressed together.

2. *Friable.* Soil material crushes easily under gentle to moderate pressure between thumb and forefinger, and coheres when pressed together.

3. *Firm.* Soil material crushes under moderate pressure between thumb and forefinger but resistance is distinctly noticeable.

K*

4. *Very Firm.* Soil material crushes under strong pressure; barely crushable between thumb and forefinger.

5. *Extremely Firm.* Soil material crushes only under very strong pressure; cannot be crushed between thumb and forefinger and must be broken apart bit by bit.

Note: the term *compact* denotes a combination of firm consistence and close packing or arrangement of particles, and should be used only in this sense. It can be given "degrees" by use of "very" and "extremely".

3. Consistence when Dry

The consistence of soil materials when dry is characterized by rigidity, brittleness, maximum resistance to pressure, more or less tendency to crush to a powder or to fragments with rather sharp edges, and inability of crushed material to cohere again when pressed together. An air-dry mass is selected and crushed in the hand. The following terms are used:

0. *Loose.* Noncoherent.

1. *Soft.* Soil mass is very weakly coherent and fragile; breaks to powder or individual grains under very slight pressure.

2. *Slightly Hard.* Weakly resistant to pressure; easily broken between thumb and forefinger.

3. *Hard.* Moderately resistant to pressure. Can be broken in the hands without difficulty, but is barely breakable between thumb and forefinger.

4. *Very Hard.* Very resistant to pressure. Can be broken in the hands only with difficulty. Not breakable between thumb and forefinger.

5. *Extremely Hard.* Extremely resistant to pressure. Cannot be broken in the hands.

4. Cementation

This refers to a hard, brittle consistence caused by some cementing substance other than clay minerals, e.g. calcium carbonate, silica or oxides or salts of iron and aluminium. The cementation is usually unaffected by moistening; the hardness and brittleness persist when it is wet. If cementation *is* greatly altered by wetting, this should be stated in the description.

The following terms are used:

1. *Weakly Cemented.* The cemented mass is brittle and hard but can be broken in the hands.

2. *Strongly Cemented.* Cemented mass is brittle and harder than can be broken in the hand, but is easily broken with a hammer.

3. *Indurated.* Very strongly cemented; brittle, does not soften under prolonged wetting, and is so extremely hard that for breakage a sharp blow with a hammer is required; the hammer generally rings as a result of the blow.

PORES AND POROSITY

All soils contain solid particles in a variety of shapes, sizes and distribution, between which are spaces or pores. Under normal field conditions, the pores are filled either with water or air, the relative amounts fluctuating continually with conditions and circumstances.

Water and air complement each other in the pore spaces. As water drains away, air replaces it, and vice versa. Both are needed by the plants and micro-organisms in a soil, and in a fertile soil adequate amounts of each are available as required.

Pores exist between (a) the grains and (b) the aggregates in a soil, and the nature and extent of the pore spaces are determined by the texture and structure of the soil. Sandy soils have large pore spaces between the individual grains, but the total pore space is lower than in clayey soils.

Fine-textured soils have more total pore space, but many of the pores are small.

These differences affect the water-holding capacities of soils. Water will flow readily through the large pores of a sandy soil, even though the proportion of pore space is relatively low.

In a fine-textured soil, many of the pores are very small, and water cannot move as freely through them. A clayey soil does not drain as rapidly as a sandy one.

HORIZON BOUNDARIES

The boundaries between horizons in a soil may vary (1) in distinctness, and (2) in the topography or shape of the horizon surfaces.

Distinctness

Some boundaries are clear and sharp, such as those between the A_2 and B_2 horizons in well-developed Podzols. Again, they may be diffuse, with one horizon merging into another, as between the A_1 and A_3 of a Chernozem, or the B_2 and B_3 of many Latosols.

The characteristic widths of boundaries between soil horizons may be described as:

    (1) *abrupt* – if less than 1 inch wide
    (2) *clear* – if about 1 to 2½ inches wide
    (3) *gradual* – if 2½ to 5 inches wide
    (4) *diffuse* – if more than 5 inches wide.

Topography

Observations of soil horizons are commonly made from profiles, but it must be remembered that the horizons are three-dimensional layers. They may vary greatly in shape and regularity.

The topography of horizon boundaries is described in the following terms:

    (1) *Smooth* – if nearly a plane
    (2) *Wavy* or *undulating* – if pockets are wider than their depth
    (3) *Irregular* – if irregular pockets are deeper than their width
    (4) *Broken* – if parts of the horizon are unconnected with other parts.

On the other hand, the larger pores of the sandy soil do not hold water so readily as the small pores in a fine-textured soil; the sandy soil does not retain so much water for use by the plant.

In a well-structured soil, water will drain away quickly to the water table, or to the drainage tiles. Yet the soil will hold back enough water to meet the requirements of crops that grow in it. This ideal is achieved by creating a crumb or aggregated structure in the soil. Between the aggregates are pore spaces large enough to allow excess water to drain away. And within the aggregates are small pores between the grains, which hold supplies of moisture against the force of gravity.

This desirable structure is achieved by proper cultivation and management. In temperate zones, aggregation depends very largely upon colloidal materials of the humus, which act as a gum that holds soil particles together. In tropical regions, sesquioxides and silica are important aggregating agents.

Particle Density

This is a measure of the density of the solid particles of the soil. It is not affected by the extent or nature of the pore space.

The particle density is the weight per unit volume of soil particles, commonly expressed as grams per cubic centimetre. Most soils have a particle density in the region of 2.65 g./c.c.

Bulk Density

This is the density of the total soil, including the pore space. It is the weight per unit volume of soil in its natural physical condition.

Fine textured soils have a bulk density in the region of 1.0 – 1.6; coarse textured soils, about 1.2 – 1.7.

Weight of Soil

The weight of a soil varies considerably with conditions. The plough-layer of an acre of fine-textured soil, to a depth of 6½ to 7 inches, weighs about 2,000,000 pounds when dry. Coarse textured soils are a little heavier; organic soils are much lighter, weighing only about 1,000,000 pounds to the acre.

Porosity

This is the percentage of pore space in the soil. It may be determined from the bulk density and the particle density, as follows:

$$\text{Porosity (\%)} = 100 - \left(\frac{\text{Bulk Density}}{\text{Particle Density}} \times 100 \right)$$

Porosity varies between 30 to 50 per cent in normal dry soils.

SOIL MOISTURE

The chemical activities that make up life take place in water. Every living thing, plant or animal, consists largely of water; and without an adequate supply of water, no animal or plant can stay alive for long.

All crop plants need an ample supply of water if they are to flourish, and they obtain this water from the soil. Much of the effort we put into our cultivation of the soil is concerned with providing water needed by the growing plant.

Under natural conditions, water reaches the soil as rain or other forms of precipitation. Some flows away over the surface, finding its way via streams and rivers to the sea, much of the rest soaks into the soil; this is the water from which the plant obtains its supplies.

If rain fell steadily and evenly over the earth's land surface, the soil would automatically provide plants with a regular supply of water. But rainfall is spasmodic, and varies greatly in quantity from one part of the world to another. In some regions, the intervals between rainy periods may extend for weeks or even months.

A soil under cultivation must be able to absorb and retain sufficient water to provide for the plant's needs throughout its growing period.

Gravitation Water

When rainwater soaks into the soil, it flows down through the pores and channels separating the particles and aggregates of solid material. This water is flowing under the force of gravity, and it is commonly described as *gravitation water.*

As it passes through different horizons of the soil, gravitation water dissolves chemicals which have been released by weathering and decay. It also carries away fine particles of clay and humus, perhaps to deposit them again in a lower horizon.

The depth to which the water flows will depend upon the nature of the soil drainage. On a sloping hillside, for example, water may flow through the soil until it reaches a sloping layer of impervious rock or clay. It will flow along the top of the layer until eventually it bubbles from the hillside as a spring.

The lie of the land may be such that water is held at a certain level beneath the soil. This depth is the *water table*; it may be many feet down, or only a matter of inches beneath the surface. If the water table is on or slightly above the surface, water will lie on the soil to form a bog.

Most of the plants we cultivate as food crops need air to support the respiration processes of their cells. If the soil is waterlogged, air cannot reach the roots, and the plants will not flourish. Moreover, organic matter and mineral substances decompose under these conditions to form substances which may be poisonous to plants. The

COLOUR PATTERNS

A soil profile consists usually of several horizons which differ in colour, and a description of the colour of each horizon is an essential part of the assessment of a soil.

A single horizon may be uniform in colour, or it may be streaked, spotted, variegated or mottled in many ways. Local accumulations of lime or organic matter may produce a spotted appearance. Streaks or tongues of colour may result from the seepage of dissolved materials or fine particles from overlying horizons.

Some combinations of mottled colours, mainly grays and browns, indicate impeded drainage. Other mottled effects result from different causes.

Mottling in soils is described by noting the colour of the matrix (i.e. the main soil mass), and the colour or colours of the principal mottles, and the pattern of the mottling.

1. COLOURS

These may be assessed and defined in the usual descriptive terms.

2. PATTERNS

These are conveniently described in terms of contrast, abundance and size.

A. *Contrast* Contrast may be described as *faint, distinct* or *prominent* as follows:

Faint Indistinct mottles are evident and recognizable only on close examination. Soil colours in matrix and mottles are closely related.

Distinct Although not striking, the mottles are readily seen. The pattern may be one of a continuous matrix with mottles or one of mixtures of two or more colours.

Prominent The conspicuous mottles are obvious and mottling is an outstanding feature of the horizon. The pattern may be one of a continuous matrix with contrasting mottles or one of mixtures of two or more colours.

B. *Abundance* Abundance of mottles may be indicated in three general classes as few, common or many as follows:

Few Mottles occupy less than about 2 percent of the exposed surface.

Common Mottles occupy about 2 to 20 percent of the exposed surface.

Many Mottles occupy more than 20 percent of the exposed surface. This last class may be further sub-divided according to whether (a) the mottles are set in a definite matrix, or (b) there is no clear matrix colour.

C. *Size* Three relative size classes are described as follows: —

Fine Mottles less than 5 mm. in diameter along the greatest dimension.

Medium Mottles range between 5 and 15 mm. in diameter along the greatest dimension.

Coarse Mottles are greater than 15 mm. in diameter along the greatest dimension

NOMENCLATURE

In defining the colour patterns of a soil horizon, mottling may be conveniently described in the sequence abundance, size, contrast and colour for example " . . . brown silt loam with few, fine, distinct reddish-brown and dark-gray mottles. . . . "

Note : In assessing soil colours, aggregates should be broken to find out whether the colour is uniform throughout. The colours of granules may be due to a thin coating which differs from the colour of the mass of soil within. The colour of a soil commonly changes with the moisture content, and it is usual to describe the colour of a moist soil.

supply of nutrient chemicals is diminished, and ion-exchange cannot operate effectively on the particle surface.

Water requires five times as much heat to raise it one degree in temperature as dry soil. A poorly-drained soil is slow to warm up in the spring.

If a soil is to be healthy and fertile, excess water must drain freely from it, allowing air to enter the spaces between the crumbs and particles. The water table must be at an adequate depth, and the soil itself must be sufficiently porous to allow water to flow through it.

If the natural water table is too high, it may be lowered by efficient drainage. Lack of proper drainage is one of the most common defects of agricultural land.

The permeability of the soil itself depends upon its texture and structure. Coarse soils of sandy texture have larger spaces between the particles than silty or clayey soils; water is able to move more freely through the larger spaces, and a sandy soil will often drain more readily than a soil of finer texture.

The structure of the soil plays an equally important role. Water flows freely through the channels between the aggregates in soil of good structure, even though the soil forming the aggregates is of fine texture.

Capillary Water

If all the water was able to drain away freely through pores and channels, the soil would be unable to hold reserves of water for the future needs of growing crops. All the water of the soil would be gravitation water.

In fact, some water remains as a film that coats the soil particles. It is held on the surface of the particles by forces of adhesion exerted between the soil material and the molecules of water, and the forces of cohesion exerted between the molecules of water themselves.

Water in the surface film, and in the wedge-shaped spaces between particles, is subject to capillary forces.

These are the forces associated with surface tension, which cause a liquid to rise up a narrow tube. Water held on the surface of soil particles will move against the pull of gravity under the influence of capillary forces; it is commonly called *capillary water*.

Capillary water is the source on which plants rely for their supplies of water. Gravity water contributes little directly to the plant, serving primarily to keep the capillary water "topped up". Root hairs of the plant lie in the layer of capillary water, stimulating the ion-exchange processes that release nutrient chemicals from the particle surfaces.

As capillary water is absorbed by plant roots, fresh supplies flow in to restore the film. Capillary movements of this sort will carry water upwards through the soil, the distance depending upon the fineness of the pores and the continuity of the film.

In a sandy soil, the movement may be restricted to a matter of inches. But in a fine-textured silty soil, capillary water may be lifted through a hundred feet or more.

Capillary effects play a part in maintaining a supply of water to the roots of plants. But the movement is so slow, particularly in soils of fine texture, that it is doubtful whether they play a really important role. The capillary layers are replenished very largely from water reaching the surface of the soil.

If capillary water is absorbed faster than fresh supplies are coming in, the film of moisture will become thinner, and the flow of water through the film will be restricted. In time, a point is reached at which the root hairs cannot overcome the forces holding the last remaining film of moisture onto the particle surfaces. The plant will wilt, even though there is still a supply of moisture in the soil.

Most of this "last ditch" moisture may be removed by evaporation, leaving only the ultimate residue of *hygro-scopic water* clinging to the particles.

As capillary water is held in the soil by surface forces,

the amount of water retained by a soil depends to a large extent on its texture and organic content. Clay and humus provide colloidal particles with vast areas of surface, and soils which are rich in clay or humus will hold more water than sandy soils deficient in humus.

On the other hand, the extra water in a fine textured soil, or a soil rich in organic matter, adds to the heat capacity of the soil. A moist soil takes a long time to heat up in spring. It is colder and later than a sandy soil which holds less moisture.

Conserving Water Supplies

In every part of the world, even in the humid regions, agriculture could benefit from additional reserves of water. This may be achieved by adding to the natural supplies, for example, by irrigation. Or it may be done by making more effective use of the water that is supplied by nature.

Only a very small proportion of the water that falls as rain is made available to plants. Some of it is lost immediately by run-off, finding its way back to the sea in streams and rivers. Much of the water that soaks into the soil is lost by drainage, or by evaporation from the soil surface.

In recent years, much progress has been made in controlling run-off water, with a view to preventing erosion and making more efficient use of available water supplies. Contour ploughing, for example, creates shallow terraces that hold the water, preventing it from flowing away rapidly downhill.

The maintenance of a good soil structure, using all available supplies of organic matter, increases the amount of water that is absorbed and held for use by crops.

When soil is dug or ploughed, the area exposed to the air is increased, and water evaporates more readily from the rough surface. Cultivation and tillage may result in loss of soil moisture in this way. But the evaporation of moisture is more rapid than the replenishment of water by capillary action, and the layer of dry soil on the surface protects the rest of the soil from losing moisture. It is a natural mulch (see page 100).

A densely packed, compacted clayey surface, on the other hand, carries capillary water to the surface, where it will evaporate steadily into the air.

The value of tillage in water-conservation extends also to the filling of cracks which form as the earth dries. Considerable quantities of water are lost by evaporation from fissures that are formed in this way.

Weeds, too, are kept down by tillage of cultivated ground, preventing loss of water by transpiration through the weeds.

Mulches are often used to protect the soil from evaporation losses. Almost any material may be used for covering the ground to provide a mulch, including peat, sawdust, straw, compost, manure and other organic materials. The mulch lies like a blanket on the surface soil, protecting it from the sun's rays and from the drying wind. When rain comes, a mulched soil is ready to absorb water which would not be able to make its way into a sun-baked soil.

13

Acidity and Nutrients

SOIL ACIDITY

When we speak of anything being "acid", in ordinary everyday terms, we think of it as something with a sharp, sour taste. But in scientific terms, "acid" has a much more precise meaning. An acid is a substance which dissolves in water with the formation of hydrogen ions. An "alkali", on the other hand, is a substance which dissolves to form hydroxyl ions.

The water molecule – H_2O – consists of two atoms of hydrogen linked with one of oxygen. Under normal circumstances, some of the molecules separate into two electrically charged particles, or ions; a hydrogen ion, H^+, carrying a positive electric charge (i.e. a cation) and a hydroxyl ion, OH^-, consisting of the remaining hydrogen and oxygen atoms linked together, which carries a negative electric charge (i.e. an anion).

In pure water, only a small proportion of all the molecules is ionized in this way; the bulk of the water remains as molecules. The number of hydrogen ions produced by the ionized water equals the number of hydroxyl ions, and the water as a whole is electrically neutral.

Some substances, when they dissolve in water, ionize to form hydrogen ions; the solution which results has more hydrogen ions than hydroxyl ions, and this in an *acid solution*. The substance that ionizes to form hydrogen ions in this way is an *acid*. Hydrochloric acid (HCl), for example, ionizes to hydrogen ions, H^+ and chlorine ions, Cl^-.

Conversely, some substances dissolve in water and ionize to form hydroxyl ions; the solution that results has more hydroxyl ions than hydrogen ions, and this is an *alkaline (or basic) solution*. The substance that ionizes to form hydroxyl ions in this way is an *alkali* (or *base*).

The pH Scale

The degree of acidity (or alkalinity) of a solution can be expressed in terms of the concentration of hydrogen ions. For this purpose, it is convenient to use the notation described as pH, which is merely a shorthand method of indicating hydrogen ion concentration by a number on a scale which extends from 0 to 14.

At pH7, midpoint in the scale, the concentration of hydrogen ions equals the concentration of hydroxyl ions, and the solution is neutral (i.e. neither acid nor alkaline).

pH values *less than* 7 indicate an excess of hydrogen ions, and the solution is *acid*. The acidity increases as the pH values get smaller. pH values *greater than* 7 indicate an excess of hydroxyl ions, and the solution is *alkaline*. As the pH value increases, the alkalinity increases.

The pH scale is based on logarithms of the concentration of hydrogen ions, and this means that the concentration increases or decreases 10 times in moving from one pH figure to the next figure on the scale. A solution of pH 5 has 10 times the hydrogen ion concentration of a solution of pH 6. A solution of pH 4 has 10 times more hydrogen ions than one of pH 5 (i.e. 100 times more than pH 6).

Soil Solution Acidity

Many substances are dissolved in water forming the soil solution. The concentration of hydrogen ions (i.e. acidity) varies over a considerable pH range, and many factors influence it.

Most soils in the temperate regions have a pH of between 4 and 8, i.e. ranging from acid (pH 4) through the neutral point (pH 7) to slightly alkaline (pH 8). Some soils, however, may be so acid that they reach pH 3.5, whereas others are so alkaline that they reach pH 9 or 10.

The hydrogen ions in a soil exist in many different chemical combinations, and are to be found not only in the soil solution, but on the surface of the colloidal particles of clay and humus. They form part of the escort of exchangeable ions that are attracted to and held by the negatively charged colloid particles.

The number of hydrogen ions in the soil solution is usually quite small by comparison with those that are held in less active form in various molecules (non-ionized) and on the surfaces of colloidal particles.

The total acidity of a soil is made up of two parts. One, the *active acidity,* consists of hydrogen ions in the soil solution. The other, *potential acidity,* consists of hydrogen ions held in various chemical combinations, and exchangeable ions adsorbed on the surface of colloidal particles.

When we estimate the pH of a soil solution, we are measuring only the active acidity; the pH figure, as such, gives no indication of potential acidity.

The potential acidity acts as a reserve supply of hydrogen ions. If free hydrogen ions are removed from the soil solution, hydrogen ions from potential acidity sources enter the solution to restore the balance. Measures taken to reduce the acidity of a soil by lowering the concentration of hydrogen ions must be planned on the basis of total acidity, rather than pH of the soil solution.

What changes Soil pH?

Most agricultural soils tends to be acid rather than alkaline, i.e. with a pH of less than 7 rather than greater than 7, especially in humid regions of the earth. This is largely the result of leaching by water that has percolated through the soil.

The colloidal particles of soil parent materials are commonly saturated with exchangeable cations such as calcium and magnesium. But through centuries of soil development, hydrogen ions carried downward by rainwater have replaced calcium and magnesium ions held by the colloidal particles. Calcium and magnesium are carried away by water that drains from the soil (see page 310).

This replacement of calcium and magnesium by hydrogen ions from water is a slow process. But soil development takes place over many centuries.

In general, the more water there is moving through the soil, the faster is the leaching process that removes calcium and magnesium. For this reason, soils of humid regions are usually more acid than those of subhumid regions; soils in arid regions are seldom acid.

When agriculture has become established on a soil, calcium and magnesium are also absorbed into the growing crops. They are essential nutrient elements, and are required in considerable amounts. Supplies of the elements are released from colloidal particles in exchange for hydrogen ions released by carbonic acid produced by the plant roots. This contributes to the gradual devolpment of soil acidity.

Some artificial fertilizers, including ammonium sulphate, add to the acidity of the soil. The increasing use of fertilizers is an important factor in this respect in modern agriculture.

Acidity and Plant Growth

A series of experiments was carried out by Dr. D. I. Arnon and his colleagues in California, with the object of discovering the effect of pH on plant growth. Plants were provided with all the nutrient chemicals they needed, but the solutions were maintained at different pH's.

The results were, in some ways, unexpected; all the plants grew well, except those grown under conditions of extreme acidity or alkalinity. Between pH 4 and pH 9,

CORN — 80 Bushels Grain

WHEAT — 40 Bushels Grain

OATS — 70 Bushels Grain

RYE — 30 Bushels Grain

SOYBEANS — 30 Bushels Seed

0   1   2   3   4   5
POUNDS

5,200 Pounds Stover

4,000 Pounds Straw

2,400 Pounds Straw

3,300 Pounds Straw

3,600 Pounds Straw

Alfalfa Hay 1 Ton

Red Clover 1 Ton

Lespedeza 1 Ton

Timothy 1 Ton

0   10   20   30
POUNDS

Calcium and Magnesium Removed in Crops

Calcium

Magnesium

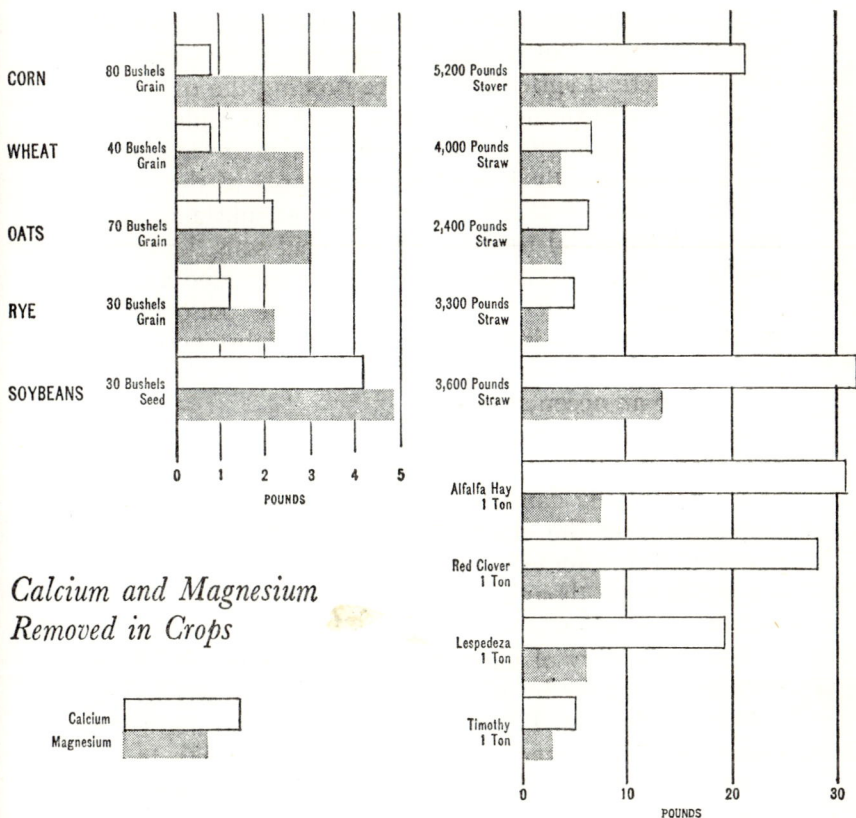

Note: Losses of calcium and magnesium vary with climate, soil permeability, soil acidity, fertility and cropping practices.

acidity did not appear to affect plant growth to any significant extent.

On the face of it, this appears to indicate that soil acidity is not an important factor in plant growth. But in fact, this is not so. In Dr. Arnon's experiments, the plants were provided with all the nutrients they required. And *under these conditions*, acidity did not have a noticeable influence, except at the extremes of the pH range.

In some soils
Practical
Horticulture.

It is now accepted that the *direct* effect of pH on plant growth is small. But soil acidity plays a vitally important role in practical agriculture, by controlling the quantities of nutrient chemicals which are made available to the plant. The solubility and availability of many important nutrients are greatly influenced by the pH of the soil.

In addition, pH affects the 'solubility of substances' that can be detrimental to the plant. In acid soils, ions such as aluminium, iron, manganese, copper and zinc may be present in quantities sufficient to become poisonous to plants. As the soil is neutralized, these substances form oxides and hydroxides, and the concentration of ions is reduced to an acceptable level.

If the pH is increased still further until neutral point is exceeded, and the solution becomes alkaline, the solubility of the potentially damaging ions may become so low that a deficiency of the elements occurs. Iron, copper, manganese and zinc, for example, are required in small amounts by plants, even though they are detrimental if present in high concentrations.

The 'availability of phosphorus,' one of the elements required in quantity by plants, is influenced greatly by the acidity of the soil. Phosphates applied as fertilizers will commonly "disappear" so far as their availability to the plant is concerned. They form insoluble compounds with iron and aluminium, and as little as 2 to 20 per cent of phosphate fertilizer applied to the soil may be available to the plant.

Formation of these insoluble phosphorus compounds takes place most readily in acid soils, and other phosphorus-holding reactions occur in highly alkaline soils. In many soils, phosphorus availability is at its highest in neutral or slightly acid conditions.

The availability of boron, molybdenum and other trace elements is affected by acidity. Boron deficiencies may result if an acid soil is neutralized. Molybdenum tends to be unavailable in acid soils, being released for use by the plant as acidity is corrected.

Bacteria and Micro-organisms

The decomposition of organic matter in soil is brought about by bacteria and other micro-organisms. Elements locked up in complex organic compounds are converted into simple chemicals which may be used as nutrients by the growing plant. A flourishing population of micro-organisms contributes greatly to the health and fertility of a soil.

Bacteria are sensitive to the pH of their environment; as a rule, they do not flourish in an acid soil. By neutralizing the acidity, we can make the soil more favourable to the growth of bacteria, and thus speed up the process which converts organic matter into plant nutrients.

The *Rhizobium* bacteria, which live in association with leguminous plants, are also stimulated into increased activity in neutral or alkaline soils. In acid soils they rarely flourish, and their nitrogen-fixing activities are at a modest level.

Effect of Soil Type

The relationships between pH and nutrient-availability are very complex. Knowledge of the acidity of a soil is of only limited value without an understanding of the chemical and physical characteristics of the soil as a whole. pH measurements, for example, cannot be related directly to soil fertility. They may give a useful indication of the reasons for poor fertility, but additional information is needed before the proper corrective treatment can be devised.

Most of the hydrogen ions responsible for a soil's acidity are held on the surface of colloidal particles of clay or humus. Fine textured soils, which are rich in clay and organic matter, will commonly have a higher total acidity than sandy soils containing little clay and organic matter.

The clays of temperate regions, usually of the montmorillonite and illite types, have a much greater capacity for
holding ions than the kaolinite-type clays of warm-temperate and tropical regions.

Crop Plants and pH

When plants are growing under normal agricultural
conditions (as distinct from experimental conditions which
guarantee them all the nutrients they need), individual
species respond most favourably to particular degrees of
acidity. Some plants grow best in an acid soil, others prefer
neutral or alkaline soils.

The pH range favoured by any plant is one that ensures
a supply of various nutrients in the quantities needed by
this particular plant for effective growth. It follows, therefore, that the preferred pH range depends upon the kind
of soil in which the plant is growing. If a crop plant is to
be grown efficiently, the acidity of the soil must be considered in relation to the kind of soil and the plant's preferred pH conditions. Practical steps are then taken to
adjust the soil pH to the value that is required.

Liming to Control Acidity

When a virgin soil is first brought under the plough, it is
generally acid. Rainwater percolating through the soil, perhaps for many centuries, has leached out calcium and
magnesium from the colloidal particles, leaving hydrogen
ions in their place.

When the soil is cultivated, further supplies of these
elements are absorbed by the crop, and eventually removed from the soil. So the acidity of the soil increases,
and in many regions of the world it can become too acid
to support a flourishing crop.

The problem of controlling soil acidity, therefore, is
commonly one of reducing the acidity of a soil that is too
acid. And for centuries, this has been achieved by applying
lime to the land.

The term "lime", when used scientifically, refers to calcium oxide. But in agricultural terminology, it is used indiscriminately for a variety of calcium compounds, including limestone (calcium carbonate), quicklime (calcium oxide) and slaked lime (calcium hydroxide). Other substances, which are not simple compounds of calcium, may also be described as lime. Dolomite, or dolomitic limestone, for example, is a carbonate of calcium and magnesium (see page 57).

When lime is added to an acid soil, it has the effect of neutralizing the hydrogen ions in the soil solution. If the solution was not in contact with solid particles of the soil, the removal of hydrogen ions would reduce its acidity. But as the concentration of hydrogen ions falls, fresh supplies are brought into the solution from the store held by colloidal particles of clay and humus.

To neutralize an acid soil effectively, therefore, enough lime must be added to deal (a) with the hydrogen ions in the soil solution (active acidity), and (b) the hydrogen ions held in reserve by the colloidal particles as well (potential acidity). Measurement of the soil pH gives an indication of only the active acidity, and this is insufficient to show how much lime is needed to effect a complete neutralization. To calculate this, it is necessary to know the potential acidity as well.

If the liming of an acid soil is to be effective, lime must be applied in adequate quantity. A meagre application may be of no value at all if it merely neutralizes hydrogen ions in the soil solution; replacement ions will make up the deficiency immediately from the stores in the colloidal particles.

In calculating total acidity, the unique role of aluminium must also be taken into account. Aluminium occurs as a replaceable cation on the colloidal particles of acid soils, commonly in greater quantity than any of the other cations. As lime is added to the soil, calcium ions from the lime

Annual Losses of Calcium and Magnesium From Soil by Leaching

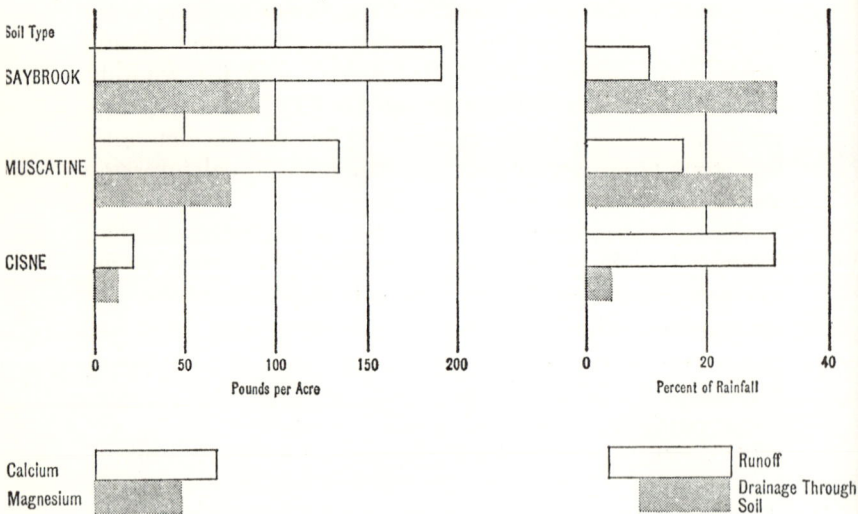

Soil Type

SAYBROOK

MUSCATINE

CISNE

0   50   100   150   200
Pounds per Acre

0   20   40
Percent of Rainfall

Calcium
Magnesium

Runoff
Drainage Through Soil

replace not only the hydrogen ions on the colloidal particles but the aluminium ions too.

Aluminium ions replaced in this way react with soil water to form insoluble oxides and hydroxides. The replacement of aluminium by calcium means that supplies of lime are used for the purpose. And in calculating the amount of lime that is needed to neutralize an acid soil, it is necessary to include enough for replacement of the aluminium ions held by colloidal particles.

The amount of lime needed to neutralize an acid soil depends to a large extent upon the amount of colloidal material in the soil. A sandy soil, with little clay or organic matter, will tend to become acid very quickly, as there is little colloidal material to be leached. But it will also require only a small amount of lime to correct the total acidity.

A fine textured soil, with a high proportion of clay, or a soil that is rich in humus, will take longer to become acid, as there is a heavier reserve of colloidal matter to be leached. When it *does* become acid, a soil of this type will need heavy dressings of lime to neutralize the total acidity.

Overliming may reduce the availability of certain nutrients, and should be avoided. This is less likely to occur on fine textured soils, or soils rich in humus which have a greater capacity for lime.

An agricultural soil that has been limed effectively will have up to 90 per cent of its cation exchange capacity occupied by calcium and magnesium. Calcium ions will outnumber magnesium ions 7 to 10 times, and potassium will account for up to 5 per cent, with hydrogen ions making up the rest.

Alkaline Soils

Some soils are naturally alkaline, and never become acid. The availability of plant nutrients in these soils may be quite high, and alkaline soils are often fertile. They differ in their characteristics from soils which have been rendered alkaline by overliming. Naturally alkaline soils, for example, may provide an adequate supply of boron, whereas an overlimed soil will often be deficient in boron.

Acidification of an alkaline soil may be achieved by adding acids such as sulphuric acid, or acid-producing substances such as sulphur to the soil (see page 186).

COLLOIDS AND CHEMICAL NUTRIENTS

The growing plant is a factory in which all manner of chemical processes are taking place. Simple substances drawn into the plant serve as raw materials from which innumerable compounds are constructed, and the sum total of all this chemical activity is seen as life itself.

The basic raw materials of all matter, including the constituents of plants, are the elementary forms of matter we

call elements. Atoms of the elements are constructional
units which, linked together, produce molecules; these are
fundamental particles of the multitude of different forms
of matter we find on earth.

The growing plant must have supplies of all the elements
it needs if its chemical life-processes are to be sustained.
These supplies come from the air that circulates through
the pores of the leaves and other surfaces, and from the
solution of simple chemicals absorbed through the roots.

From the air, plants obtain carbon and oxygen in the
form of carbon dioxide and oxygen gas. From the soil, they
draw all the other elements they need. Some, like nitrogen,
phosphorus, potassium and calcium, are required in comparatively large amounts; others, like molybdenum or
cobalt, are needed only in very small quantities.

The rocks of the earth's crust contain supplies of all
the elements, most of them combined with one another to
form compounds. But the distribution of elements is uneven, only a few of them making up the bulk of surface
rocks. Oxygen, silicon, aluminium, iron, calcium, magnesium, potassium and sodium are the main constituents
of the earth's solid crust to a depth of a few miles.

As rocks are weathered, some of the more resistant
materials – notably silica – are released as particles of primary (i.e. unchanged) mineral. Other constituents undergo
chemical changes which convert them into new compounds, providing, for example, fine particles of clay.

When the chemical study of soil began, about a century
ago, it was commonly supposed that a chemical analysis
of the soil would provide a reliable index of fertility. The
total quantity of every element in the surface soils could be
assessed, and this would represent the amount available to
growing crops. The quantity of each element needed annually by a specific crop could be estimated, and the amount
available in the soil would indicate how many crops could
be grown before supplies must be renewed.

PLATE 19

PLOUGH PAN.

Under continuous cultivation, soil may become compacted by the sliding action of the plough bottom, or by pressure from the wheels of farm implements, forming a hard layer beneath the tilled surface soil. This restricts the flow of water and air, and prevents plant roots from penetrating into the lower layers of the soil.

Left : Cotton plant roots in a soil without a plough pan.

Right : Cotton plant roots in a soil with a plough pan. The roots turn sideways on reaching the impenetrable layer.

Below : In this soil profile, a plough pan consisting of a compacted layer nearly 1 inch thick has separated completely from the tilled soil above and the subsoil below. The pan has been caused by 40 years of cropping under poor management conditions – *U.S.D.A.*

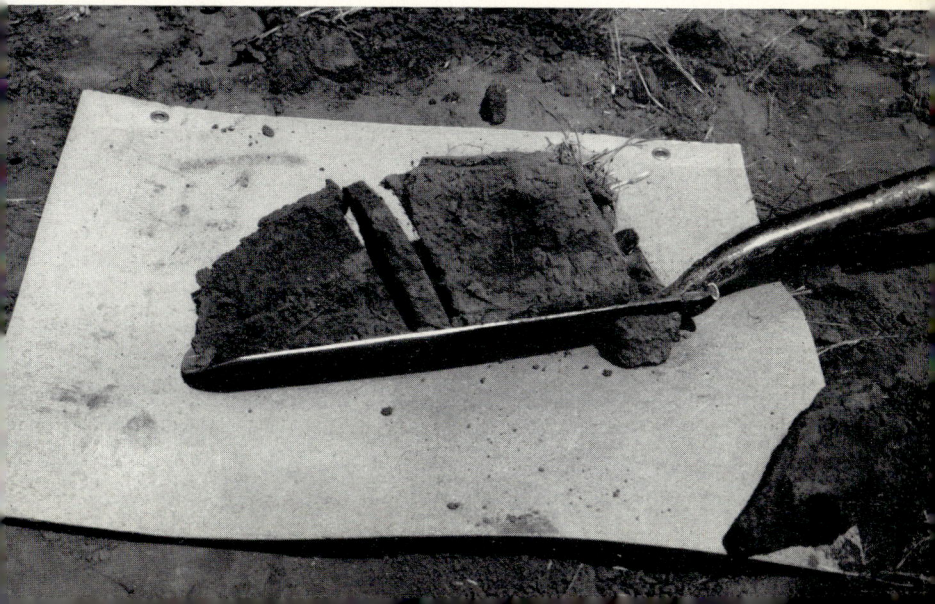

Land capability classes photograph showing a region divided into eight capability classes, with labels: CLASS VII LAND, CLASS VIII LAND, CLASS VII LAND, CLASS VI LAND, CLASS IV LAND, CLASS II LAND, CLASS V LAND, CLASS I LAND, CLASS III LAND.

LAND CAPABILITY CLASSES			
SUITABLE FOR CULTIVATION		NO CULTIVATION - PASTURE, HAY, WOODLAND AND WILDLIFE	
I	REQUIRES GOOD SOIL MANAGEMENT PRACTICES ONLY	V	NO RESTRICTIONS IN USE
II	MODERATE CONSERVATION PRACTICES NECESSARY	VI	MODERATE RESTRICTIONS IN USE
III	INTENSIVE CONSERVATION PRACTICES NECESSARY	VII	SEVERE RESTRICTIONS IN USE
IV	PERENNIAL VEGETATION - INFREQUENT CULTIVATION	VIII	BEST SUITED FOR WILDLIFE AND RECREATION

LAND CAPABILITY CLASS AREAS

This photograph shows a region divided into the eight capability classes.

Class I Land. Congaree fine sandy loam ; 1% slope ; no recent detrimental deposits. Crops are corn and small grain, and lespedeza.

Class II Land. Cecil sandy loam ; 4% slope ; only slight detrimental erosion. Corn.

Class III Land. Cecil sandy loam ; 9% slope ; moderate erosion. Field planted in contour strips of cotton and small grain.

Class IV Land. Cecil clay loam ; 12% slope ; moderately severe erosion. Apple orchard in sod, and pasture land.

Class V Land. Undifferentiated alluvial soils ; poorly drained, less than 1% slope ; recent detrimental deposits. Mostly idle land ; small patch of corn in area chlorotic and stunted.

Class VI Land. Cecil sandy loam ; 20% slope ; moderate erosion. Pasture.

Class VII Land. Cecil sandy loam and Louisburg sandy loam ; 30 to 60% slope ; no apparent erosion. Original forest (oak, hickory, poplar, short leaf pine etc.).

Class VIII Land. Granite rock outcrop.

PLATE 20

This "balance sheet" attitude to the chemical raw materials of the soil was abandoned as knowledge of soil science grew. It was found that the *total* quantity of an element present in a soil did not necessarily indicate the quantity that was *available* to the growing plant. A crop might fail for lack of a particular element, for example, even though the soil contained a rich supply of the element in its mineral particles. If the element was locked away as a constituent of an insoluble, resistant mineral it could not be absorbed into the plant.

Chemical nutrients find their way from soil to plant through the root hairs, which bathe in the film of moisture clinging to the surface of solid particles in the soil. And the nutrients are made available as a result of physical-chemical activity taking place on the particle surface.

The importance of this surface activity in plant feeding cannot be over-estimated. The total amount of surface available on the particles in a soil is a major factor in determining the extent of the nutrient-releasing activity. The greater the amount of surface, the more prolific will be the release of nutrients to the plant. Soil fertility depends as much upon the surface area of particles as upon the quantity of nutrients present in the soil.

The Importance of Surface

The amount of surface on a mass of matter depends upon the size of its constituent particles. The smaller the particles, the greater is the amount of surface available.

Consider a roughly circular piece of rock, for example, with a diameter of 1 foot. Its surface area will be about 3 square feet. If we cut it in two, we add another 1½ square feet, and if we cut the two halves again we add a further 1½ square feet. Continuing in this way, we can go on increasing the surface area by making the pieces smaller and smaller. We would pass through the sizes recognized as stones and gravel, then through the soil textural classes of

L

sand, silt and finally clay. If we continued until the rock was chopped into particles comparable with clay, say, 0.001 mm. diameter, we would have a total surface area of several acres! (See page 65.)

The amount of surface presented by the mineral particles depends upon the proportions of sand, silt and clay (i.e. upon the soil texture), the surface area increasing in that order. The richer a soil is in clay, the greater its surface area will be. And it is for this reason that the productivity of a soil is greatly influenced by the proportion of clay it contains. The richer a soil is in clay, the more surface its particles make available, and the more productive it will be.

The humus of soil is also in the form of very fine particles, often too small to be seen individually through an optical microscope. It too improves the productivity of a soil by increasing the total surface area.

Colloids

Clay and humus are both *colloids*; they consist of particles so small that they may be dispersed in water, and remain suspended without settling out.

The colloidal particles of clay and humus are the seat of much of the chemical activity of the soil. They act as a storehouse of nutrient chemicals needed by the plant.

Clay

In general, the particles of sand and silt in a soil are primary minerals – they are tiny pieces of parent rock which have not undergone any chemical change. Silt particles, being smaller than sand, have a greater surface area and are more chemically active than sand. But the amount of activity provided by silt particles is not sufficient to release plant nutrients in the quantities required by crop plants. Soils which are predominantly silty or sandy are not, as a rule, as productive as those of clayey texture.

Clay is a secondary material; it is formed by chemical

modification of constituents of the parent rock. The structure of a clay depends not only upon the nature of the
parent rock, but upon the chemical changes involved in
the weathering processes. Climatic conditions, for example,
may influence the type of clay that is produced.

In many parts of the tropics, weathering is intense and
clays will often consist of hydrated sesquioxides of iron
and aluminium. But in the temperate regions, clays are
mainly alumino-silicates – substances derived from
alumina (aluminium oxide) and silica (silicon dioxide) in
which substitution of other constituents may have taken
place to varying degrees.

The atoms in the alumina-silica structure of a clay particle are arranged in orderly fashion, and this regular
arrangement is reflected in the shape of the particle itself.
It is crystalline, with a characteristic plate-like structure.
If we could see a clay particle as though through an electron microscope, its structure would resemble a stack of
sheets of paper made up of sheets of two different colours.
One colour would represent a layer of silica; the other
colour would represent a layer of alumina.

This plate-like shape of the clay particle provides an
immense amount of surface, the area increasing with the
thinness of the plate (see page 316). In some types of clay,
the layers forming the particle are held tightly together,
and the effective surface is the outer surface of the particle
itself. But in other types of clay, the layers are held less
rigidly, and it is possible for substances to make their way
between the layers of the particle. This exposes the surfaces of the layers themselves, and increases still further
the available surface area.

The stability of the clay particle in this respect depends
upon the precise arrangement of the layers of alumina and
silica within the particle. This arrangement is influenced
very largely by the conditions under which the clay is
formed.

CATIONS AND CLAY

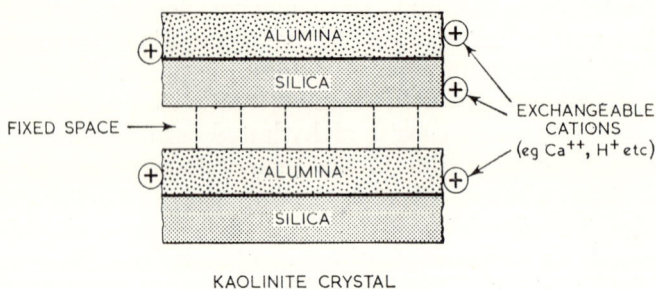

KAOLINITE CRYSTAL

Kaolinite crystals are composed of pairs of silica and alumina sheets held together by hydrogen bonds. The space between the crystal units is fixed, and is largely inaccessible to cations. It is not available for surface reactions.

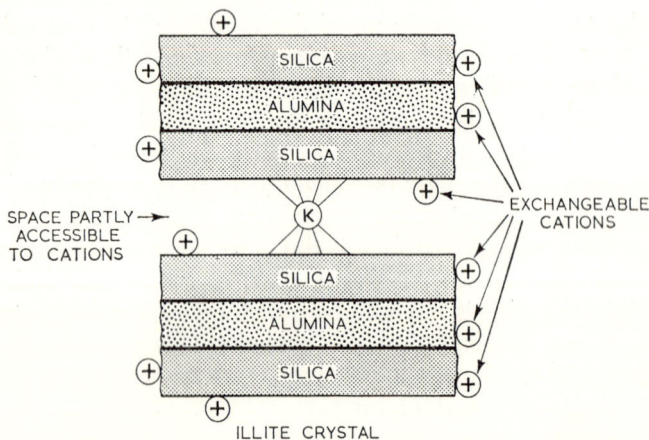

ILLITE CRYSTAL

Illite crystals are composed of units in which a layer of alumina is sandwiched between two layers of silica. Adjacent crystal units are held together by potassium bridges, and the space between the units is partly accessible for surface reactions. The available surface area in illite is greater than in kaolinite.

CATIONS AND CLAY (*Continued*)

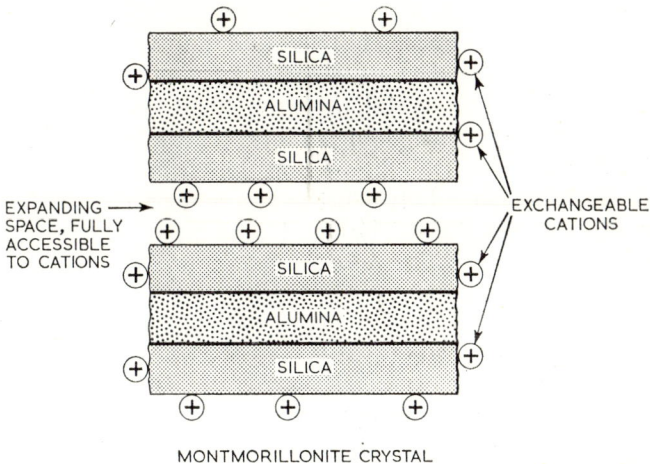

MONTMORILLONITE CRYSTAL

Montmorillonite crystals are composed of units in which a sheet of
alumina is sandwiched between two sheets of silica. Adjacent crystal units are free to move to and fro, and the space between the
units varies with the amount of water present. The entire surface
of the crystal unit is available for surface reactions, and is fully
accessible to cations. The available surface area is greater than in
illite or kaolinite.

Three of the most important types of clay mineral are
kaolinite, montmorillonite and illite. They differ from each
other in the proportions of alumina and silica, and the
physical arrangement of the layers of these constituents
in the crystal.

Kaolinite is a clay mineral developed largely in hot,
tropical regions. Its crystals consist of twin layers of
alumina and silica arranged one above the other. The twin
layers are held firmly together, and the layers within the
crystal are largely inaccessible for surface reactions. The
available surface is that of the clay particle itself.

Illite is a form of clay produced more commonly in temperate climates. Its crystals are built up from triple layers consisting of a sheet of alumina sandwiched between two sheets of silica. The triple layers lie one on top of another within the crystal, the outer sheets of silica of each layer being adjacent to each other. The triple layers are held together by potassium atoms which form a bridge or link, and the space between the layers is partly accessible for surface reactions. The total amount of surface area presented by the illite particle is greater than that of a comparable kaolinite particle.

Montmorillonite is another form of clay that is common in temperate climates. Like illite, it is constructed of triple layers consisting of a sheet of alumina sandwiched between two sheets of silica. But the layers are held less rigidly together than in the case of kaolinite or illite. Water will have the effect of prising the layers apart, making the surfaces of individual layers within the crystal available for surface reactions.

Humus

As organic matter decomposes in the soil, it forms a mass of brown or black material that we call humus. The precise chemical composition of humus is not known. It is recognized as a part-way stage in the decomposition of organic matter, which is itself decomposing slowly to release supplies of chemical nutrients into the soil.

Apart from its role as a source of plant nutrients, humus is of great importance in adding to the surface area that is available in the soil. Like clay, humus is in the form of very small particles with a large surface area, and it adds to the fertility of a soil by increasing the extent of the surface at which nutrient-releasing activity may take place.

Ion Exchange

The release of nutrient chemicals on the surface of clay

and humus particles takes place by an electrical process in which *ions* take part.

Ions are particles consisting of atoms or groups of atoms which carry an electric charge, either negative or positive. A negatively charged ion is an *anion*, and a positively charged ion is a *cation*. Together, the two forms of ion represent an electrally neutral molecule.

Ions are formed when salts, such as common salt, potassium chloride, or sodium nitrate dissolve in water. The molecule of common salt, for example, separates into a cation, Na^+ – a positively charged sodium atom – and an anion, Cl^- – a negatively charged chlorine atom.

If an electrically charged object is placed into a solution of salt, ions will be attracted towards it, or repelled by it, depending on the nature of the electric charge. A negatively-charged metal rod, for example, will attract the positively-charged cations (i.e. sodium ions) towards it, and repel the negatively charged anions (i.e. chlorine ions). This simple but familiar phenomenon controls the process that makes nutrients available on the surface of colloidal particles of clay or humus. These particles carry a negative electric charge, and as they float around in water they attract the positively-charged cations of salts dissolved in the soil water. If lime has been added to the soil, there will be calcium ions in the water, carrying a positive electric charge; if a potash fertilizer has been used, the soil water will contain a concentration of positively-charged potassium ions.

If there are colloidal particles of clay or humus suspended in the water, the negative charges they carry will attract the positively-charged ions towards them. Each particle will acquire an escort of ions which are held at the particle surface by the attraction of the opposing electric charges. The colloidal particle becomes a carrier of supplies of the positively-charged ions – cations – which are present in the soil water.

Cations held in this way by a colloidal particle may be replaced by other cations. A particle carrying an escort of calcium ions and hydrogen ions, for example, may release these ions if it meets a concentration of sodium ions in the form of a solution of common salt. The sodium ions replace the calcium and hydrogen ions surrounding the particle.

This process, called *ion-exchange,* is controlled by a number of factors, including (1) the number of charges carried by the ions, (2) the relative concentrations of ions involved, (3) the mobility of the ions. Cations may be arranged in order of replacement power, indicating the inherent ability of individual ions to oust other ions from a surface.

The hydrogen ion rates as the most powerful replacer of all. This means that a concentration of hydrogen ions released into a solution carrying suspended colloid particles will replace all other cations held by the particle. Hydrogen ions, therefore, act like money paid across the counter at a grocer's shop; they are exchanged for supplies of food.

When plants are growing in a soil, carbon dioxide gas is set free as a waste product from respiration. The roots of plants release a supply of carbon dioxide into the soil, adding to the carbon dioxide which enters the soil from decomposing organic matter.

Carbon dioxide dissolves in water to form carbonic acid, which provides a supply of hydrogen ions. And these are able to replace other cations which are held against the surface of clay or humus particles. The released cations – for example, calcium, potassium, magnesium – may then be absorbed by the roots of plants.

The plant root thus carries a built-in trigger mechanism which acts on colloidal particles in the soil, releasing supplies of nutrient chemicals they are carrying.

Cation Exchange Capacity

The ability of a soil to hold exchangeable cations may

CATION EXCHANGE REACTIONS WHEN AN ACID
SOIL IS LIMED

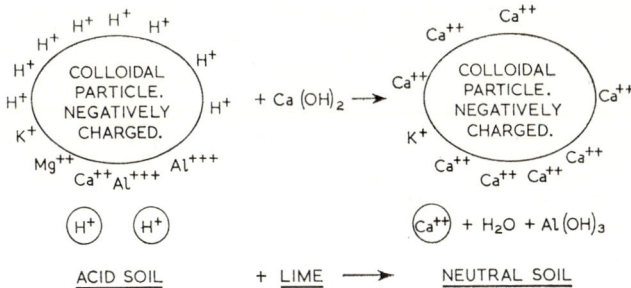

(H^+)	= HYDROGEN ION IN SOIL SOLUTION
H^+	= REPLACEABLE HYDROGEN ION HELD ON PARTICLE SURFACE (ie POTENTIAL ACIDITY)
(Ca^{++})	= CALCIUM ION IN SOLUTION
Ca^{++}	= REPLACEABLE CALCIUM ION HELD ON PARTICLE SURFACE
Mg^{++}	= REPLACEABLE MAGNESIUM ION
Al^{+++}	= REPLACEABLE ALUMINIUM ION
K^+	= REPLACEABLE POTASSIUM ION
H_2O	= WATER
$Al(OH)_3$	= ALUMINIUM HYDROXIDE

Particles of clay or organic matter carry a negative electric charge. This attracts positively charged ions in the soil solution, which are held at the particle surface. Hydrogen ions available in an acid soil are held in this way, forming a reservoir of potential acidity. When lime is added to the soil, calcium ions displace the hydrogen ions from the particle surface.

Aluminium ions play a unique role in this process. Replaceable aluminium ions are displaced by calcium ions, and they react with soil water to form aluminium hydroxide, which is insoluble in the soil water.

L*

be measured experimentally, and expressed in terms of milliequivalents per 100 grams of soil at neutrality (pH 7). This is called the *Cation Exchange Capacity* (C.E.C.).

The Cation Exchange Capacity often gives a good general indication of soil fertility. Soils with a high C.E.C. are usually fertile, and they are able to hold supplies of exchangeable nutrients which might otherwise be lost through leaching. They are soils with good staying power.

The C.E.C. of a soil derives almost entirely from the colloidal particles, especially humus and clays. Hydrated oxides of iron and aluminium play some part, but it is usually an insignificant one. The relative effectiveness of the different colloids as cation exchange constituents may be seen from their C.E.C.s. The following figures are typical (m.e. per 100 g.):

Humus	210
Clay – Montmorillonite	100
Illite	30
Kaolinite	10
Hydrated oxides of iron and aluminium	5

Anion Exchange

The ion exchange activities of soils are predominantly concerned with cations, the positively-charged particles that are attracted to the negatively-charged colloidal particles of clay and humus. But ion exchange may also involve negatively-charged particles, or anions. This takes place to a smaller extent than cation exchange, being most effective in soils rich in kaolinite.

14

Assessment of Soil Resources

If soils were distinct individual entities, with clear-cut boundaries separating one from another, the assessment of soils over an area of land would be a comparatively simple matter. All we would have to do would be to discover the boundaries between the individual soils, and then carry out a single profile examination of each in order to determine its type.

Unfortunately, there is no such thing as an individual soil. The layer of material that we call "the soil" is infinitely variable, and it is not possible to delineate the properties of any particular area of soil exactly. All we can do is to classify areas of soil on the basis of their general similarities, and study how the characteristics change as one type of soil merges into another.

A knowledge of the soil of a district can be of inestimable practical value. By understanding the nature of the soil, we can plan the use of land in the most effective way. Knowledge of the soil may indicate where new towns and factory sites should be sited, and where new roads could best be built. The farmer with an understanding of his soil can plan his agricultural programme to give the most effective returns, and to sustain the productivity of his land over the years. He knows which crops to grow, and how to cultivate and feed his soil to maximum effect.

In the United Kingdom and the U.S.A. and in other technically advanced countries, the value of a proper understanding of the soil is now well realized, and every effort is made to assess national soil resources effectively. Official bodies are responsible for surveying and classifying soils, and a fast-growing area of the earth's land surface is being "soil-mapped" in this way.

SOIL SURVEY

The object of a survey is to study the soil that lies over a particular area of land, with a view to finding out the essential characteristics of the different kinds of soil, classifying them and showing how they are distributed over the area under survey and assessing how they may best be used.

The basis of a survey is the field work carried out by soil surveyors. Using a map or aerial photograph as a base-map, the surveyor examines the surface soil at selected points. He studies complete soil profiles by boring out samples with special augers, or by digging pits to expose a section of the soil through as great a depth as possible.

When surveys are carried out on behalf of an official soil survey organization, the assessments are made according to a predetermined plan. The surveyor carries out an examination which is intended to provide all the information needed, and a standardized form is commonly used.

Much of the information needed can be obtained on the spot by an experienced soil surveyor. He can make simple chemical tests in the field to determine degree of acidity and presence of lime, salts and some toxic compounds.

The answer to some of his questions, however, can be found only in the laboratory, and samples are collected for subsequent analysis.

From his examination of a profile, or a number of profiles, the surveyor identifies the series to which the soil belongs. He may decide, for example, that it is a "Fayette" soil. And by determining the texture of the surface soil,

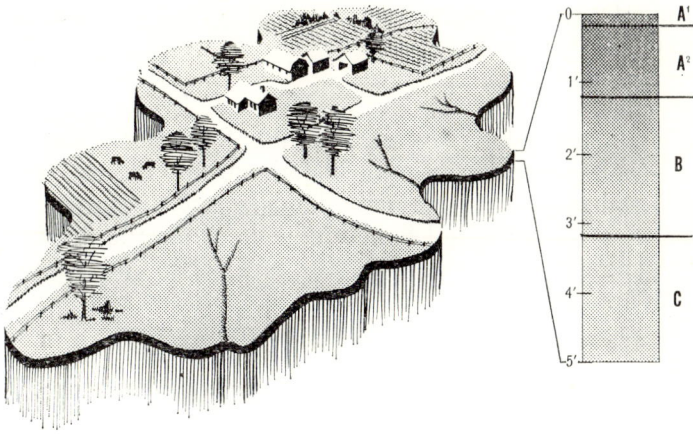

Soil Type. A single area of soil type as it occurs in nature. At the right is an enlarged sketch of the profile with its major horizons.

---

he can assign a type name by adding the appropriate texture description the series name, e.g. it might be a "Fayette" silt loam.

The allocation of a type name establishes the final category of the soil in the classification system, and completes the "identification" of the soil. But, there is still a great deal of information needed to establish the status of the soil. Variations due to factors outside the basic classification characteristics must be noted, including slope, degree of erosion that has been taken place, depth to bedrock, and stoniness. The influence of these factors is included in the *phase* descriptions which modify the *type* name, e.g. Fayette silt loam, 4 – 14 per cent slopes, eroded phase.

The surveyor's assessment includes the type of vegetation or crop that the soil is supporting, climate, parent material, relief, aspect, erosion, permeability, drainage, ground water, moisture, root distribution, salt or alkali and stoniness.

SOIL MAPS

When a survey has been carried out, information about the soils in a particular area is collated, and used as the basis of a soil map. This shows the kinds of soil that are to be found in the area, and the boundaries where the different soils merge into one another. The types of soil are named, with appropriate modifications to indicate the phases, e.g. Sharpsburg silty clay loam, eroded rolling phase. To the farmer, this information is as useful as are the names and descriptions he uses for a variety of plant, e.g. old Jonathan apple trees.

Soil series, types and phases do not occur at random on the landscape. They have an orderly pattern of arrangement that is related to the land form, the parent material

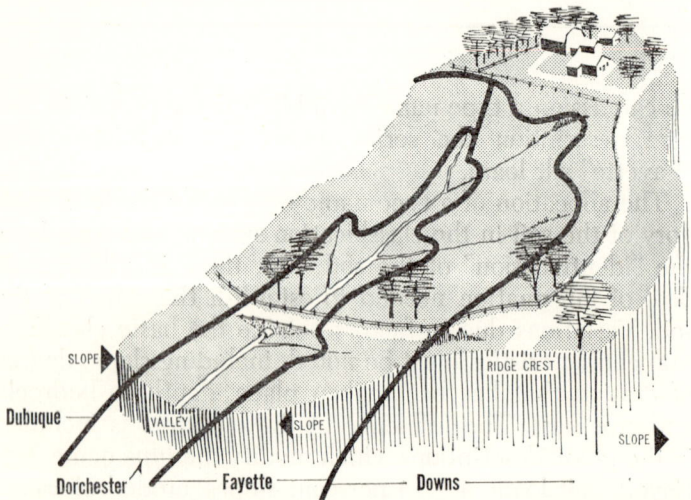

Soil Type. This sketch shows how bodies of soil types fit together in a small landscape, much like the pieces in a jigsaw puzzle. Boundaries between adjacent bodies are gradations rather than sharp lines.

from which the soil was created, the influence of plants that grew on the soils and the animals that lived on them, and the way that man has used the soil.

On any farm, the different kinds of soil commonly have a repeating pattern which is associated with the slope of the ground. Anyone familiar with soils can visualize a landscape from a soil map. And conversely when he sees a landscape he can predict roughly where the boundaries between different kinds of soils may be.

It should be remembered always that soils are not precisely-defined, individual entities. Two soils of the same type are not absolutely identical; they can be likened to two oak trees, which are essentially similar without being exactly the same. But just as all oak trees in a district will generally respond to the same treatment in a similar way, so will two soils of the same type respond to the same cultivation practices and management in a like manner.

Using the information provided by the soil map, and additional information derived from the survey, the modern soil scientist can proceed a stage further by predicting the most efficient way in which a farmer may use his soil resources. He does this by considering all the information provided by the survey, and using it to construct a second map showing the *capability classes* of different areas of the land covered by the survey.

LAND CAPABILITY
Land Capability Class

If the information obtained from a soil survey is to be applied effectively in practice, it must be condensed and presented in such a form that the farmer is able to make use of it. This is done by means of the capability classification.

Areas of land are grouped into capability classes, subclasses and units which indicate to the farmer how the areas should be used to obtain the most desirable results

AN OUTLINE OF LAND-CAPABILITY CLASSIFICATION

Major land use suitability (Broad grouping of limitations)	Land-capability class (Degree of limitations)		Land-capability subclass (Grouping of land-capability units according to kind of limitation. This table shows examples only.)	Land-capability unit (Land-management groups based on permanent physical characteristics. This table shows examples only.)
Suited for cultivation	I	Few limitations. Wide latitude for each use. Very good land from every standpoint.		
	II	Moderate limitations or risks of damage. Good land from all-around standpoint.		
	III	Severe limitations or risks of damage. Regular cultivation possible if limitations are observed.	Limited by hazard of water erosion; moderately sloping land.	Moderately sloping, slightly acid soils on limestone.
				Moderately sloping, highly acid soils on sandstone or shale.
			Limited by excess water; drainage needed for cultivation.	
			Limited by low moisture capacity; sandy land.	
	IV	Very severe limitations. Suited for occasional cultivation or for some kind of limited cultivation.		
Not suited for cultivation	V	Not suited for cultivation because of wetness, stones, overflows, etc. Few limitations for grazing or forestry use.	Grouping of sites according to kind of limitation.	Sites significant in management of ranges, pastures, forests, etc.
	VI	Too steep, stony, arid, wet, etc., for cultivation. Moderate limitations for grazing or forestry		
	VII	Very steep, rough, arid, wet, etc. Severe limitations for grazing or forestry.		
	VIII	Extremely rough, arid, swampy, etc. Not suited for cultivation, grazing, or forestry. Suited for wildlife, watersheds, or recreation.		

from his land. The capability classification takes into account both immediate and long-term aspects of agricultural practice, including soil conservation and the prevention of erosion.

Eight capability classes are recognized by the U.S. Dept. of Agriculture. They are commonly shown on soil and land-capability maps by Roman numerals (see page 328).

The restrictions and limitations on the use of land increase in going from Class I to Class VIII. That is to say, the farmer has a wider choice of uses available to him on Class I land than he has on Class II; Class II offers more choice than Class III, and so on up to Class VIII.

The increasing restrictions placed on the use of land as we go from one class to another of higher number are due to features such as slope of the land, erosion hazards, inadequate drainage etc.

Land in Classes I to IV can all be used safely for cultivated crops – which leave the soil bare part of the time – or for crops that keep the soil covered all the time. But in going from Class I to Class IV the choices become fewer, and the conservation practices needed on cultivated soils become more difficult to apply and keep working efficiently.

Class V land is not suited to ordinary cultivation, usually because it is wet too much of the time, because it is too stony, or because the growing season is too short. But it can produce good pasture, and it is suitable for trees when the climate is right.

Land in Classes VI and VII is most safely used for some kind of permanent cover. With very special management, including elaborate soil and water conservation practices, some of it can be cultivated to certain crops.

Class VIII land is not suited to any plant crop that can be sold. Usually, it is very severely eroded or is extremely sandy, wet, arid, rough, steep, or stony. Much of it is valuable for wildlife food and cover, for watershed protection or for recreation.

SOIL CAPABILITY MAP

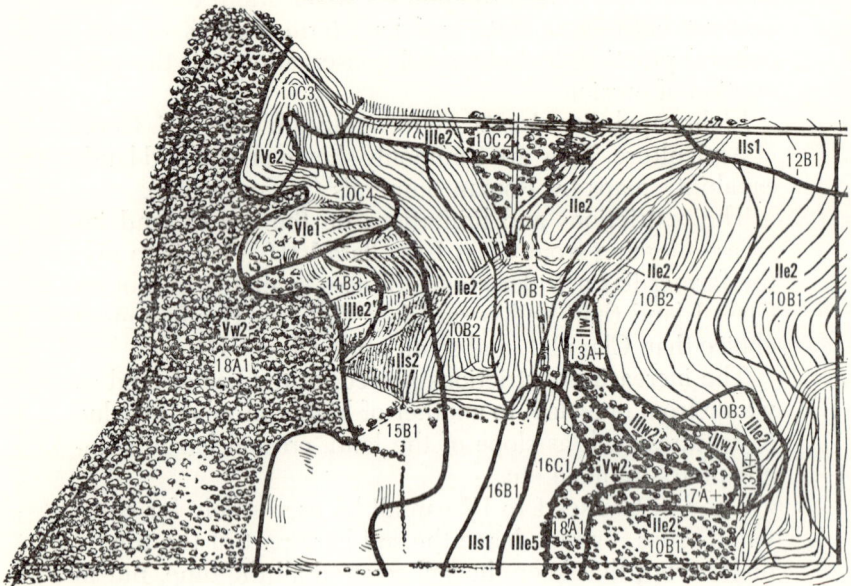

The symbols on this map refer to various aspects of soil and topography. For example, 10B1 refers to the kind of soil; the number 10 refers to soil type, the letter B to steepness of slope, and number 1 to degree of erosion. The symbol 11e2 refers to the land capability unit; 11 designates the land capability class; e indicates the subclass, and 2 indicates the unit. Heavy lines on the map indicate boundaries of a capability unit.

Land Capability Sub-Class

Within the capability classes, sub-divisions are made into sub-classes and units which recognize the different kinds of limitations that are imposed upon the use of the land. An area of Class III land, for example, is rated as subject to severe limitations in cultivation; this may be due to danger of water erosion, or too much water, or low moisture capability, or impermeable subsoil, and the sub-classes of Class III are distinguished according to these different limiting factors.

CONSERVATION PLAN MAP

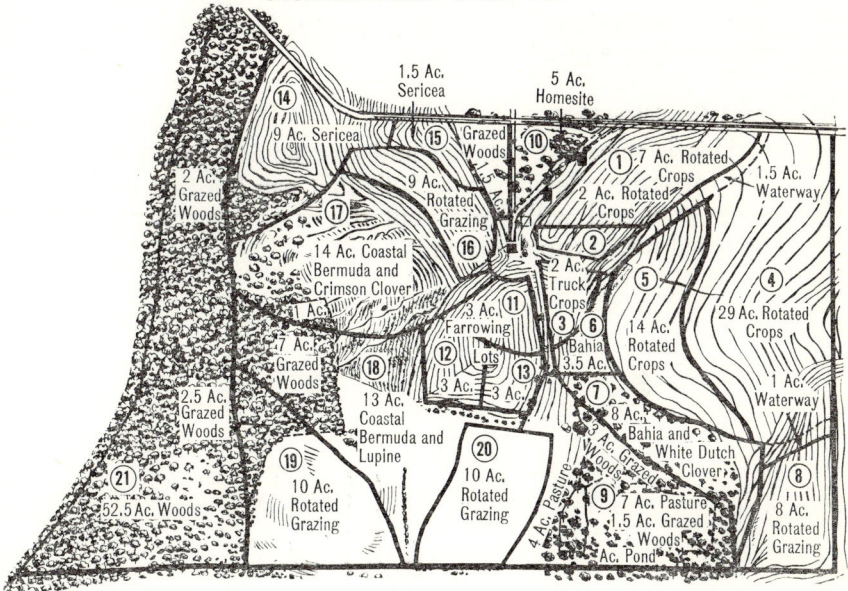

The decisions made by the farmer concerning the use and management of the land, together with field unit arrangement, are shown on this map. The decisions were based on the soil and capability map opposite. Needs of the farmer relative to his farm enterprise were also considered.

Four kinds of problem are recognized in the sub-classes, and are indicated by symbols as follows:

	Limitation Feature	Symbol
1.	Erosion and runoff	e
2.	Wetness and drainage	w
3.	Root zone and tillage limitations, e.g. shallowness, stoniness, droughtiness and salinity	s
4.	Climatic limitations	c

The sub-class thus provides more specific information about the kind and degree of limitation for the use of soil than does the capability class.

Land Capability Unit

This is the most detailed and specific soil grouping of the capability classification. Soils that can be used in the same way and will give about the same crop yield are grouped into a capability unit.

PART 4

REFERENCE SECTION

ABC OF SOIL SCIENCE

A HORIZON.   Mixed mineral-organic surface horizon of a mineral soil.

ABC SOIL.   A soil with a distinctly developed profile, including an A, B, and C horizon.

ABSORBING COMPLEX.   The materials in the soil that hold water and chemical compounds, mainly on their surfaces. They are chiefly the fine mineral matter and organic matter.

AC SOIL.   A soil where the A horizon rests directly on the parent material as, for example, immature soils on recent alluvium or on steep rocky slopes.

ACCELERATED EROSION. Erosion more rapid than that which existed under natural conditions. Accelerated erosion occurs as a result of destruction of vegetal cover, or of some activity of man. It may consist of any of the recognized types of erosion such as sheet erosion, rill erosion, gully erosion, wind erosion, or landslides, or combinations of them.

ACID SOIL.   Generally, a soil that is acid throughout most or all of the parts of it that plant roots occupy. Commonly applied to only the surface-ploughed layer or to some other specific layer or horizon of a soil. Practically, this means a soil more acid than pH 6.6; precisely, a soil with a pH value less than 7.0. A soil having a preponderance of hydrogen over hydroxyl ions in the soil solution.

ACRE-FOOT.   The quantity of water, soil or other material that will cover one acre one foot deep.

ACRE-INCH.   The quantity of water, soil or other material that will cover one acre one inch deep.

ACTINOMYCETES.   A group of soil micro-organisms which produce an extensive threadlike network. They resemble the soil moulds in some respects but are more like the bacteria in size.

ADSORB. Removal of a substance in solution to a solid surface or a separate phase; to accumulate on a surface.

ADSORPTION. The attachment of compounds or ionic parts of salts to a surface or another phase. Nutrients in solution (ions) carrying a positive charge become attached to (adsorbed by) negatively charged soil particles.

ADSORPTION COMPLEX. The group of substances in soil which are capable of adsorbing materials. The organic matter and colloidal clay form the greater part of the adsorption complex; the materials in silt and sand size exhibit adsorption, but to a greatly reduced extent in most soil material.

AEOLIAN (EOLIAN) SOIL MATERIAL. Parent material of soil accumulated through wind action. Commonly refers to sandy material usually in dunes.

AERATION, SOIL. The process by which air and other gases in the soil are renewed. The rate of soil aeration depends largely on the size and number of soil pores and on the amount of water clogging the pores. A soil with many large pores open to permit rapid aeration is said to be well aerated, while a poorly aerated soil either has few large pores or has most of those present blocked by water. The composition of the air in a well-aerated soil is similar to that in the atmosphere; in a poorly aerated soil, the air in the soil is considerably higher in carbon dioxide and lower in oxygen than the atmosphere above the soil.

AEROBIC. (1) Conditions with oxygen gas as a part of the environment. (2) Living or acting only in the presence of air or free oxygen. (3) Pertaining to the activity of organisms that grow under aerobic conditions, such as aerobic decomposition.

AGGREGATE (OF SOIL). Many fine soil particles held in a single mass or cluster, such as a clod, crumb, block, or prism. Many properties of the aggregate differ from those of an equal mass of unaggregated soil.

AGGREGATION, SOIL. The tight cementing or binding together of a number of individual soil particles into a secondary unit, aggregate or granule. The water-stable aggregates, which will not disintegrate easily, are of special importance to soil structure.

AIR-DRY. State of dryness after prolonged exposure to air, or any exposure sufficient to bring a material into moisture equilibrium with the air. Moisture content at air dryness is indefinite since it depends on relative humidity.

ALKALI CLAYPAN. A claypan containing 15 per cent or more of exchangeable sodium.

ALKALI SOIL.   Generally, a highly alkaline soil. Specifically, an alkali soil has so high a degree of alkalinity—pH 8.5 or higher—or so high a percentage of exchangeable sodium—15 per cent or higher—or both, that the growth of most crop plants is reduced. (In former years this term was also applied loosely to both alkali and saline soils. The term is also applied by some to those uncommon soils that contain highly alkaline salts, such as sodium carbonate.)

ALKALINE SOIL.   Generally, a soil that is alkaline throughout most or all of the parts of it occupied by plant roots; although the term is commonly applied to only a specific layer or horizon of a soil. Precisely, any soil horizon having a pH value greater than 7.0; practically, a soil having a pH above 7.3.

ALLUVIAL SOILS.   Soils developing from transported and relatively recently deposited material (alluvium) with little or no modification of the original materials by soil-forming processes. (Soils with well-developed profiles that have formed from alluvium are grouped with other soils having the same kinds of profiles, not with alluvial soils.)

ALLUVIUM.   Sand, mud, and other sediments deposited on land by streams.

ALUMINO-SILICATES.   Compounds containing aluminium, silicon, and oxygen atoms as main constituents.

AMENDMENT.   Any material, such as lime, gypsum, sawdust, or synthetic conditioners, that is worked into the soil to make it more productive. Strictly, a fertilizer is also an amendment, but the term "amendment" is used most commonly for added materials other than fertilizer.

AMINO ACIDS.   Amino acids are nitrogen-containing organic compounds, large numbers of which link together in the formation of a protein molecule. Each amino acid molecule contains one or more amino ($-NH_2$) groups and at least one carboxyl ($-COOH$) group. In addition, some amino acids (cystine and methionine) contain sulphur.

AMMONIA FIXATION.   Adsorption of ammonium ions by soils or minerals in such form that they are neither water soluble nor readily exchangeable.

AMMONIFICATION.   The formation by organisms of ammonium compounds from nitrogen-containing organic materials.

AMMONIUM ION.   The positively charged NH_4^+ ion. The form in which nitrogen occurs in many commercial fertilizers.

ANAEROBIC.   Living or functioning in the absence of air or free oxygen.

ANGULAR COBBLY.　See Cobbly.

ANHYDROUS.　Dry, or without water. Anhydrous ammonia is water free in contrast to the water solution of ammonia commonly known as household ammonia.

ANION.　An ion carrying a negative charge of electricity.

ANTHROPIC SOIL.　A soil whose diagnostic features result from the activities of man. Examples include deep, black surface soils resulting from centuries of manuring, and naturally acid soils that have lost their distinguishing features because of many centuries of liming and use for grass.

ANTIBIOSIS.　Opposed to living. Antibiotics suppress some micro-organisms.

APATITE.　A native phosphate of lime. The name is given to the chief mineral of phosphate rock and the inorganic compound of bone.

AQUA AMMONIA.　A water solution of ammonia.

AQUIFER.　A water-bearing formation through which water moves more readily than in adjacent formations of lower permeability.

ARID CLIMATE.　A very dry climate like that of desert or semidesert regions where there is only enough water for widely spaced desert plants. The limits of precipitation vary widely according to temperature, with an upper limit for cool regions of less than 10 inches and for tropical regions of as much as 20 inches.

ARID REGION.　Area where the potential water losses by evaporation and transpiration are greater than the amount of water supplied by precipitation.

ASH.　The nonvolatile residue resulting from the complete burning of organic matter. It is commonly composed of oxides of such elements as silicon, aluminium, iron, calcium, magnesium, and potassium.

ASSIMILATION.　Conversion of substances taken in from the outside into living tissue of plants or animals.

AUTOTROPHIC.　Cabable of utilizing carbon dioxide as a source of carbon and of obtaining energy for the reduction of carbon dioxide and other life processes from oxidation of inorganic elements or compounds, e.g., sulphur, hydrogen, ammonium, and nitrite salts, or from light.

AVAILABLE NUTRIENT (SOILS).　The part of the supply of a plant nutrient in the soil that can be taken up by plants at rates and in amounts significant to plant growth.

AVAILABLE WATER (SOILS). The part of the water in the soil that can be taken up by plants at rates significant to their growth; usable; obtainable.

AZONAL SOILS. Soils without distinct genetic horizons. A soil order.

B HORIZON. A sub-surface horizon with one or more of the following characteristics:
1. accumulations of clay, iron, aluminium or humus from the A horizon above.
2. coatings of iron oxides that give brighter colours than the horizons above or below.
3. a blocky or prismatic structure.
  In soils with distinct profiles, the B horizon is roughly equivalent to the general term "subsoil".

BACTERIA. A large group of unicellular microscopic oganisms widely distributed in air, water, soil, the bodies of living animals and plants, and dead organic matter. Most bacteria are either parasitic or saprophytic. Bacteria may cause diseases of plants and animals, fix free nitrogen from the air and cause decay of organic matter.

BADLAND. A land type nearly devoid of vegetation, especially a region where erosion has cut the land into an intricate maze of narrow ravines, sharp crests, and pinnacles.

BANDING (OF FERTILIZERS). The placement of fertilizers in the soil in continuous narrow ribbons, usually at specific distances from the seeds or plants. The fertilizer bands are covered by the soil but are not mixed with it.

BASE SATURATION. The relative degree to which soils have metallic cations adsorbed. The proportion of the cation-exchange capacity that is saturated with metallic cations.

BASIN IRRIGATION. The application of irrigation water to level areas that are surrounded by border ridges or levees. Usually irrigation water is applied at rates greater than the water intake rate of the soil. The water may stand on uncropped soils for several days until the soil is well soaked; then any excess may be used on other fields. The water may stand a few hours on fields having a growing crop.

BASIN LISTING. A method of tillage that creates small basins by damming lister furrows at regular intervals of about 4 to 20 feet. This method is a modification of ordinary listing and is carried out approximately on the contour on nearly level or gently sloping soils as a means of encouraging water to enter the soil rather than to run off the surface.

BC SOIL. A soil with a B and a C horizon but with little or no A horizon. Most BC soils have lost their A horizons by erosion.

BEDDING SOIL. Arranging the surface of fields by ploughing and grading into a series of elevated beds separated by shallow ditches for drainage.

BED LOAD. Soil, rock particles or other debris rolled along the bottom of a stream by the moving water, as contrasted with the "silt load" carried in suspension.

BEDROCK. The solid rock underlying soils and other earthy surface formations.

BENCH TERRACES. An embankment constructed across sloping soils with a steep drop on the downslope side.

BIOLOGICAL INTERCHANGE. The interchange of elements between organic and inorganic states in a soil or other substrate through the agency of biological activity. It results from biological decomposition of organic compounds and the liberation of inorganic materials on one hand (mineralization), and the utilization of inorganic materials in the synthesis of microbial tissue on the other (immobilization). Both processes commonly proceed continuously in normal soils.

BIOLOGICAL MINERALIZATION. The conversion of an element occurring in organic compounds to the inorganic form as a result of biological decomposition.

BLACK EARTH. Used by some authors as synonymous with Chernozem; but by a few (in Australia) for self-mulching black clays.

BLACK SOILS. A term used in Canada for soils with dark-coloured surface horizons of the Black (Chernozem) zone; includes Black Earth or Chernozem, Wiesenboden, Solonetz, etc.

BLEICHERDE. The light-coloured, leached, A_2 horizon, of the Podzol.

BLUFF PODZOL. See Depression Podzol.

BOG IRON ORE. Impure ferruginous deposits developed in bogs or swamps by the oxidizing action of algae, bacteria, or the atmosphere on iron carried in solution.

BOG SOIL. An intrazonal group of soils with mucky or peaty surface soils underlain by peat. Bog soils usually have swamp or marsh vegetation and are commonest in humid regions.

BORDER IRRIGATION. Irrigation in which the water flows over narrow strips that are nearly level and are separated by parallel, low-bordering banks or ridges.

BOTTOMLAND. See flood plain.

BRECCIA. A rock composed of coarse angular fragments cemented together.

BROAD-BASE TERRACE. A low embankment, with such gentle slopes that it can be farmed, constructed across sloping soils approximately on the contour. Broad-base terraces are used on pervious soils to reduce runoff and soil erosion.

BROWN EARTHS. Naturally acid, well-drained soils with more or less uniformly coloured profiles. They are coloured by hydrated iron oxides although the brown colour may be masked by humus or by colours inherited from the parent material. The chemical composition of the clay fraction remains nearly constant throughout the profile, indicating that little or no differential eluviation of sesquioxide has occurred.

BROWN FOREST SOILS. An intrazonal group of soils that have dark-brown surface horizons, relatively rich in humus, grading through lighter coloured soil into the parent material. They are characterized by a slightly acid or neutral reaction and a moderately high amount of exchangeable calcium. They are commonly developed under deciduous forests from parent materials relatively rich in bases, especially calcium.

BROWN PODZOLIC SOILS. A zonal group of soils with thin mats of partly decayed leaves over thin, greyish-brown mixed humus and mineral soil. They lie over yellow or yellowish-brown, acid B horizons, slightly richer in clay than the surface soils. These soils develop under deciduous or mixed deciduous and coniferous forests in cool-temperate humid regions.

BROWN SOILS. A zonal group of soils having a brown surface horizon that grades below into lighter coloured soil. These soils have an accumulation of calcium carbonate at 1 to 3 feet. They develop under short grasses, bunchgrasses, and shrubs in a temperate to cool semi-arid climate.

BRUNIGRA. See Prairie soils.

BUFFER, BUFFERING. Substances in the soil that act chemically to resist changes in reaction or pH. The buffering action is due mainly to clay and very fine organic matter. Highly weathered tropical clays are less active buffers than most less weathered silicate clays. Thus with the same degree of acidity, or pH, more lime is required to neutralize (1) a clayey soil than a sandy soil, (2) a soil rich in organic matter than one low in organic matter, or (3) a sandy loam in Michigan, say, than sandy loam in Central Alabama.

BUFFER COMPOUNDS. The clay, organic matter, and such compounds as carbonates and phosphates, which enable the soil to resist appreciable change in pH value.

BUFFER STRIPS. Established strips of perennial grass or other erosion-resisting vegetation, usually on the contour in cultivated fields, to reduce runoff and erosion.

BULK DENSITY. The mass or weight of oven-dry soil per unit bulk volume, including air space. This mass in relation to the weight of a unit volume of water, was formerly called "apparent density" or "volume weight". Mass per unit bulk volume of soil that has been dried to constant weight at 105°C. Symbol—D_b.

BULK SPECIFIC GRAVITY. The ratio of the mass of a dry bulk volume of oven-dried (105°C.) soil to the mass of an equal volume of water.

BULK VOLUME. The volume of an arbitrary soil mass including the volume of the solid particles and of the pores (interstices, voids).

C HORIZON. A relatively little-altered horizon of consolidated or unconsolidated rock material in the lower part of the soil profile that is either like or unlike the material in which overlying, more-altered horizons have developed.

CALCAREOUS SOIL. A soil containing calcium carbonate, or a soil alkaline in reaction because of the presence of calcium carbonate. A soil containing enough calcium carbonate to effervesce (fizz) when treated with dilute hydrochloric acid.

CALICHE. A broad term for the more or less cemented deposits of calcium carbonate in many soils of warm-temperate areas. When it is very near the surface or exposed by erosion, the material hardens. (Caliche is also used for deposits of sodium nitrate in Chile and Peru.)

CAPABILITY, LAND. See Land Capability.

CAPILLARY POROSITY. The volume of small pores within the soil that hold water against the force of gravity.

CAPILLARY WATER. The portion of soil water which is held by cohesion as a continuous film around the particles and in the capillary spaces. Most of this water is available to plants.

CARBOHYDRATES. Compounds containing carbon, hydrogen, and oxygen. Usually the hydrogen and oxygen occur in the proportion of 2 to 1 such as in glucose ($C_6H_{12}O_6$).

CARBON. One of the commonest chemical elements, occurring in lamp-black, coal, and coke in varying degrees of purity. Compounds of carbon are the chief constituents of living tissue.

CARBON CYCLE. The sequence of transformation undergone by carbon utilized by organisms wherein it is used by one organism, later liberated upon the death and decomposition of the organism, and returned to its original state to be reused by another organism.

CARBON DIOXIDE. A colourless gas (CO_2) composed of carbon and oxygen and normally found in small amounts in the air. It is one of the end products of the burning (oxidation) of organic matter, or carbon-containing compounds.

CARBON-NITROGEN RATIO. The ratio of the weight of organic carbon to the weight of total nitrogen in a soil or in an organic material.

CATALYST. A material that increases the rate of a chemical reaction.

CATEGORY. A sub-division in any field of knowledge. (General.) Any one of the sub-divisions of the system of classification in which soils are grouped or arranged on the basis of their characteristics. (Soil.)

CATENA. A group of soils, within a specific soil zone, formed from similar parent materials but with unlike soil characteristics because of differences in relief or drainage.

CATION. An ion carrying a positive charge of electricity. The common soil cations are calcium, magnesium, sodium, potassium, and hydrogen.

CATION EXCHANGE. The exchange of cations held by the soil-adsorbing complex with other cations. Thus if a soil-adsorbing complex is rich in sodium, treatment with calcium sulphate (gypsum) causes some calcium cations to exchange with some sodium cations.

CATION EXCHANGE CAPACITY. A measure of the total amount of exchangeable cations that can be held by the soil. It is expressed in terms of milliequivalents per 100 grams of soil at neutrality (pH 7) or at some other stated pH value. (Formerly called base-exchange capacity.)

CEMENTED. Having a brittle hard consistence because of some cementing substance such as carbonate silica oxides, iron and aluminium, or humus. The hardness and brittleness persist when wet.

CHANNERY. See Coarse Fragments.

CHELATES.   A type of chemical compound in which a metallic atom is firmly combined with a molecule by means of multiple chemical bonds. The term refers to the claw of a crab illustrative of the way in which the atom is held.

CHEMICALLY PRECIPITATED PHOSPHORUS.   Phosphorus compounds formed by reactions between constituents in solution into chemically homogeneous solid particles. Antithesis of forms of phosphorus formed from solution on to solid surfaces consisting of other minerals or compounds. Examples: precipitated compounds of calcium and magnesium above pH 6.0 to 6.5, or of iron and aluminium below pH 5.8 to 6.1, excluding monolayer precipitates of these constituents which are of chemisorbed or exchangeable forms. A form of fixed phosphate.

CHEMISORBED PHOSPHORUS.   A chemically precipitated monolayer on surface of another crystalline species, formed by reaction of phosphorus compounds with solid constituents. A form of adsorbed phosphorus, involving surface valence forces and chemical affinities between the phosphate ion and the lattice constituents on which adsorption takes place.

CHERNOZEM SOILS.   A zonal group of soils having deep, dark to nearly black surface horizons and rich in organic matter, which grades into lighter coloured soil below. At 1.5 to 4 feet, these soils have layers of accumulated calcium carbonate. They develop under tall and mixed grasses in a temperate to cool subhumid climate.

CHERT.   A structureless form of silica, closely related to flint, which breaks into angular fragments. Soils developed from impure limestones containing fragments of chert and having abundant quantities of these fragments in the soil mass are called cherty soils.

CHERTY SOILS.   See Chert.

CHESTNUT SOILS.   A zonal group of soils with dark-brown surface horizons, which grade into lighter coloured horizons beneath. They have layers of accumulated calcium carbonate at 1 to 4 feet. They are developed under mixed tall and short grasses in a temperate to cool and subhumid to semiarid climate. Chestnut soils occur in regions a little more moist than those having Brown soils and a little drier than those having Chernozem soils.

CHISEL.   A tillage machine with one or more soil-penetrating points that can be drawn through the soil to loosen the subsoil, usually to a depth of 12 to 18 inches.

CLASS.   A group having a definite range in a property or attribute, such as acidity, slope, texture, structure, land capability, degree of erosion, and drainage of soils.

CLASSIFICATION. The assignment of objects or units to groups within a system of categories distinguished by their properties. In the classification of soils a fundamental unit is the series. Series are grouped into families, families into great soil groups, these into suborders, and suborders into orders (of which there are three, the Zonal, Azonal, and Intrazonal).

CLAY. As a soil separate, the mineral soil particles less than 0.002 mm. in diameter. As a soil textural class, soil material that contains 40 per cent or more of clay, less than 45 per cent of sand, and less than 40 per cent of silt.

CLAYEY. Includes all clay textural classes, i.e. sandy clay, silty clay, and clay.

CLAY LOAM. A textural class. Soil material that contains 27 to 40 per cent of clay and 20 to 45 per cent of sand.

CLAY MINERAL. Naturally occurring inorganic crystalline material in soils or other earthy deposits of clay size—particles less than 0.002 mm. in diameter.

CLAYPAN. A compact, slowly permeable soil horizon rich in clay and separated more or less abruptly from the overlying soil. Claypans are commonly hard when dry and plastic or stiff when wet.

CLIMATE. The sum total of all atmospheric or meteorological influences, principally temperature, moisture, wind, pressure, and evaporation, which combine to characterize a region and give it individuality by influencing the nature of its land forms, soils, vegetation and land use. Contrast with Weather.

CLIMOSEQUENCE. A sequence of soils whose properties are functionally related to climate as a soil formation factor.

CLINOSEQUENCE. A sequence of soils whose properties are functionally related to the amount of slope on which they were formed.

CLOD. A mass of soil produced by ploughing or digging, which usually slakes easily with repeated wetting and drying, in contrast to a ped, which is a natural soil aggregate.

COARSE FRAGMENTS. Masses of mineral or rock material greater than 2 mm. in diameter.

COARSE SAND. See Soil Separates and Soil Textures.

COBBLES. Rounded mineral or rock fragments between 3 and 10 inches in diameter. See Coarse Fragments.

M

COBBLY.   Soils having rounded or partially rounded fragments of rock ranging from 3 to 10 inches in diameter. Angular cobbly, formerly included as stony, is similar to cobbly except that fragments are not rounded. A single piece of either is a cobblestone or small stone. See Coarse Fragments.

COLLOID, SOIL.   Colloid refers to organic or inorganic matter having very small particle size and a correspondingly large surface area per unit of mass. Most colloidal particles are too small to be seen with the ordinary compound microscope. Soil colloids do not go into true solution as sugar or salt do, but they may be dispersed into a relatively stable suspension and thus be carried in moving water. By treatment with salts and other chemicals, colloids may be flocculated, or aggregated, into small crumbs or granules that settle out of water. (Such small crumbs of aggregated colloids can be moved by rapidly moving water or air just as other particles can be.) Many mineral soil colloids are really tiny crystals and the minerals can be identified with X-rays and in other ways.

COLLUVIUM.   Mixed deposits of soil material and rock fragments near the base of rather steep slopes. The deposits have accumulated through soil creep, slides, and local wash.

COLUMNAR (SOIL STRUCTURE).   Similar to prismatic structure except that the tops of the blocks are rounded.

COMPLEX, SOIL.   An intimate mixture of soil series whose areal extent is too small to be shown separately on a soil map. The whole group of soils must be shown together as one mapping unit and described as a soil complex.

COMPOST.   A mass of rotted organic matter made from waste plant residues. Inorganic fertilizers, especially nitrogen, and a little soil (usually) are added to it. The organic residues usually are piled in layers, to which the fertilizers are added. The layers are separated by thin layers of soil. The whole pile is kept moist and allowed to decompose. The pile is usually turned once or twice. The principal purpose in making compost is to permit the organic materials to become crumbly and to reduce the carbon-nitrogen ratio of the material. Compost is sometimes called artificial manure.

CONCRETIONS.   Hard grains, pellets, or nodules from concentrations of compounds in the soil that cement the soil grains together. The composition of some concretions is unlike that of the surrounding soil. Concretions can be of various sizes, shapes, and colours.

CONDITIONER (FERTILIZER).   A material added to a fertilizer to prevent caking and to keep it free flowing.

CONSISTENCE. The combination of properties of soil material that determine its resistance to crushing and its ability to be moulded or changed in shape. Consistence depends mainly on the forces of attraction between soil particles. Consistence is described by such words as loose, friable, firm, soft, plastic, and sticky.

CONSOLIDATE. To place into a compact mass and thus increase density and reduce pore space.

CONTINENTAL CLIMATE. A general term for the climate typical of great land masses where wide ranges in temperature and other weather conditions occur because the area is not greatly influenced by nearness to the sea.

CONTOUR. An imaginary line connecting points of equal elevation on the surface of the soil. A contour terrace is laid out on a sloping soil at right angles to the direction of the slope and level throughout its course. In contour ploughing the ploughman keeps to a level line at right angles to the direction of the slope, which usually results in a curving furrow.

CONTOUR FARMING. Conducting field operations, such as ploughing, planting, cultivating and harvesting on the contour or at right angles to the natural direction of slope.

CONTOUR FURROWS. Furrows ploughed on the contour on pasture or range land to prevent soil loss and allow water to penetrate the soil. Sometimes used in planting trees or shrubs on the contour.

CONTOUR STRIP CROPPING. The production of crops in comparatively narrow strips planted on the contour and at right angles to the natural direction of slope. Usually strips of grass or close growing crops are alternated with those in cultivated crops. Graded Strip Cropping is a form of contour strip cropping in which the strips have a grade of not more than 1 per cent laid out from a guide line in the centre of the strip. All rows and furrows are continuous to a grassed waterway. Graded Strip Cropping is used on sloping land which is slightly or moderately wet. It serves to control erosion and also provides drainage by allowing surface water to follow the rows at a safe velocity.

COPPICE MOUNDS. Small mounds of soil material stabilized around desert shrubs.

CORRASION. The process by which a flowing substance loaded with abrading material detaches or wears away rock. A stream carrying sand and gravel has power to cause corrasion.

CORROSION. The process by which surface or ground water dissolves and chemically alters rock materials with which it comes into contact.

CRADLE KNOLL. The earth raised and left in a knoll by an uprooted tree.

CREEP. The downward mass movement of sloping soil. The movement is usually slow and irregular and occurs most commonly when the lower soil is nearly saturated with water.

CROTOVINA. A former animal burrow in one soil horizon, which has been filled with material from another horizon (also spelt "Krotovina").

CROUTE CALCAIRE. Hardened caliche, often found in thick masses or beds overlain by only a few inches of earth. See Caliche.

CRUMB STRUCTURE. Very porous spheroidal aggregates of soil.

CRUST. A thin, brittle layer of hard soil that forms on the surface of many soils when they are dry. An exposed hard layer of materials cemented by calcium carbonate, gypsum, or other binding agents. Most desert crusts are formed by the exposure of such layers through removal of the upper soil by wind or running water and their subsequent hardening.

CRYSTALLINE ROCK. A rock composed of closely fitting, mineral crystals that have formed in the rock substance. Such a rock is in contrast to one made up of cemented grains of sand, volcanic glass, or other material.

CULTIVATION. A mechanical stirring of the soil in place as in seedbed preparation or weed control.

D LAYER. Any stratum underlying the soil profile.

DEALKALIZATION. Removal of exchangeable sodium (or alkali) from the soil, usually by chemical treatment and leaching.

DEBRIS, ROCK. The material resulting from the decay and disintegration of rocks. It may occur in the place where it was produced, or it may be transported by streams of water or ice and deposited in other localities.

DEBRIS CONE (GEOLOGY). A fan-shaped deposit of soil, sand, gravel, and boulders built up at the point where a mountain stream meets a valley, or otherwise where its velocity is reduced sufficiently to cause such deposits. Similar to alluvial fan, but consists of coarser material lying on steeper slopes.

DEEP PERCOLATION. A general term for the downward movement of water beyond the reach of plant roots.

DEEP SOIL.   Generally, a soil deeper than 40 inches to rock or other strongly contrasting material. Also, a soil with a deep black surface layer; a soil deeper than about 40 inches to the parent material or to other unconsolidated rock material not modified by soil forming processes; or a soil in which the total depth of unconsolidated material, whether true soil or not is 40 inches or more.

DEFLATION.   Removal of fine soil particles from soil by wind erosion.

DEFLOCCULATE.   To separate or to break up soil aggregates into the individual particles; to disperse the particles of granulated clay to form a clay that runs together or puddles.

DEGRADATION (SOIL).   The change of one kind of soil to a more highly leached kind, such as the change of a Chernozem to a Podzol.

DEHYDRATION.   Removal or loss of water.

DELTA.   An alluvial deposit formed where a stream or river drops its sediment load on entering a body of more quiet water, formed largely beneath the water surface, and often resembling the shape of the Greek letter Delta.

DENITRIFICATION.   The process by which nitrates or nitrites in the soil or organic deposits are reduced to ammonia or free nitrogen by bacterial action. The process results in the escape of nitrogen into the air and is therefore wasteful.

DEPOSIT.   Material left in a new position by some natural transporting agent such as water, wind, ice, or gravity.

DEPTH, EFFECTIVE SOIL.   The depth of soil material which plant roots can penetrate readily to obtain water and plant nutrients. It is the depth to a layer that differs from the overlying material in physical or chemical properties sufficiently to prevent or seriously retard the growth of roots.

DESALINIZATION.   Removal of salts from saline soil, usually by leaching.

DESERT.   An area with an extremely arid climate. Vegetation, if present at all, is generally sparse and includes very hardy, drought resistant types such as cactus and rapid-growing annuals that can grow, bloom, and produce seed on the moisture from a single good rain or a brief rainy period.

DESERT CRUST.   A hard layer, containing calcium carbonate, gypsum, or other binding material exposed at the surface in desert regions.

DESERT SOIL. A zonal group of soils that have light-coloured surface soils and usually are underlain by calcareous material and frequently by hard layers. They are developed under extremely scanty scrub vegetation in warm to cool, arid climates.

DESILTING AREA. An area used for removing the sediment from flowing water, especially by vegetation.

DESORPTION. The removal of adsorbed materials from surfaces.

DETACHMENT. The removal from a soil mass of transportable fragments of soil material by an eroding agent, usually falling raindrops, running water, or wind. Through detachment, soil particles or aggregates are made ready for transport.

DIATOMS. Algae having a siliceous cell wall which persists as a skeleton after death. Any of the microscopic unicellular or colonial algae constituting the class Bacillariae. They occur abundantly in fresh and salt waters and are widely distributed in soils.

DIATOMACEOUS EARTH. A geological deposit derived chiefly from the remains of diatoms.

DIFFUSION. The transport of matter as a consequence of the movement of the constituent particles. The intermingling of two gases or liquids in contact with each other takes place by diffusion.

DIPOLAR. Having two poles as a result of separation of electric charge. A dipolar molecule orients in an electric field.

DISPERSE. To break up compound particles.

DISPERSION MEDIUM. Fluid in which particles are dispersed.

DISPERSION OF SOIL. Deflocculation of the soil and its suspension in water.

DOLOMITE. A rock containing a high percentage of calcium and magnesium carbonates. Ground dolomitic limestone, containing considerable magnesium carbonate as well as calcium carbonate, is widely used as agricultural lime, especially on soils with a low magnesium content.

DRAIN (VERB). (1) To provide outlet channels so that excess water can be removed by surface flow or by downward internal flow through the soil. (2) To lose water by percolation.

DRAINAGE (A PRACTICE). The removal of excess surface water or excess water from within the soil, by means of surface or subsurface drains.

DRAINAGE, SOIL. (1) The rapidity and extent of the removal of water from the soil by runoff and flow through the soil to underground spaces. (2) As a condition of the soil, soil drainage refers to the frequency and duration of periods when the soil is free of saturation. For example, in well-drained soils, the water is removed readily, but not rapidly; in poorly-drained soils, the root zone is water-logged for long periods and the roots of ordinary crop plants cannot get enough oxygen; and in excessively drained soils, the water is removed so completely that most crop plants suffer from lack of water.

DRAINAGE, TERRACE. Constructed channel for conducting surplus surface water from land with minimum erosion.

DRAIN TILE. Concrete or pottery pipe for water outlets from soil.

DRIFT. Material of any sort deposited by geological processes in one place after having been removed from another. Glacial drift includes the materials deposited by glaciers and by the streams and lakes associated with them.

DROUGHT. A period of dryness, especially a long one. Usually considered to be any period of soil moisture deficiency within the plant root zone. A period of dryness of sufficient length to deplete soil moisture to the extent that plant growth is seriously retarded.

DRY AGGREGATE. A soil aggregate not broken down by dry sieving.

DRY FARMING. Generally, producing crops that require some tillage in sub-humid or semiarid regions without irrigation. The system usually involves periods of fallow between crops during which water from precipitation is absorbed and retained.

DRY SANDS. Sandy deposits, with low water-holding capacity, in which there has been no clear development of soil characteristics since deposition.

DRY WEIGHT PERCENTAGE (OF WATER IN SOIL). The weight of water expressed as a percentage of the oven-dry weight of soil.

DUNE. A mount or ridge of loose sand piled up by the wind. During periods of extreme drought, granulated soil material of fine texture may be piled into low dunes, sometimes called clay dunes.

DUNE SAND. (1) Areas of wind-drifted sand in dunes, hummocks and ridges, usually free from vegetation and undergoing active erosion and re-deposition by winds. (2) Sand, predominantly from 0.1 to 0.4 mm. diameter, that has been piled up by wind into dunes.

DUST MULCH. A loose, dry surface layer of a cultivated soil.

EARTHFLOW. See Landslide.

ECOLOGY. The branch of biology that deals with the mutual relations among organisms and between organisms and their environment.

ECTODYNAMORPHIC SOIL. Soils whose properties are influenced mainly by factors other than parent material. See Endodynamorphic Soil.

EDAPHIC. A term pertaining to the influence or relationship of soil or other similar media to plant growth in contrast to atmospheric influences.

EDAPHOLOGY. The scientific study of the relationships between soils and living things, including man's use of the land.

EFFLUENT. The outflowing of water from a subterranean storage space. (Also used generally for gases and other liquids.)

ELECTROLYTE. Any conductor of electric current in which chemical change accompanies the passage of the current and the amount of the change is proportional to the amount of current passed. Usually electrolytes are solutions of substances in a liquid, such as salt in water. A substance that forms a conductor of electricity when added to a solvent. Thus, common table salt becomes an electrolyte when added to water.

ELUVIAL HORIZON. Soil horizon from which fine material has been removed either in solution or water suspension. Horizon depleted of clay or sesquioxides by leaching.

ELUVIATION. The movement of material from one place to another within the soil in either true solution or colloidal suspension. Soil horizons that have lost material through eluviation are said to be eluvial; those that have received material are illuvial. With an excess of rainfall over evaporation, eluviation may take place either downward or laterally according to the direction of water movement. The term refers especially to the movement of soil colloids in suspension; leaching refers to the removal of soluble materials such as salt in true solution.

ENDODYNAMORPHIC SOILS. Soils whose properties are influenced mainly by parent material.

ENVIRONMENT. All external conditions that may act upon an organism or soil to influence its development, including sunlight, temperature, moisture and other organisms.

ENZYMES. Substances produced by living cells which can bring about or speed up chemical reaction. They are organic catalysts.

EOLIAN SOIL MATERIAL. See Aeolian Soil Material.

EQUILIBRIUM. A state of balance between opposing forces or actions, e.g. in soils.

ERODIBLE (SOIL). Susceptible to erosion. A soil, for example, that is quite susceptible to erosion is referred to as erodible, while one that is resistant to erosion is said to be relatively non-erodible.

EROSION. (1) The wearing away of the land surface by running water, wind, or other geological agents, including such processes as gravitational creep. (2) All processes by which earthy materials or rocks are loosened and moved from place to place. (3) Detachment and movement of soil or rock material by water, wind, ice, or gravity. See Accelerated Erosion; Geological Erosion; Gully Erosion; Natural Erosion; Normal Erosion; Rill Erosion; Sheet Erosion; Splash Erosion.

EROSION CLASS. An erosion condition or set of conditions used in mapping the effects of accelerated erosion, or the absence of any effects of it, as part of the land information obtained in a soil conservation survey. An erosion class may consist of a group of similar erosion conditions, such as moderate sheet erosion, or of a characteristic combination of erosion conditions, such as moderate sheet erosion with closely spaced gullies. For convenience in mapping, the classes that designate no apparent erosion, recent alluvial deposits, normal erosion and certain disturbed areas are also commonly called "erosion classes". The erosion class is an appraisal at a specified time of the cumulative effect of accelerated erosion on the area mapped.

EROSION PAVEMENT. A layer of coarse fragments, as gravel or stones, on the surface of the ground, remaining after the removal of fine particles by erosion.

EROSIVE (WIND OR WATER). Used in reference to wind or water having sufficient velocity to cause erosion. Not to be confused with erodible as a quality of soil.

EVAPOTRANSPIRATION. The loss of water from a soil by evaporation and plant transpiration.

EXCHANGE CAPACITY. See Cation-Exchange Capacity.

EXCHANGEABLE. This word describes the ions in the adsorbing complex of the soil that can be exchanged with other ions. For example, when acid soils are limed, calcium ions exchange for hydrogen ions in the complex; when alkali soils are treated with gypsum, calcium ions exchange for sodium ions that can be leached away.

M*

EXCHANGEABLE PHOSPHATE. Phosphate anions held on the surface of solid particles of soils, capable of taking part in ion exchange reactions with other anions.

EXCHANGEABLE POTASSIUM. The potassium which is held mainly by the colloidal portions of the soil and which is easily exchanged with other positively charged ions. It is readily available to growing plant roots.

EXCHANGEABLE SODIUM. Sodium that is attached to the surface of soil particles which can be exchanged with other positively charged ions in the soil solution, such as calcium and magnesium.

FALLOW. Cropland left idle in order to restore productivity, mainly through accumulation of water, nutrients, or both. Summer fallow is a common stage before cereal grain in regions of limited rainfall. The soil is tilled for at least one growing season to control weeds, to aid decomposition of plant residues, and to encourage the storage of moisture for the succeeding grain crop. Bush or forest fallow is a rest period under woody vegetation between crops.

FELDSPARS. Primary alumino-silicate minerals having a three-dimensional framework structure.

FERRIC IRON. An oxidized or high-valence form of iron (Fe^{+3}) responsible for red, yellow, and brown colours in soils.

FERROUS IRON. A reduced or low-valence form of iron (Fe^{+2}), imparting a blue-grey colour to some soil horizons that are more or less permanently saturated with water.

FERTILITY, SOIL. The quality of a soil that enables it to provide compounds, in adequate amounts and in proper balance, for the growth of specified plants, when other growth factors such as light, moisture, temperature, and the physical condition of the soil are favourable.

FERTILIZER. Any natural or manufactured material added to the soil in order to supply one or more plant nutrients. The term is generally applied to largely inorganic materials other than lime or gypsum (mineral fertilizers) sold in the trade.

FERTILIZER FORMULA. The quantity and grade of the crude stock materials used in making a fertilizer mixture. For example, one formula for a fertilizer whose analysis is 5–10–5 could be 625 pounds 16 per cent nitrate of soda, 1111 pounds of 18 per cent superphosphate, 200 pounds 50 per cent muriate of potash, and 64 pounds of filler per ton.

FERTILIZER GRADE. An expression that indicates the percentage of plant nutrients in a fertilizer. Thus a 10–20–10 grade contains 10 per cent nitrogen (N), 20 per cent phosphoric oxide (P_2O_5), and 10 per cent potash (K_2O). This convention is in common use even though the nitrogen, phosphorus, and potassium are present in other forms.

FERTILIZER UNIT. One per cent of a ton of fertilizer, or 20 pounds. For example, a 5–10–5 fertilizer contains 5 units (100 lbs.) of nitrogen (N), 10 units (200 lbs.) of available phosphoric acid (P_2O_5), and 5 units (100 lbs.) of water soluble potash (K_2O).

FIELD CAPACITY. The amount of moisture remaining in a soil after the free water has been allowed to drain away into drier soil material beneath; usually expressed as a percentage of the oven-dry weight of soil or other convenient unit. It is the highest amount of moisture that the soil will hold under conditions of free drainage after excess water has drained away following a rain or irrigation that has wet the whole soil. For permeable soils of medium texture, this is about 2 or 3 days after a rain or thorough irrigation. Although generally similar for one kind of soil, values vary with previous treatments of the soil.

FIELD MOISTURE. The water that soil contains under field conditions.

FIELD STRIP CROPPING. A system of strip cropping in which crops are grown in parallel strips laid out across the general slope but which do not follow the contour. Strips of grass or close-growing crops are alternated with those in cultivated crops.

FILM WATER. The water held on the surface of soil particles that does not drain away, although it moves rapidly under suction gradients. Most of it is available to plant roots.

FINE SAND. (1) A soil separate. See Soil Separate. (2) A soil texture. See Soil Texture.

FINE TEXTURE. (1) Predominating in fine fractions, as fine clay. (2) Includes all clay loams and clays, i.e. clay loam, sandy clay loam, silty clay loam, sandy clay, silty clay, and clay textural classes. Sometimes sub-divided into clayey and moderately fine textures.

FINE TEXTURED SOIL. Roughly, clayey soil containing 35 per cent or more of clay.

FIRE, GROUND (FORESTRY). A fire that not only consumes all the organic materials of the forest floor, but also burns into the underlying soil itself, as, for example, a peat fire. (Usually combined with, but not to be confused with, a surface fire.)

FIRM.   A consistence term used in describing moist soil which crushes under moderate pressure between thumb and forefinger, but with a resistance distinctly noticeable. See Consistence.

FIRST BOTTOM.   The normal flood plain of a stream, subject to frequent or occasional flooding. (U.S.).

FIXATION (IN SOIL).   The conversion of a soluble material, such as a plant nutrient like phosphorus, from a soluble or exchangeable form to a relatively insoluble form.

FIXED PHOSPHORUS.   (1) That phosphorus that has changed to less soluble forms as a result of reaction with the soil; moderately available phosphorus. More specifically, that quantity of soluble phosphorus compounds which when added to soil becomes chemically or biologically attached to the solid phase of soil so as not to be recovered by extracting the soil with a specified extractant under specified conditions. Such extractants include: water, carbonated water, or dilute solutions of strong mineral acids with or without fluoride or other exchangeable anion. (2) Applied phosphorus which is not taken up by plants during the first cropping year. (3) Soluble phosphorus which has become attached to the solid phase of soil in forms highly unavailable to crops; unavailable phosphorus; phosphorus in other than readily or moderately available forms.

FLAGGY.   See Coarse Fragments.

FLAGSTONE.   A relatively thin fragment 6 to 15 inches long, of sandstone, limestone, slate, shale, or (rarely) of schist. See Coarse Fragments.

FLOCCULATE.   To aggregate or clump together individual tiny soil particles, especially fine clay, into small groups or granules. The opposite of deflocculate, or disperse.

FLOOD IRRIGATION.   Irrigation by running water over nearly level soil in a shallow flood.

FLOOD PLAIN.   The nearly flat lands along streams that overflow during floods.

FLUORAPATITE.   A member of the apatite group of minerals, rich in fluorine. Most common mineral in raw rock phosphate.

FOREST FLOOR.   (1) All dead vegetable matter on the mineral soil surface. Includes litter and unincorporated humus. (2) All organic matter, inclusive of litter, on the mineral soil surface of a forest.

FOREST LAND. Land bearing a stand of trees at any age or stature, including seedlings, and of species attaining a minimum of 6 feet average height at maturity; or land from which such a stand has been removed but on which no other use has been substituted. The term is commonly limited to land not in farms; forests on farms are commonly called woodland or farm forests.

FLUVIO-GLACIAL. See Glacio-Fluvial Deposits.

FOREST SOILS. (1) Any soil developed under trees. (2) Soils found under temperate forest (European usage).

FRAGIPANS. Dense and brittle pans or layers in soils that owe their hardness mainly to extreme density or compactness rather than to high clay content or cementation. Removed fragments are friable, but the material in place is so dense that roots cannot penetrate and water moves through it very slowly because of small pore size.

FRIABILITY. The ease of crumbling of soils. (Note: coherence would determine crushing strength.)

FROST, CONCRETE. That type of frost in the soil which is so filled with ice as to be virtually a solid block.

FROST, HONEYCOMB. Frost in the soil of a crystalline nature giving it a loose structure, permitting the ready entrance of water.

GALLED SPOTS. Small areas that are bare because erosion has removed soil.

GENESIS, SOIL. The mode of origin of the soil, with special reference to the processes responsible for the development of the solum, or true soil, from the unconsolidated parent material.

GEOLOGICAL EROSION. See Natural Erosion.

GILGAI. Microrelief of clays that have high coefficients of expansion and contraction with changes in moisture; usually a succession of microbasins, and microknolls in nearly level areas or of microvalleys and microridges that run with the slope. See Microrelief.

GLACIAL DRIFT. A general term for the rock debris that has been transported by glaciers and is deposited, either directly from the ice or from the melt-water, on melting, of the glacier. It may be heterogeneous or it may be assorted.

GLACIAL SOIL. Obsolete: soil formed from glacial drift.

GLACIAL TILL.   See Till.

GLACIATION.   (1) The covering of large areas of land by glacial ice. (2) The geological action of glaciers, including the wearing down of the earth's surface by moving ice, the transportation of loosened soil and rock material, and the later deposition of this material as till and outwash and, indirectly, the deposition of lacustrine material in glacial lakes.

GLACIO-FLUVIAL DEPOSITS.   Material moved by glaciers and subsequently sorted and deposited by streams flowing from the melting ice. These deposits are stratified and may be in the form of outwash plains, deltas, kames, eskers, and kame terraces. See Glacial Drift and Till.

GLEYING.   The soil formation processes leading to the development of a gley soil. See: Humic Gley, Dark Grey Gleysolic Soil.

GLEY SOIL.   A soil horizon in which waterlogging and lack of oxygen have caused the material to be a neutral grey in colour. The term "gleyed" is applied, as in "moderately gleyed soil," to soil horizons with yellow and grey mottling caused by intermittent waterlogging. Gley soils are a Major Soil Group in the U.K. and are subdivided into surface-water gleys and ground-water gleys.

GRADE.   (1) The slope of a road, channel, or natural ground. (2) The finished surface of a canal bed, roadbed, top of embankment, or bottom of excavation; any surface prepared for the support of construction like paving or laying a conduit.

GRANULAR FERTILIZER.   A fertilizer composed of particles of roughly the same composition, about one-tenth inch in diameter. This kind of fertilizer contrasts with fine or powdery fertilizer.

GRANULAR STRUCTURE.   Soil structure in which the individual grains are grouped into spherical aggregates. Highly porous granules are called crumbs. A well-granulated soil has the best structure for most ordinary crop plants.

GRAVELLY.   A coarse fragment class used in soil textural class names. See Coarse Fragments.

GRAVITATIONAL WATER.   The water in the large pores of the soil that drains away under the force of gravity with free under-drainage. Well-drained soils have such water only during and immediately after rains or applications of irrigation water. In poorly drained soils, this water accumulates in the pores at the expense of the air. Under such conditions, the soil lacks oxygen for the roots of most crop plants and is said to be waterlogged.

GREAT SOIL GROUPS. Any one of several broad groups of soil with fundamental characteristics in common. Examples are Chernozem, Grey-Brown Podzolic, and Podzol.

GREEN MANURE. A crop grown for the purpose of being turned under while green, or soon after maturity, for improving the soil.

GREY-BROWN PODZOLIC SOILS. A zonal group of soils having thin organic coverings and thin organic-mineral layers over greyish-brown leached layers that rest upon brown B horizons richer in clay than the soil horizon above. These soils have formed under deciduous forests in a moist temperate climate.

GROUND WATER. Water that fills all the unblocked pores of under-lying material below the water table, which is the upper limit of saturation.

GROUND-WATER PODZOL. An intrazonal group of soils, developed from imperfectly drained sandy deposits in humid regions, with thin organic and organic-mineral layers over light-grey or white leached layers that rest on dark-brown B horizons irregularly cemented with iron, organic matter, or both.

GULLY. A channel or miniature valley cut by running water, but through which water commonly flows only during and immediately after heavy rains or during the melting of snow. A gully may be dendritic or branching or it may be linear, rather long, narrow and of uniform width. The distinction between gully and rill is one of depth. A gully is sufficiently deep that it would not be obliterated by normal tillage operation whereas a rill is of lesser depth and would be smoothed by ordinary farm tillage. See Gully Erosion; Rill Erosion.

GULLY EROSION. Removal of soil by running water, with formation of channels that cannot be smoothed out completely by normal cultivation.

HALOPHYTE. A plant able to grow in salty soil.

HARDPAN. A hardened soil horizon caused by cementation of soil particles with organic matter or with materials such as silica, sesquioxides, or calcium carbonate (see caliche). Hardness or rigidity of horizon does not appreciably change with changes in the water content; pieces of the hard layer do not slake in water.

HEAVY SOIL. An old term formerly used for clayey or fine-textured soils. (The term originated from the heavy draught on the horses when ploughing.)

HORIZON, SOIL. A layer of soil, approximately parallel to the soil surface, with distinct characteristics produced by soil-forming processes.

HUMIC ACID. Alkali soluble end products of the decomposition of organic matter in soil and in composts. The term sometimes is used interchangeably for humus.

HUMIC-GLEY SOILS. Includes Wiesenboden and those soils formerly grouped with Half-Bog soils, that have a thin muck or peat A_0 horizon and an A_1 horizon. Developed in wet meadows and forested swamps.

HUMID CLIMATE. A climate with enough precipitation to support a forest vegetation, although there are exceptions where the plant cover includes no trees, as in the Arctic or high mountains. The lower limit of precipitation may be as little as 15 inches in cool regions and as much as 60 inches in hot regions. A climate having a high average relative humidity.

HUMIFICATION. A process or condition of decay in which plant or animal remains are so thoroughly decomposed that their initial structures or shapes can no longer be recognized.

HUMIN. In reference to soil organic matter has had varied usage but usually is applied to that part of the organic matter not dissolved upon extraction of soil with dilute alkali.

HUMUS. (1) Organic matter that has reached a more or less stable advanced stage of decomposition. It is usually characterized by its dark colour, considerable content of nitrogen, a carbon-nitrogen ratio approaching 10:1 and by various physical and chemical properties, such as high cation exchange capacity, water absorption and swelling. (2) The plant and animal residues in the soil that have undergone some appreciable degree of decomposition.

HUMUS LAYER. The top portion of the soil which owes its characteristic features to the humus contained in it. The humus may be incorporated or unincorporated in the mineral soil. See Mor; Mull.

HUMUS, RAW. See Mor.

HYDRAULIC EQUILIBRIUM (OF WATER IN SOIL). The condition for zero flow rate of liquid or film water in soil. This condition is satisfied when the pressure gradient force is just equal and opposite to the gravity force.

HYDROGENIC SOILS. Soil developed under the influence of water standing within the profile for considerable periods, mainly in cold, humid regions.

HYDROLOGIC CYCLE. The circuit of water movement from the atmosphere to the earth and return to the atmosphere through various stages or processes as precipitation, interception, run-off, infiltration, percolation, storage, evaporation, and transpiration.

HYDROMORPHIC SOILS. Soils developed in the presence of excess water.

HYDRONIUM IONS. The predominant form of occurrence of hydrogen ions in solution, each hydrogen ion being associated with a single water molecule; H_3O^+.

HYDROUS. Containing water.

HYDROXYAPATITE. A member of the apatite group of minerals rich in hydroxyl groups. A nearly insoluble calcium phosphate.

HYGROSCOPIC. Capable of taking up moisture from the air.

HYGROSCOPIC COEFFICIENT. The amount of moisture in a dry soil when it is in equilibrium with some standard relative humidity near a saturated atmosphere (about 98 per cent), expressed in terms of percentage on the basis of oven-dry soil.

HYGROSCOPIC WATER. Water which is so tightly held by the attraction of soil particles that it cannot be removed except as a gas, by raising the temperature above the boiling point of water. This water is unavailable to plants.

IGNEOUS ROCK. Rock produced through the cooling of molten mineral matter. When the cooling process is slow, the rock contains fair-sized crystals of the individual minerals, as in granite.

ILLITE. A series of mica-like, nonexpandable, or slightly expandable alumino-silicate clay minerals in which two silica layers alternate with one alumina layer; also called hydrous micas.

ILLUVIAL HORIZON. Horizon that has received material in solution or suspension from some other part of the soil, e.g. clay, sesquioxides or humus.

IMMATURE SOIL. A soil lacking clear individual horizons because of the relatively short time for soil-building forces to act upon the parent material since its deposition or exposure.

IMMOBILIZATION (OF PLANT NUTRIENTS). The conversion of an available plant nutrient in the soil from an inorganic to an organic form in living tissue. Thus the addition of fresh straw or sawdust to the soil may greatly increase the number of bacteria. These remove available nitrogen and phosphorus from the soil and immobilize them within their cells.

IMPEDED DRAINAGE. Condition in which downward movement of gravitational water is hindered.

IMPERVIOUS SOIL. A soil through which water, air, or roots penetrate slowly or not at all. No soil is absolutely impervious to water and air all the time.

INDURATED SOIL. Soil cemented into a hard mass that will not soften on wetting. See Hardpan; Fragipan.

INFILTRATION. The downward entry of water into soil.

INFILTRATION CAPACITY. The maximum rate at which water can infiltrate into a soil under a given set of conditions.

INFILTRATION RATE. The maximum rate at which a soil, in a given condition at a given time, can absorb water. Also, the maximum rate at which a soil will absorb water impounded on the surface at a shallow depth when adequate precautions are taken regarding border or fringe effects. Defined as the volume of water passing into the soil per unit of area per unit of time, it has the dimensions of velocity (LT^{-1}).

INFILTRATION VELOCITY. The volume of water moving downward into the soil surface per unit of area per unit of time. The local instantaneous volume is the limit approached as the area and time interval are made small. The maximum infiltration velocity is the infiltration rate.

INHERITED SOIL CHARACTERISTICS. Any characteristic of a soil that is due directly to the nature of the material from which it formed, as contrasted to the characteristics that are wholly or partly the result of soil-forming processes acting on parent material. For example, some soils are red because the parent material was red; although the colour of most red soils is due to soil-forming processes.

INORGANIC. Refers to substances occurring as minerals in nature or obtainable from them by chemical means. Refers to all matter except the compounds of carbon, but includes carbonates.

INORGANIC NITROGEN. Nitrogen in combination with mineral elements, not in animal or vegetable form. Ammonium sulphate and sodium nitrate are examples of inorganic nitrogen combinations, while proteins contain nitrogen in organic combination.

IN PLACE (IN SITU). (1) Formed or accumulated on the spot. A rock may decay and break down into small particles where it is first exposed in the land surface. It is then said to have weathered in place or in situ. (2) As a mass appears in the soil before any disturbance. For example, the deeper part of a profile may be massive and show no signs of structure in place but break down into lumps of regular size and shape when removed.

INTAKE RATE. The rate, usually expressed in inches per hour, at which rain or irrigation water enters the soil. This rate is controlled partly by surface conditions (infiltration rate) and partly by subsurface conditions (permeability). It also varies with the method of applying water. The same kind of soil has different intake rates under sprinkler irrigation, border irrigation, and furrow irrigation.

INTERGRADE. Soils which possess moderately well-developed distinguishing characteristics of two or more genetically related groups.

INTRAZONAL SOIL. Any one of the great groups of soils having more or less well-developed soil characteristics that reflect a dominating influence of some local factor of relief or of parent material over the normal influences of the climate and the vegetation on the soil-forming processes. Such groups of soils may be geographically associated with two or more of the zonal groups of soils having characteristics dominated by the influence of climate and vegetation.

ION. An electrically charged particle. As used in soils, an ion refers to an electrically charged element or combination of elements resulting from the breaking up of an electrolyte in solution. Since most soil solutions are highly dilute, many of the salts exist as ions. For example, all or part of the potassium chloride (muriate of potash) in most soils exists as potassium ions and chloride ions. The positively charged potassium ion is called a cation and the negatively charged chloride ion is called an anion.

IRRIGATION. Artificial application of water to the soil for supplying water to crops.

IRRIGATION EFFICIENCY. The ratio of the water consumed by crops of an irrigated farm or project to the water diverted from a river or other natural source into the farm or project canals.

IRRIGATION METHODS. *Border-strip*—Water applied at the upper end of a strip with earth borders to confine the water to the strip.
　　Check basin—Water applied rapidly to relatively level plots surrounded by levees. The basin is a small check.
　　Corrugation—Water applied to small, closely packed furrows, frequently in grain and forage crops, to confine the flow of irrigation water to one direction.

IRRIGATION METHODS *(Continued)*.

Flooding—Water released from field ditches and allowed to flood over the land.

Furrow—Water applied in small ditches made by cultivation implements for tree and row crops.

Sprinkler—Water sprayed over the soil surface through nozzles from a pressure system.

Subirrigation—Water applied in open ditches or tile lines until water table is raised sufficiently to wet the soil.

Wild Flooding—Irrigation water is released at high points in the field without controlled distribution.

ISOTOPE. One of two or more forms of a chemical element having the same atomic number and position in the periodic table of elements, but distinguishable by differences of weight.

KAME. An irregular ridge or hill of stratified glacial drift.

KAOLIN MINERALS. A group of nonswelling clay minerals in which one layer or sheet of silicon and oxygen alternates with a sheet made up of aluminium, oxygen, and hydrogen.

LACUSTRINE DEPOSITS. Materials deposited from lake water. Many nearly level soils have developed from such deposits from old lakes that have long since disappeared.

LAGG. The depressed margin of a raised bog.

LAND. The total natural and cultural environment within which production takes place. Land is a broader term than soil. In addition to soil, its attributes include other physical conditions such as mineral deposits and water supply; location in relation to centres of commerce, populations, and other land; the size of the individual tracts or holdings; and existing plant cover, works of improvement, and the like. Some use the term loosely in other senses: as defined above, but without the economic or cultural criteria, especially in the expression "natural land"; as a synonym for "soil"; for the solid surface of the earth; and also for earthy surface formations, especially in the geomorphological expression "land form".

LAND CAPABILITY. The suitability of land for use without damage. Land-capability is an expression of the effect of physical land conditions, including climate, on the total suitability for use without damage for crops that require regular tillage, for grazing, for woodland, and for wildlife. Land capability involves consideration of (a) the risks of land damage from erosion or other causes, and (b) the difficulties in land use owing to physical land characteristics including climate.

LAND CAPABILITY CLASS. One of the eight classes of land in the land-capability classification. These eight land-capability classes, distinguished according to the risk of land damage or the difficulty of land use are:

A. *Land suitable for cultivation and other uses*

    I. (Light green on maps.) Very good land for cultivation. Nearly level and productive; not subject to erosion. Needs only ordinary good farming methods.

    II. (Yellow.) Good land for cultivation. Mostly gently sloping, not more than moderately subject to erosion. Some rather wet. Can be farmed safely with easily applied practices.

    III. (Red.) Moderately good land for cultivation. Mostly moderately sloping. Some too wet or too dry. Can be farmed safely with practical conservation measures, carefully applied. Usually a combination of two or more measures is needed.

    IV. (Blue.) Fairly good land, suitable for occasional cultivation. Generally strongly sloping; often shallow or very sandy. Often dry climate.

B. *Land not suitable for cultivation*

    V. (Dark Green.) Land very well suited for grazing or forestry. Requires good range or woodland management.

    VI. (Orange.) Land well suited for grazing or forestry. Steeply sloping land, stony or shallow soil, eroded land, droughty land, or wet land. Requires careful management.

    VII. (Brown.) Land fairly well suited for grazing or forestry. Severely limited in use by such factors as very steep slope, shallow or droughty soil, wetness, severe erosion, or excessive salinity. Requires very careful management.

    VIII. (Purple.) Land not suitable for cultivation, grazing, or forestry. May be useful for wildlife, recreation, or protection of water supplies.

LAND CAPABILITY CLASSIFICATION. A grouping of kinds of soil into special units, sub-classes, and classes according to their capability for intensive use and the treatments required for sustained use.

LAND CAPABILITY MAP. A map showing land-capability units, sub-classes, and classes; or a soil conservation survey map coloured to show land-capability classes.

LAND CAPABILITY SUBCLASS. A sub-division of a land-capability class according to the kind of difficulty or risk that is involved in using the land. The four USDA subclasses are: e—dominant limitation is susceptibility to erosion, by either water or wind; w—dominant limitation is excess water, such as that produced by seepage, high water table, or floods; s—dominant limitation is an outstandingly unfavourable soil characteristic, such as low moisture capacity, excess gravel or stone, shallow effective depth; c—dominant limitation is climate, chiefly extremes in precipitation or temperature. Subclasses are not recognized in land-capability Class I. The subclass e does not occur in Class V.

LAND CAPABILITY UNIT. A land capability unit consists of land that is sufficiently uniform in climate, soil, slope, erosion, and other permanent land characteristics to have continuing limitations or hazards of similar degree and nature, and similar inherent potentialities. Thus, the land in a Land Capability Unit is sufficiently uniform (a) to permit use of the same crops and cropping systems on land suitable for cultivation; (b) to result in a particular climax vegetation (range site); or (c) to result in a given composition and volume of tree crops.

LANDSCAPE. The sum total of the characteristics that distinguish a certain kind of area on the earth's surface and give it a distinguishing pattern in contrast to other kinds of areas. Any one kind of soil is said to have a characteristic natural landscape, and under different uses it has one or more characteristic cultural landscapes.

LANDSLIDE. (1) Rapid movement down slope of a mass of soil, rock and debris. (2) Mass of material that has slipped down hill.

LAND TYPE. See Soil Classification.

LAND-USE PLANNING. The development of plans for the uses of land that, over long periods, will best serve the general welfare, together with the formulation of ways and means for achieving such uses.

LAND, WILD. Uncultivated land; it may or may not be maintained by the owner for its protective vegetative cover, or for wood, forage production, recreation, or wildlife.

LATTICE, CLAY. The structural framework of a clay mineral which is made up by the orderly arrangement of the various ionic components of the mineral. The mineral is held together by the chemical bonds exerted toward each other by the various ions in the mineral. The structural pattern repeats itself indefinitely and regularly; the atoms are linked according to definite angles and distances. For example, micas and alumino-silicate clay minerals have layer lattices consisting of alternate silica and alumina layers.

LATTICE ENERGY. The energy required to separate the ions of a crystal to an infinite distance from each other.

LATTICE STRUCTURE. Orderly arrangement of atoms in crystalline material.

LEACHED SALINE SOILS. (1) Soils which have had the soluble salts removed by leaching. (2) Soils which have been saline and which still possess the major physical characteristics of saline soils but from which the soluble salts have been leached, generally as a result of reclamation.

LEACHED SOIL. A soil from which most of the soluble constituents have been removed throughout the entire profile or removed from one part of the profile and accumulated in another part.

LEACHING. The removal of materials in solution by the passage of water through soil.

LEAFMOULD. See Humus Layer.

LEGUME. A member of the legume or pulse family, *Leguminosae*. One of the most important and widely distributed plant families. The fruit is a "legume" or pod that opens along two sutures when ripe. Flowers are usually papilionaceous (butterfly-like). Leaves are alternate, have stipules, and are usually compound. Includes many valuable food and forage species, such as the peas, beans, peanuts, clovers, alfalfas, sweet clovers, lespedezas, vetches, and kudzu. Practically all legumes are nitrogen-fixing plants, and many of the herbaceous species are used as cover and green manure crops. (Even legumes without feed or forage value, such as crotalaria and some lupines, are used for soil improvement.) The legume family contains timber trees such as locust, honey locust, and many tropical trees, and in addition, ornamental plants, including redbud, mimosa and wisteria.

LEGUME INOCULATION. The addition of the proper strain of nitrogen fixing bacteria to legume seed or to the soil in which the seed is to be planted. May be accomplished by (1) the addition of bacteria from pure cultures; (2) the addition of soil from a field on which the particular legume species has recently grown successfully. Inoculation is done so that the legume, with the aid of the associated bacteria, can fix nitrogen from the air instead of taking it from the soil.

LEVEL TERRACE. A broad surface channel or embankment constructed across sloping soil on the contour, as contrasted to a graded terrace, which is built at a slight angle to the contour. A level terrace can be used only on soils that are permeable enough for all of the storm water to soak into the soil so that none breaks over the terrace to cause gullies.

LEVELLING (OF LAND). The reshaping or modification of the land surface to a planned grade to provide a more suitable surface for the efficient application of irrigation water and to provide good surface drainage.

LEY. A term used for pastures or meadows. A short ley is roughly equivalent to "rotation" pasture or meadow, and a long ley to "longtime" pastures and meadows, often incorrectly called permanent.

LIGHT SOIL.   Obsolete in scientific use; see Coarse Texture. A soil which has a low drawbar pull; a soil easy to cultivate.

LIME.   Generally the term lime, or agricultural lime, is applied to ground limestone (calcium carbonate), hydrated lime (calcium hydroxide), or quick lime (calcium oxide), with or without mixtures of magnesium carbonate, magnesium hydroxide, or magnesium oxide, and materials such as basic slag, used as amendments to reduce the acidity of acid soils. In strict chemical terminology, lime refers to calcium oxide (CaO), but by an extension of meaning it is now used for all limestone-derived materials applied to neutralize acid soils.

LIME CONCENTRATION.   An aggregate cemented by precipitation of calcium carbonate.

LIME PAN.   A hardened layer cemented by calcium carbonate.

LIME REQUIREMENT.   The amount of standard ground limestone required to bring a 6.6-inch layer of an acre (about 2,000,000 pounds in mineral soils) of acid soil to some specific lesser degree of acidity, usually to slightly or very slightly acid. In common practice, lime requirements are given in tons per acre of nearly pure limestone, ground finely enough so that all of it passes a 10-mesh scmreen and at least half of it passes a 100-mesh screen.

LIMING.   The application of lime to land, primarily to reduce soil acidity and to supply calcium for plant growth. (Dolomitic limestone supplies both calcium and magnesium.) May also improve soil structure, organic matter content, and nitrogen content of the soil by encouraging the growth of legumes and soil micro-organisms. Liming an acid soil to a pH value of about 6.5 is desirable for maintaining a high degree of availability of most of the nutrient elements required by plants.

LIQUID LIMIT.   Minimum moisture weight percentage at which a small sample of soil material will barely flow under a standard treatment. Sometimes called "upper plastic limit". See Plastic Limit; Plasticity Index.

LISTER.   A double plough, the shares of which throw the soil in opposite directions, leaving the field with a series of alternate ridges and furrows. Row crops may be seeded in the bottoms of the furrows as they are opened up; when no seed is planted, the operation is sometimes referred to as *Blank Listing*. A modification, the *Basin Lister*, has an attachment which forms earth dams across the lister furrows at intervals of 15 to 25 feet, leaving basins with a large water capacity.

LITHOSEQUENCE.   A sequence of soils whose properties are functionally related to differences in the parent rock as a soil-formation factor.

LITHOSOL. A soil having little or no evidence of soil development and consisting mainly of a partly weathered mass of rock fragments or of nearly barren rock.

LOAM. The textural class name for soil having a moderate amount of sand, silt and clay. Loam soils contain 7 to 27 per cent of clay, 28 to 50 per cent of silt, and less than 52 per cent of sand. (In the old literature, especially English literature, the term "loam" applied to mellow soils rich in organic matter, regardless of the texture. The modern term refers only to the relative amounts of sand, silt and clay; loam soils may or may not be mellow.)

LOAMY SOIL. A general expression for soils of intermediate texture between the coarse-textured or sandy soils, on the one hand, and the fine-textured or clayey soils on the other. Sandy loams, loams, silt loams, and clay loams are regarded as loamy soils.

LOESS. A wind-blown deposit of fine earth in which silt-sized particles predominate.

LOOSE. See Consistence.

LUXURY CONSUMPTION. The intake by a plant of an essential nutrient in amounts exceeding what it needs. Thus if potassium is abundant in the soil, alfalfa may take in more than is required.

MACROPORE. Large or non-capillary pores. The pores, or voids, in a soil from which water usually drains by gravity. Is differentiated from micropore, or capillary pore, which consists of voids small enough to hold water against gravity by capillarity. Sandy soils have a large macropore, or non-capillary, pore space and a small micropore, or capillary, pore space. Nongranular clayey soils are just the reverse.

MADE-LAND. Areas filled with earth, trash, or both.

MANURE. Generally, the refuse from stables and barnyards, including both animal excreta and straw or other litter. In some countries the term "manure" is used more broadly and includes both farmyard or animal manure and "chemical manures" (fertilizers).

MARL. An earth deposit, consisting mainly of calcium carbonate commonly mixed with clay or other impurities. It is formed chiefly at the margins of fresh-water lakes. It is commonly used for liming acid soils.

MARSH. Periodically wet or continually flooded areas with surface not deeply submerged. Covered dominantly with sedges, cattails, rushes, or other hydrophytic plants. Subclasses include fresh water and salt water marshes.

MATURE SOIL. Any soil with well-developed soil horizons having characteristics produced by the natural processes of soil formation and in near equilibrium with its present environment.

MAXIMUM WATER-HOLDING CAPACITY. The average moisture content of a disturbed sample of soil, 1 cm. high which is at equilibrium with a water table at its lower surface.

MEADOW PODZOL. See Depression Podzol.

MEANDER-LAND. Unsurveyed land, usually between a lake shore or stream border, at the time of a cadastral survey, and the present lower shore or border.

MECHANICAL ANALYSIS. The physical analysis of soil materials to determine the amounts of the various soil separates, or grain-size fractions.

MECHANICAL STABILITY. Resistance of soil to breakdown by mechanical forces such as tillage or abrasion from windborne soil particles; strength of coherence; mechanical strength.

MEDITERRANEAN CLIMATE. A general term for warm-temperature climates that are dry in the warm season and moist in the cool season.

MEDIUM TEXTURED. Intermediate between fine-textured and coarse-textured soils. Includes very fine sandy loams, loam, silt loam, and silt textural classes.

MELLOW SOIL. A porous, softly granular soil easily worked without becoming compacted.

MESOPHILIC BACTERIA. Bacteria whose optimum temperatures for growth fall in an intermediate range of approximately 20° to 40°C.

METAMORPHIC ROCK. A rock that has been altered from its previous condition through the action of heat and pressure. For example, marble is a metamorphic rock produced from limestone, gneiss is one produced from granite, and slate is produced from shale.

MICAS. Primary alumino-silicate minerals in which two silica layers alternate with one alumina layer. They separate readily into thin sheets or flakes.

MICROCLIMATE. The local climatic condition near the ground resulting from the modification of the general climatic condition by local differences in relief, exposure, and cover.

MICROFAUNA. The part of an animal population comprised of individuals so small that they cannot be distinguished without the use of a microscope. Usually applied to protozoa, nematodes, etc.

MICROFLORA. The part of a plant population comprised of individuals so small that they cannot be distinguished without the use of a microscope. Usually applied to algae, fungi, bacteria, etc.

MICRONUTRIENTS. Nutrients that plants need in only small, trace, or minute amounts. Often referred to as 'trace elements'.

MICRO-ORGANISMS. Forms of life too small to be seen with the unaided eye.

MICRORELIEF. Small-scaled differences in relief, such as small mounts, swales, or pits that are a few feet across and have differences in elevation of a few inches to around 3 feet that are significant to soil-forming processes, to growth of plants, or to preparing the soil for cultivation.

MINE-DUMPS. Areas of waste rock, with little or no segregation, that come from ore and coal mines, quarries, and smelters. See Miscellaneous Land Type.

MINE-WASH. Accumulations of sandy, silty, or clayey material recently eroded in mining operations; may clog streams, channels, and damage land on which it is deposited.

MINERAL (GEOLOGY). A natural inorganic compound usually having definite physical properties, crystalline structure, and chemical composition (within the limits of isomorphism).

MINERALIZATION. The conversion of an element that is immobilized in some organic combination to available form as a result of microbial decomposition.

MINERALOGICAL ANALYSIS. Estimation of the kinds or amounts of minerals in soil or rock.

MINERAL SOIL. A general term for a soil composed chiefly of mineral matter, in contrast to an organic soil, which is composed chiefly of organic matter.

MISCELLANEOUS LAND TYPE. A mapping unit for areas of land that have little or no natural soil or that are too nearly inaccessible for orderly examination, or where for other reasons it is not feasible to classify the soil. See Badland, Made-Land, Meander-Land, Mine-Wash, Oil-Wasteland, Slickens, Stony-Land, Swamp, Tidal Flats, Urban-Land, Volcanic-Ash-Land, and Waste-Land.

MODERATELY COARSE TEXTURED. Includes all sandy loams except the very fine sandy loam textural class. See Coarse Texture.

MODERATELY FINE TEXTURED. Includes all clay loams, i.e., clay loam, sandy clay loam, and silty clay loam textural classes. See Fine Textured.

MOISTURE EQUIVALENT. Percentage of water retained in a soil sample 1 cm. thick after it has been saturated and subjected to a centrifugal force 1,000 times gravity for 30 minutes.

MOISTURE STRESS. The tension at which water is held by the soil.

MOISTURE TENSION. The force at which water is held by soil; usually expressed as the equivalent of a unit column of water in centimetres; 1,000 cm. equal 1 atmosphere equivalent tension. Moisture tension increases with dryness and indicates the degree of work required to remove soil moisture for use by plants.

MOISTURE VOLUME PERCENTAGE OR WATER RATIO. The per cent of the soil bulk volume that is occupied by moisture. Symbol P_v. Numerically it is equal to depth percentage. The ratio of the volume of water in a soil to the total bulk volume of the soil system.

MOISTURE WEIGHT PERCENTAGE. Moisture content expressed as a percentage of oven-dry (105° to 110°C.) weight of soil. Same as Dry Weight Percentage.

MOLE DRAINAGE. The method of draining land by constructing underground tubular channels in the soil. The channels are constructed with a mole plough consisting of a short pointed cylinder of iron, 4 or 6 inches in diameter, and connected to the beam by a sharp shank about 4 feet long. The plough is pulled along the course of the desired drain with the cylinder at a depth of from 2 to 3 feet.

MONTMORILLONITE. Alumino-silicate clay mineral that expands and contracts with the absorption and loss of water. It has a high cation-exchange capacity and is plastic and sticky when moist.

MOR. Raw humus; a type of forest humus layer of unincorporated organic material, usually matted or compacted or both; distinct from the mineral soil, unless the latter has been blackened by washing in organic matter.

MORPHOLOGY, SOIL. The constitution of the soil including the texture, structure, consistence, colour, and other physical, chemical and biological properties of the various soil horizons that make up the soil profile.

MOTTLED HORIZONS. Soil horizons irregularly marked with spots of colour. A common cause of mottling is imperfect or impeded drainage although there are other causes, such as soil development from an unevenly weathered rock. Different kinds of minerals may cause mottling.

MOUNTAIN SOILS. Obsolete: General term, usually referring to skeletal soils formed mainly by physical weathering in cool mountain regions.

MUCK. Highly decomposed organic soil material developed from peat. Generally, muck is decomposed to the point that the original plant parts cannot be identified. (U.S.).

MUDFLOW. Flow of a torrent so heavily charged with earth and debris that the mass is thick and viscous. Rocks several feet in diameter may be carried in it. Mudflows may result from run-off of very heavy rains or from explosive volcanic eruptions.

MULCH. A natural or artificially applied layer of plant residues or other materials on the surface of the soil. Mulches are generally used to help conserve moisture, control temperature, prevent surface compaction or crusting, reduce runoff and erosion, improve soil structure, or control weeds. Common mulching materials include compost, sawdust, wood chips, and straw. Sometimes paper, fine brush, or small stones are used.

MULCH FARMING (MULCH TILLAGE). Tillage of the soil and treatment of crop residues in ways to leave plant materials within or on the soil surface to form a mulch.

MULL. A humus-rich layer consisting of mixed organic and mineral matter. A mull blends into the upper mineral-layers without an abrupt change in soil characteristics.

MYCELIA. The threadlike bodies of simple organisms, such as the common bread mould.

MYCORHIZA (MICORRHIZA). The morphological association, usually symbiotic, of fungi and roots of seed plants. The feeding roots are enshrouded and partially penetrated by fine filaments of fungi; such roots commonly are more branched and lose their root hairs.

NEMATODES. Very small worms abundant in many soils and important because many of them attack and destroy plant roots.

NEUTRAL SOIL. A soil that is neither significantly acid nor alkaline. Strictly, a neutral soil has pH of 7.0; in practice a neutral soil has a pH between 6.6 and 7.3.

NITRATE REDUCTION.   The biological reduction of nitrates to the nitrite form.

NITRIFICATION.   The formation of nitrates and nitrites from ammonia (or ammonium compounds), as in soils by micro-organisms.

NITROGEN CYCLE.   The sequence of transformation undergone by nitrogen wherein it is used by one organism, later liberated upon the death and decomposition of the organism and is converted by biological means to its original state of oxidation to be re-used by another organism.

NITROGEN FIXATION.   Generally, the conversion of free nitrogen to nitrogen combined with other elements. Specifically in soils, the assimilation of free nitrogen from the soil air by soil organisms and the formation of nitrogen compounds that eventually become available to plants. The nitrogen-fixing organisms associated with legumes are called symbiotic; those not definitely associated with the higher plants are nonsymbiotic.

NODULE.   A structure developed on the roots of most legumes and a few other plants in response to the stimulus of root nodule bacteria. Legumes bearing these nodules are nitrogen-fixing plants, utilizing atmospheric nitrogen instead of depending on nitrogen compounds in the soil.

NODULE BACTERIA.   See Rhizobia.

NON-SYMBIOTIC ORGANISMS.   Independent or free-living organisms; commonly refers to organisms capable of fixing nitrogen apart from leguminous plants.

NUTRIENT, PLANT.   Any element taken in by a plant, essential to its growth and used by it in elaboration of its food and tissue.

OCEANIC CLIMATE.   The type of climate characteristic of land areas near oceans which contribute to the humidity and at the same time have a moderating influence on temperature and range of temperature variation. Also referred to as Marine or Maritime Climate.

OIL WASTELAND.   See Miscellaneous Land Type.

ORDER.   The highest category in some soil classifications. Three orders are zonal soils, intrazonal soils, and azonal soils.

ORGANIC MATTER.   A general term for plant and animal material in or on the soil, in all stages of decomposition. Readily decomposed organic matter is often distinguished from the more stable forms that have already passed through the stage of rapid decomposition. Also see Humus.

ORGANIC PHOSPHORUS. Phosphorus present as a constituent of an organic compound or a group of organic compounds. Examples: glycerophosphoric acid, inositol phosphoric acid, cytidylic acid.

ORGANIC SOIL. A general term applied to a soil or to a soil horizon that consists primarily of organic matter, such as peat soils, muck soils, and peaty soil layers.

ORTSTEIN. The B horizon of Podzols that are cemented by sesquioxides and/or organic matter.

OVEN-DRY SOIL. A soil dried at 105° to 110°C. until it is in moisture equilibrium at that temperature.

OXIDATION. A chemical change of an element or compound involving the addition of oxygen or its chemical equivalent. A chemical change that involves an increase of positive valence or a decrease of negative valence. For example, if iron is changed from the ferrous state (in which it has 2 positive valences) to the ferric state (in which it has 3 positive valences), the iron is said to be oxidized. The reverse process is reduction. During the burning of fuel, oxygen is added to carbon to form carbon dioxide; in the rusting of iron, the addition of oxygen forms a red iron oxide.

OXIDE. A compound of any element with oxygen alone.

PAN. A layer or soil horizon within a soil that is firmly compacted or is very rich in clay. Examples include hardpans, fragipans, claypans, and traffic pans.

PARENT MATERIAL. The material from which the soil profile develops.

PARENT ROCK. The rock from which parent materials of soils are formed.

PARTIAL STERILIZATION. The incomplete elimination of microorganisms in soil or other substrates usually by treatment with heat or chemicals. The process is selective in action, certain organisms, or groups of organisms, being destroyed to a greater extent than others or, in some cases, being completely eliminated.

PARTICLE DENSITY. The average density of the soil particles not including fluid space. Particle density is usually expressed in grams per cubic centimetre and is sometimes referred to as "real density or grain density".

PARTICLE SIZE. The effective diameter of a particle measured by sedimentation, sieving, or micrometric methods.

PARTS PER MILLION (ppm.) A notation for indicating small amounts of materials. The expression gives the number of units by weight of the substance per million weight units of oven-dry soil. The term may be used to express the number of weight units of a substance per million weight units of solution.

PEAT. Undecomposed or only slightly decomposed organic matter accumulated under conditions of excessive moisture.

PED. An individual natural soil aggregate such as a crumb, prism, or block, in contrast to a clod, which is a mass of soil brought about by digging or other disturbance.

PEDOLOGY. The study of soil, i.e. soil science.

PENEPLAIN. A land surface which has become nearly level, as the result of denudation.

PENETRABILITY. The work required to push a probe a unit distance into the soil.

PERCOLATION. The downward movement of water through soil.

PERMAFROST. (1) Permanently frozen material underlying the solum. (2) Perennially frozen soil horizon.

PERMAFROST TABLE. The upper boundary of the permafrost, coincident with the lower limits of seasonal thaws.

PERMANENT PASTURE. Pasture that occupies the soil for a long time in contrast to rotation pasture, which occupies the soil for only a year or two in a rotation cycle with other crops. As used in the humid parts of the United States, the term "permanent pasture" is equivalent to the European "long ley".

PERMEABILITY. The quality of a soil horizon that enables water or air to move through it. It can be measured quantitatively in terms of rate of flow of water through a unit cross section in unit time under specified temperature and hydraulic conditions. Values for saturated soils usually are called hydraulic conductivity. The permeability of a soil may be limited by the presence of one nearly impermeable horizon even though the others are permeable.

pH. A numerical designation of relatively weak acidity and alkalinity as in soils and other biological systems. Technically, pH is the common logarithm of the reciprocal of the hydrogen-ion concentration of a solution. A pH of 7.0 indicates precise neutrality, higher values indicate increasing alkalinity, and lower values indicate increasing acidity.

PHASE, SOIL. The sub-division of a soil type or other classification soil unit having variations in characteristics not significant to the classification of the soil but significant to the use and management of the soil. Examples of the variations recognized by phases of soil types include differences in slope, stoniness, and thickness because of accelerated erosion.

PHYSICAL WEATHERING. The breakdown of rock and mineral soil into smaller fragments by physical forces, as by frost action. See Weathering.

PHYSISORPTION. Process of attachment of molecules to a surface by other-than-ionic processes. Examples are polar attachment of water molecules to solid phase surfaces of soil, acetic acid molecules to clay (ionic processes may also attach large molecules to clay surfaces, but these are not processes of physisorption). Physisorption is active in attachment of certain organic phosphorus compounds such as nucleic acid to clays, but is not active in the attachment of phosphate ions.

PHYTOGENIC SOILS. Soils developed under the dominant influence of the natural vegetation, mainly in temperate regions.

PHYTOMORPHIC SOILS. Canadian term for the well-drained soils of an association which have developed under the dominant influence of the natural vegetation characteristics of a region. The zonal soils of an area.

PITCHY. Dense and hard when dry, breaking with smooth somewhat lustrous fracture into sharp-angled (conchoidal) fragments. Wet pitchy peat is very plastic and if squeezed in the hand oozes out between the fingers.

PITTING. The making of shallow pits in the soil to retain rainwater or snowmelt. In short-grass rangelands pitting is done mainly with an offset disc or pitting machine.

PLANOSOL. An intrazonal group of soils with eluviated surface horizons underlain by claypans or fragipans, developed on nearly flat or gently sloping uplands in humid or sub-humid climates.

PLASTIC. Capable of undergoing deformation without rupture.

PLASTIC LIMIT. Minimum moisture weight percentage permitting deformation of a small sample of soil material without rupture. Sometimes called lower plastic limit; see Liquid Limit and Plasticity Index.

PLASTICITY INDEX (OR PLASTICITY NUMBER). The numerical difference between the liquid and the plastic limits.

N

PLASTICITY RANGE. Range of moisture weight percentage within which a small sample of soil materials exhibits plastic properties.

PLATE COUNT. A method for estimating the number of micro-organisms, in a given weight of soil, which will form colonies or semi-solid nutrient media.

PLATY SOIL STRUCTURE. Soil aggregates with thin vertical axes and long horizontal axes. Flat, tabular; a three-dimensional object that has one dimension much smaller than the other two.

PLOUGH LAYER. Surface soil.

PLOUGHPAN. A compacted layer formed in the soil immediately below plough depth. A ploughpan is caused by such operations as the sliding action of the plough bottom, or by the trampling of horses or the pressure and vibration of tractor wheels. Syn. Ploughsole.

PODZOL. A zonal group of soils having surface organic mats and thin, organo-mineral horizons above grey leached horizons that rest upon illuvial dark-brown horizons developed under coniferous or mixed forests or under heath vegetation in a cool-temperate, moist climate.

PODZOLIC SOIL. Soils that have part or all of the characteristics of the Podzol soils, especially leached surface soils that are poorer in clay than the B horizons beneath.

PODZOLIZATION. The process of podzolization involves the breakdown of the alumino-silicate clay minerals by extremely acid leaching under a layer of raw plant debris of particular type. The aluminium and iron ions released from the clay are translocated with humus to the sub-soil, whereas the silica remains in the sub-surface horizon. Thus, the clay-sized fraction of the bleached sub-surface horizon is relatively siliceous and deficient in iron and aluminium sesquioxides, the latter having accumulated in the illuvial subsoil horizon, which has a relatively high sesquioxide clay fraction.

POLYNUTRIENT FERTILIZER. A fertilizer containing more than one major plant nutrient.

PORE SPACE. The fraction of the bulk volume or total space within soils that is not occupied by solid particles.

POROSITY. The degree to which the soil mass is permeated with pores or cavities. Porosity can be generally expressed as a percentage of the whole volume of a soil horizon that is unoccupied by solid particles. In addition, the number, sizes, shapes, and distribution of the voids is important. Generally, the pore space of surface soil is less than one-half of the soil mass by volume, but in some soils it is more than half. The part of the pore space that consists of small pores that hold water by capillarity is called capillary porosity. The part that consists of larger pores that do not hold water by capillarity and free drainage is called noncapillary porosity.

POTASSIUM FIXATION. The process of converting exchangeable or water-soluble potassium to moderately available potassium, a form not easily exchanged from the soil complex with a cation of a neutral salt solution.

POTASSIUM-SUPPLYING POWER OF SOILS. The capacity of the soil to supply potassium to growing plants from both the exchangeable and the moderately available forms.

PRAIRIE SOILS. A zonal group of soils having dark-coloured surface horizons grading through brown soil material to lighter coloured parent material at 2 to 5 feet, formed under tall grasses in a temperate, humid climate. The term has a restricted meaning in soil science and does not apply to all soils developed in treeless landscapes.

PRECIPITATION. (1) A general term for all forms of falling moisture which more specifically include rain, snow, hail, sleet and their modifications. (2) The quantity of water that is precipitated. The amount of precipitation during some unit of time such as a day, month, or year is generally expressed in depth (measured as liquid water) precipitated upon a horizontal surface or into a gauge having a horizontal opening. (3) The process by which water in liquid form is discharged out of the atmosphere, upon a land or water surface.

PRECIPITATION, EXCESSIVE. (1) Rainfall in which the rate of fall is greater than certain adopted limits, chosen with regard to the normal precipitation (excluding snow) of a given place or area. (2) The accumulated amount of precipitation for each 5 minutes during all storms in which the rate of fall equalled or exceeded 0.25 inch in any 5 minutes period, or 0.30 inch in any 10 minute period, or 0.35 inch in any 15 minute period, etc. The storms in which excessive precipitation occurs are called Excessive Storms.

PRECIPITATION, TRACE OF. An amount not large enough to be measured in a gauge. Usually less than 0.005 inch.

PRIMARY MINERAL. A mineral which occurs, or originally occurred, in igneous rocks; examples are micas and feldspars.

PRISMATIC SOIL STRUCTURE. Prismlike structural aggregates with the vertical axes of the aggregates longer than the horizontal axes.

PRODUCTIVE SOIL. A soil in which the chemical, physical, and biological conditions are favourable for the economic production of the crops suited to a particular area.

PRODUCTIVITY (OF SOIL). Soil productivity is the capacity of a soil for producing a specified plant or sequence of plants under a specified system of management. In the definition of productivity the specifications are necessary, since no soil can produce all crops with equal success nor can a single system of management produce the same effects on all soils. Productivity emphasizes the capacity of soil to produce crops and should be measured in terms of unit yields.

PROFILE (SOIL). A vertical section of the soil through all its horizons and extending into the parent material.

PROTEIN. Any of a group of nitrogen-containing compounds that yield amino acids on hydrolysis and have high molecular weights. They are essential parts of living matter and are one of the essential food substances of animals.

PUDDLED SOIL. Dense soil artificially compacted when wet and having no regular structure. The condition commonly results from the tillage of a clayey soil when it is wet.

PUDDLING. The act of destroying soil structure. Puddling reduces porosity and permeability. This process is sometimes used to reduce leakage of reservoirs and canals.

PULVERANT. A term applied to ungranulated fertilizers, those which are largely powdered. Pulverant fertilizers are dusty and blow readily.

PURINES. A group of closely related compounds containing carbon, hydrogen, and nitrogen. Uric acid, an example, is formed from proteins as an end product of animal metabolism. Uric acid is the chief nitrogenous compound in the excrement of birds.

QUICK TESTS. Simple and rapid chemical tests of soils designed to give an approximation of the nutrients available to plants.

RAINFALL INTERCEPTION. Interception of the fall of raindrops by a canopy vegetation or vegetative residue.

RANGE (OR RANGELAND). Land that produces primarily native forage plants suitable for grazing by livestock, including land that has some forest trees.

REACTION, SOIL. The degree of acidity or alkalinity of a soil mass, expressed in either pH value or in words as follows:

	pH
Extremely acid	Below 4.5
Very strongly acid	4.5—5.0
Strongly acid	5.1—5.5
Medium acid	5.6—6.0
Slightly acid	6.1—6.5
Neutral	6.6—7.3
Mildly alkaline	7.4—7.8
Moderately alkaline	7.9—8.4
Strongly alkaline	8.5—9.0
Very strongly alkaline	9.1 and higher.

RED EARTH. Leached, red, deep, clayey soils of the humid tropics, low in silica.

RED PODZOLIC SOILS. Formerly used for a zonal group of soils having thin organic and organic-mineral horizons over a yellowish-brown leached horizon that rests upon an illuvial red horizon developed under deciduous or mixed deciduous and coniferous forests in a warm to warm-temperate humid climate. These are now placed in the Red-Yellow Podzolic group.

REDUCTION. Any chemical change involving the removal of oxygen or its chemical equivalent. A chemical change involving a decrease of positive valence or an increase of negative valence. The reverse of oxidation.

REGOLITH. The unconsolidated mantle of weathered rock and soil material on the earth's surface; loose earth materials above solid rock. This is approximately equivalent to the term "soil", as used by many engineers.

REGOSOLS. An azonal group of soils lacking definite genetic horizons and deriving from deep soft mineral deposits, such as loess or glacial drift.

REGUR. An intrazonal group of dark calcareous soils high in clay, which is mainly montmorillonitic in character, and formed mainly from rocks low in quartz; occurring extensively on the Deccan Plateau of India.

RELIEF. Elevations or inequalities of the land surface, considered collectively.

RENDZINA SOILS. (1) (Europe.) A group of calcareous soils with dark grey to nearly white surface horizons that are usually stony and that grade into partially disintegrated limestone at shallow depths. These would be called Lithosols in the U.S. (2) (U.S.) An intrazonal group of soils with brown or black friable surface horizons underlain by light gray to pale yellow calcareous material; developed from soft, highly calcareous parent material under grass vegetation or mixed grasses and forest in humid and semiarid climates.

RESIDUAL FERTILIZER. The amount of fertilizer that remains in the soil after one or more cropping seasons.

RESIDUAL MATERIAL. Unconsolidated and partly weathered parent material for soils presumed to have developed from the same kind of rock as that on which it lies. The term "residual" is sometimes incorrectly applied to soils, but it can be applied correctly only to the material from which soils are formed.

RESIDUAL SOIL. Obsolete: Soil resting on consolidated rock of the same kind as from which it was formed. See Residual Material.

RETICULATE MOTTLING. A network of streaks of different colours; most commonly found in the deeper profiles of latosolic soils.

REVERSION. The interaction of a soluble plant nutrient with the soil which causes a precipitation of the nutrient in a less soluble form. The term is usually restricted to the conversion of monocalcium phosphate to the less soluble dicalcium phosphate.

RHIZOBIA. Bacteria that can live in symbiotic relations with leguminous plants within nodules on their roots. The normal result of the association is the fixation of nitrogen from the air into forms that can be used by living plants.

RHIZOSPHERE. The bounding surface of root plants. The soil space in the immediate vicinity of the plant roots in which the abundance and composition of the microbial population are influenced by the presence of roots.

RILL. A small, intermittent water course with steep sides and no obstacle to agricultural machinery; usually a few inches in depth.

RILL EROSION. Formation of rills by the uneven removal of surface soil by running water.

RIVER WASH. Barren alluvial land, usually coarse textured, exposed along streams at low water and subject to shifting during normal high water. See Miscellaneous Land Type.

ROCK LAND. Areas containing frequent rock outcrops and shallow soils. Rock outcrops usually occupy 25 to 90 per cent of the area.

ROLLING. Having moderately steep complex slopes; intermediate between undulating and hilly.

ROOT ZONE. The part of the soil that is invaded by plant roots.

ROUGH-BROKEN LAND. Very steep land, ordinarily not stony, broken by numerous intermittent drainage channels but having a vegetative cover. See Miscellaneous Land Type, Badlands.

RUBBLE-LAND. Areas with 90 per cent or more of the surface covered by stones and boulders.

RUNOFF. The surface flow of water from an area; or the total volume of surface flow during a specified time.

SALINE SOIL. A soil containing sufficient soluble salts, usually chlorides and sulphates, to reduce the growth of most crop plants. It is not highly alkaline, pH less than 8.5. The soil is flocculated and has favourable structure thus allowing movement of air and water. Saline soils have been called "white alkali" due to the quite common formation of white or grey salt crustations on the surface. Contrast with Alkali Soil.

SALINE-ALKALI SOIL. A soil having a combination of a harmful quantity of salts and either a high degree of alkalinity or a high amount of exchangeable sodium, or both, so distributed in the soil profile that the growth of most crop plants is less than normal.

SALINIZATION. The process of accumulation of salts in soil.

SALT-AFFECTED SOIL. Soil that has been adversely modified for growth of most crop plants by the presence or action of soluble salts. The term includes soil having an excess of salts, or an excess of exchangeable sodium or both. See Saline Soil and Sodic Soil.

SALTATION. The movement of soil and mineral particles by intermittent leaps from the ground when the particles are being moved by wind or water.

SAND.   Individual rock or mineral fragments in soils having diameters ranging from 0.5 mm. to 2.0 mm. Usually sand grains consist chiefly of quartz, but they may be of any mineral composition. The textural class name of any soil that contains 85 per cent or more of sand and not more than 10 per cent of clay.

SANDY.   A term which refers to sand and loamy sand textures.

SANDY CLAY.   Soil of this textural class contains 35 per cent or more of clay and 45 per cent or more of sand.

SANDY CLAY LOAM.   Generally, soil of this textural class contains 20 to 35 per cent clay, less than 28 per cent silt, and 45 per cent or more of sand.

SANDY LOAMS.   Generally, soil of the sandy loam class of texture has 50 per cent sand and less than 20 per cent clay.

SANDY SOILS.   A broad term for soils of the sand and loamy sand classes; soil material with more than 70 per cent sand and less than 15 per cent clay.

SATURATE.   (1) To fill all the voids between soil particles with liquid. (2) To form the most concentrated solution possible under a given set of physical conditions in the presence of an excess of the substance.

SCORIA LAND.   Areas of slaglike clinkers, burned shale and fine-grained sandstone; characteristic of burned-out coal beds. It commonly supports a sparse cover of grasses, but is of low value for crops.

SECOND BOTTOM.   The first terrace above the normal flood plain of a stream (U.S.).

SEDIMENTARY ROCK.   A rock composed of particles deposited from suspension in water. Chief groups of sedimentary rocks are conglomerates, from gravels; sandstone, from sand; shales, from clay; and limestones, from soft masses of calcium carbonate. There are many intermediate types. Some wind-deposited sands have been consolidated into sandstones.

SEEPAGE.   The escape of water through the soil, or water emerging from an area of soil along an extensive line of surface, in contrast to springs where the water emerges from a local spot.

SELF-MULCHING SOIL. (1) A soil that cracks deeply and becomes so granular at the surface when very dry that the granular mulch washes into the cracks when rains begin, the whole soil swelling enough as it becomes moist to force material upward between the former cracks. (2) A soil in which the surface layer becomes so well aggregated that it does not crust and seal under the impact of rain.

SEMI-ARID CLIMATE. A climate characteristic of the regions intermediate between the true deserts and sub-humid areas. The upper limit of the average annual precipitation in cool semi-arid regions is as low as 15 inches and in warm regions as much as 45 inches. The vegetation is close-growing or scattered short grass, bunchgrass, or shrubs. Soils in such regions that can take in nearly all of the rain that falls and that can hold it for crop plants can be used for crops under dry-farming methods but irrigation is common where water is available.

SEPARATE, SOIL. One of the individual-size groups of mineral soil particles—sand, silt, or clay.

SERIES, SOIL. A group of soils that have soil horizons similar in their differentiating characteristics and arrangement in the soil profile, except for the texture of the surface soil, and are formed from a particular type of parent material. Soil series is an important category in detailed soil classification. Individual series are given proper names from place names near the first recorded occurrence. Thus names like Houston, Cecil, Barnes, and Miami are names of soil series that appear on soil maps and each connotes a unique combination of many soil characteristics.

SERPENTINE ROCKS. Rocks consisting of acid magnesium silicate.

SESQUIOXIDES. Oxides of trivalent cations, such as iron and aluminium.

SHALY. A coarse fragment class used in soil texture class names. See Coarse Fragments.

SHEAR. Force, as of a tillage implement, acting at right angles to the direction of movement.

SHEET EROSION. The gradual uniform removal of the earth's surface by water without the formation of rills or gullies.

SIEROZEM SOILS. A zonal group of soils having brownish-grey surface horizons that grade through lighter coloured material into accumulated calcium carbonate, developed under mixed shrub vegetation in a temperate to cool-arid climate.

N*

SILICA.   An important soil constituent composed of silicon and oxygen. The essential material of the mineral quartz.

SILICA-ALUMINA RATIO.   (1) The molecular ratio of silica to alumina in a soil, clay, or other alumino-silicate mineral. (2) The quotient obtained when the number of mol-fractions of silica are divided by the number of mol-fractions of alumina, both determined by standard fusion analysis of the soil or some part of it.

SILICA-SESQUIOXIDE RATIO.   The ratio of the number of molecules of silica to the number of molecules of alumina plus iron oxide in a soil or in the clay fraction of a soil. The more highly weathered materials of warm-temperate humid regions and especially of the Tropics generally have low ratios. The clay in soils with low ratios usually are less active, physically and chemically, than those with high ratios.

SILT.   (1) Individual mineral particles of soil that range in diameter between the upper size of clay, 0.002 mm., and the lower size of very fine sand, 0.05 mm. (2) Soil of the textural class silt contains 80 per cent or more of silt and less than 12 per cent of clay. (3) Sediments deposited from water in which the individual grains are approximately of the size of silt, although the term is sometimes applied loosely to sediments containing considerable sand and clay.

SILTING.   The deposition of water-borne sediments, chiefly silt, in lakes, reservoirs, stream channels, or overflow areas.

SILT LOAM.   Soil material having (1) 50 per cent or more of silt and 12 to 27 per cent of clay, or (2) 50 to 80 per cent of silt and less than 12 per cent of clay.

SILTY CLAY.   Soil of this textural class has 40 per cent or more of clay and 40 per cent or more of silt.

SILTY CLAY LOAM.   Soil of this textural class has 27 to 40 per cent of clay and less than 20 per cent of sand.

SINGLE GRAIN SOIL.   A structureless soil in which each particle exists separately, as in dune sand.

SLATY.   A coarse fragment class used in soil texture class names. See Coarse Fragments.

SLICKENS.   Accumulations of fine-textured materials separated in placermine and ore-mill operations; may be detrimental to plant growth but are usually confined in specially constructed basins.

SLICK SPOTS. Small areas in a field that are slick when wet, due to alkali or high exchangeable sodium.

SLIP. The downslope movement of a mass of soil under wet or saturated conditions; a microlandslide that produces micro-relief in soils.

SLOPE. The incline of the surface of a soil. It is usually expressed in percentage of slope, which equals the number of feet of fall per 100 feet of horizontal distance.

SOD. A surface layer of soil matted or held together by roots, rhizomes and stolons of grasses and other herbs.

SODIC SOIL. Soil that contains sufficient sodium to interfere with the growth of most crop plants; soils for which the exchangeable-sodium-percentage is 15 or more.

SODIUM (SODIC) CLAYPAN. See Alkali Claypan.

SOIL. (1) The natural medium for the growth of land plants. (2) A dynamic natural body on the surface of the earth in which plants grow, composed of mineral and organic materials and living forms. (3) The collection of natural bodies occupying parts of the earth's surface that support plants and that have properties due to the integrated effect of climate and living matter acting upon parent material, as conditioned by relief, over periods of time.

A soil is an individual three-dimensional body on the surface of the earth unlike the adjoining bodies.

A kind of soil is the collection of soils that are alike in specified combinations of characteristics. Kinds of soil are given names in the system of soil classification. The terms "the soil" and "soil" are collective terms used for all soils, equivalent to the word "vegetation" for all plants.

SOIL AIR. The combination of gases occurring in the gaseous phase in soil.

SOIL ALKALINITY. The degree or intensity of alkalinity of a soil expressed in terms of the pH scale. See Reaction, Soil.

SOIL ASSOCIATE. Obsolete: A Canadian term for an individual taxonomic unit which forms part of a soil association, particularly if the association is made up of soils on similar parent material; corresponds to a series within a catena.

SOIL ASSOCIATION. A group of defined and named kinds of soil associated together in a characteristic geographic pattern. Except on detailed soil maps, it is not possible to delineate the various kinds of soil so that on all small-scale soil maps the areas shown consist of soil associations or two or more kinds of soil that are geographically associated.

SOIL AUGER. A tool for boring into the soil and withdrawing a small sample for field or laboratory observation; augers are of two general types, those with worm-type bits and those of a hollow cylinder type with cutting edge at one end.

SOIL CHARACTERISTIC. A feature of a soil that can be seen and/or measured in the field or in the laboratory on soil samples. Examples include soil slope and stoniness as well as the texture, structure, colour, and chemical composition of soil horizons.

SOIL CLASSIFICATION. Study of soils and their interrelationships, description of their properties, naming, and grouping them systematically. The taxonomic units are frequently regrouped for various purposes such as drainage requirements, crop adaptations, highway construction or forestry purposes.

SOIL CLIMATE. The moisture and temperature conditions existing within the soil.

SOIL CONSERVATION. The efficient use and stability of each area of soil that is needed for use at its optimum level of developed productivity according to the specific patterns of soil and water resources of individual farms, ranches, forests, and other land-management units. The term includes the positive concept of improvement of soils for use as well as their protection and preservation.

SOIL CONSERVATION SURVEY. A record on a map or aerial photograph of the physical land features that are significant in determining land capability and in recommending land use and soil conservation practices. The features include the kind of soil, steepness of slope, type and degree of soil erosion, and overflow hazards or salinity if they are present. Used without modifying terms such as general or reconnaissance, a soil conservation survey is one that shows the physical land features in enough detail and with enough precision to furnish basic land information for planning land use and conservation measures for the specific land on a farm or ranch. General surveys of this kind are made also, and are called Reconnaissance Soil Conservation Surveys.

SOIL EXTRACT. The solution separated from a soil suspension or a soil at a particular moisture content by filtration, centrifuging, or displacement.

SOIL FORMATION FACTOR. The independent variables that define the soil system. Five main groups of soil formation factors are generally recognized by soil scientists, viz., parent rock, climate, organisms, topography, and time.

SOIL HORIZON. A layer of soil approximately parallel to the land surface with observable characteristics that have been produced through the operation of soil forming processes. Each horizon differs in one or more characteristic from the one above or below. The letters A, B, and C are often used to designate soil horizons.

A. The A horizon is the upper part. It consists of mineral layers of maximum organic accumulation; or layers from which clay minerals, iron and aluminium have been lost; or both. (The loose surface organic matter in unploughed areas is not strictly part of the A horizon.

B. The B horizon lies under the A. It consists of weathered material with an accumulation of clay, iron or aluminium; or with more or less blocky or prismatic structure; or both. Usually it is more strongly coloured than the horizon above or below.

C. The C horizon, under the B, is the layer of unconsolidated, weathered parent material.

In addition the letter D is used to designate any such stratum under the soil as hard rock, sand or clay that is not parent material, but which may have some significance to the overlying soil.

Note: Not all these horizons are present in all soils.

SOIL IMPROVEMENT. The processes for, or the results of, making the soil more productive for growing plants by fertizilation, drainage, addition of organic matter, irrigation, and the like.

SOIL MANAGEMENT. The preparation, manipulation, and treatment of soils for the production of plants, including crops, grasses, and trees.

SOIL MAP. A map designed to show the distribution of soil types or other soil mapping units in relation to the prominent physical and cultural features of the earth's surface. The following kinds of soil maps are recognized:

Soil Map—Detailed. A soil map on which the boundaries between all soil types that are significant to potential use (generally field-management systems) are shown. The scale of the map depends upon the purpose to be served, the intensity of land use, the pattern of soils, and the scale of other cartographic materials available. Traverses are made usually at one-quarter mile or more frequent intervals. Commonly a scale of 4 inches = 1 mile (1:15,840) is now used for field mapping.

Soil Map—Detailed Reconnaissance. In a detailed reconnaissance map some portions satisfy the specifications for detailed soil maps while other portions are reconnaissance soil maps.

SOIL MAP (*Continued*).

Soil Map—Generalized. Small scale maps made to bring out the contrasts within large areas by generalization of more detailed maps. They vary from soil association maps of a county, on a scale of 1 inch = 1 mile (1:63,360), to maps of larger regions showing associations dominated by one or more great soil groups.

Soil Map—Reconnaissance. Made by observation of the area at intervals such that the complete land area is not examined as in the case with detailed surveys. The intervals of traversing vary from about one-half mile to several miles. The units shown are soil associations. The maps are usually made for exploratory purposes to outline areas of soil suitable for more intensive development. The scale is usually smaller than for detailed maps.

Soil Map—Schematic. Very small scale maps (1:1,000,000 or smaller) compiled from the scant existing knowledge of new and undeveloped regions by the application of existing information about the relationship of soil properties to the soil formation factors (climate, living organisms, relief, parent rocks, and time) of the area.

SOIL MONOLITH. A verticle section taken out of a soil profile and mounted for display or study.

SOIL ORGANIC MATTER. The organic fraction of the soil. Includes plant and animal residues at various stages of decomposition, cells and tissues of soil organisms, and substances synthesized by the soil population. Commonly determined as those organic materials which accompany the soil when put through a 2 mm. sieve.

SOIL PIPING OR TUNNELING. Accelerated erosion which results in subterranean voids and tunnels.

SOIL POPULATION. All of the organisms living in the soil; the combined soil fauna and flora.

SOIL PORES. Interstices between soil particles (voids).

SOIL POROSITY. The fraction or percentage of the total volume of a soil material not occupied by soil particles.

SOIL QUALITY. An attribute of a soil that cannot be seen or measured directly from the soil alone but which is inferred from soil characteristics and soil behaviour under defined conditions. Fertility, productivity, and erodibility are examples of soil qualities (in contrast to soil characteristics).

SOIL SALINITY. The amount of soluble salts in a soil, expressed in terms of percentage, parts per million, or other convenient unit.

SOIL SEPARATES. Mineral particles, less than 2 mm. in equivalent diameter ranging between specified sized limits. The names and sizes of separates commonly recognized are: very coarse sand (2.0–1.0 mm.), coarse sand (1.0–0.5 mm.), medium sand (0.5–0.25 mm.), fine sand (0.25–0.10 mm.), very fine sand (0.10–0.05 mm.), silt (0.05–0.002 mm.), and clay (<0.002 mm.). The separates recognized by the International Society of Soil Science are: I (2.0–0.2 mm.), II (0.2–0.02 mm.), III (0.02–0.002 mm.), IV (<0.002 mm.).

Very coarse sand—prior to 1947 this separate was called fine gravel; now fine gravel includes particles between 2.00 mm. and about 12.5 mm. in diameter.

Clay—Prior to 1937 clay included particles less than 0.005 mm. in diameter, and silt, those particles from 0.05–0.005 mm.

SOIL SURVEY. A general term for the systematic examination of soils in the field and in the laboratories, their description and classification, the mapping of kinds of soil, and the interpretation of soils according to their adaptability for various crops, grasses, and trees, their behaviour under use or treatment for plant production or for other purposes, and their productivity under different management systems.

SOIL TEXTURE. The relative proportions of the various soil separates, in a soil material. The proportions of sand, silt, and clay in different soil-texture classes of fine soil are shown in diagram on page 274. The sands, loamy sands, and sandy loams are further sub-divided on the basis of the proportions of the various sand separates. All these textural soil class names are modified by the addition of suitable adjectives to the name where coarse fragments are also present in the soil material. See Coarse Fragments, Muck, Peat.

(a) Loamy Sands: Loamy Coarse Sand—25 per cent or more very coarse and coarse sand, and less than 50 per cent any other one grade of sand. Loamy sand—25 per cent or more very coarse, coarse, and medium, and less than 50 per cent fine or very fine sand. Loamy fine sand—50 per cent or more fine sand (or) less than 25 per cent very coarse, coarse, and medium sand and less than 25 per cent very fine sand. Loamy very fine sand—50 per cent or more very fine sand.

(b) Sands: Coarse sand—25 per cent or more very coarse and coarse sand, and less than 50 per cent of any other material or sand separate. Sand—25 per cent or more of very coarse, coarse, and medium sand, and less than 50 per cent of fine or very fine sand. Fine sand—50 per cent or more of fine sand or less than 25 per cent very coarse, coarse, and medium sand and less than 50 per cent very fine sand. Very fine sand—50 per cent or more very fine sand.

(c) Sandy Loam: Coarse sandy loam—25 per cent or more very coarse and coarse sand and less than 50 per cent of any other one grade of sand.

SOIL VARIANT. A soil whose properties are believed sufficiently different from other known soils to justify a new series name but whose geographic area is so limited that creation of a new series is not believed to be justified.

SOLCLIME. The temperature and moisture conditions of the soil; the soil climate.

SOLONCHAK SOILS. An intrazonal group of soils with high concentrations of soluble salts in relation to those in other soils, usually light coloured, without characteristic structural form, developed under salt-loving plants, and occurring mostly in a sub-humid or semi-arid climate. In soil classification, the term applies to a broad group of soils and is only approximately equivalent to the common term saline soils.

SOLONETZ SOILS. An intrazonal group of soils having surface horizons of varying degrees of friability underlain by dark-coloured hard soil, ordinarily with columnar structure (prismatic structure with rounded tops). This hard layer is usually highly alkaline. Such soils are developed under grass or shrub vegetation, mostly in sub-humid or semi-arid climates. This term is used for a broad group of soils that include many so-called alkali soils in the western part of the United States. (Where the hard, clayey layer is overlain with a light-coloured leached layer, the soils are called solodized Solonetz.)

SOLUM (PL. SOLA). The upper part of a soil profile, above the parent material, in which the processes of soil formation are active. The solum in mature soils includes the A and B horizons. Usually the characteristics of the material in these horizons are quite unlike those of the underlying parent material. The living roots and other plant and animal life characteristic of the soil are largely confined to the solum.

SPLASH EROSION. The removal of soil particles from their position by the beating effect of rain drops.

SPOIL BANK. Rock-waste banks and dumps from the excavation of ditches.

STICKY POINT. The moisture content of well-mixed, kneaded soil material that barely fails to adhere to a polished nickel or stainless steel surface when the shearing speed is 5 cm. per second. It is a property of plastic soils.

STONES. Rock fragments greater than 10 inches in diameter if rounded, and greater than 15 inches along the longer axis if flat. See Coarse Fragments.

STONINESS. The relative proportion of stones present; used in classification of soils. See Coarse Fragments.

STONY. Soils containing sufficient stones to interfere with or prevent tillage. Stones usually occupy more than 0.01 per cent of the surface.

STONY-LAND. Areas containing so many stones that use of machinery is impractical, usually 15 to 90 per cent of the surface is covered with stones. See Stoniness, Rubble-land, Miscellaneous Land Type.

STORAGE CAPACITY. The amount of water that can be stored in the soil for future use by plants and evaporation.

STRATIFIED. Composed of, or arranged in, strata, or layers, such as stratified alluvium. The term is confined to geological materials. Layers in soils that result from the processes of soil formation are called horizons; those inherited from the parent material are called strata.

STRESS (SOIL MOISTURE). A term used for the total energy with which water is held in the soil, including tension of soil moisture and additional effects of salts in the soil water. It can be expressed in any convenient pressure unit.

STRIP CROPPING. The practice of growing crops in a systematic arrangement of strips, or bands. Commonly cultivated crops and sod crops are alternated in strips to protect the soil and vegetation against running water or wind. The alternate strips are laid out approximately on the contour on erosive soils or at approximate right angles to the prevailing direction of the wind where soil blowing is a hazard.

STRUCTURE, SOIL. The arrangement of primary soil particles into compound particles or clusters that are separated from adjoining aggregates and have properties unlike those of an equal mass of unaggregated primary soil particles. The principal forms of soil structure are platy, prismatic, columnar (prisms with rounded tops), blocky (angular or subangular), and granular. Structureless soils are (1) single grain—each grain by itself, as in dune sand, or (2) massive—the particles adhering together without any regular cleavage as in many claypans and hardpans. ("Good" or "bad" tilth are terms for the general structural condition of cultivated soils according to particular plants or sequences of plants.)

STUBBLE MULCH. A mulch consisting of the stubble and other crop residues left in and on the surface of the soil as a protective cover during the preparation of a seedbed and during at least part of the growing of the succeeding crop.

SUBARCTIC BROWN FOREST SOILS. Similar to Brown Forest except for more shallow sola and temperatures average less than 5°C., 18 inches or more below the surface.

SUB-HUMID CLIMATE. A climate intermediate between semi-arid and humid with sufficient precipitation to support a moderate to heavy growth of short and tall grasses, or shrubs, or of these and widely spaced trees or clumps of trees. The upper limit of rainfall in sub-humid climates may be as low as 20 inches in cold regions and as high as 60 inches in hot regions.

SUBIRRIGATION. Irrigation through controlling the water table in order to raise it into the root zone. Water is applied in open ditches or through tile until the water table is raised enough to wet the soil. Some soils along streams are said to be naturally "subirrigated".

SUBSOIL. The B horizons of soils with distinct profiles. In soils with weak profile development, the subsoil can be defined as the soil below the ploughed soil (or its equivalent of surface soil), in which roots normally grow. Although a common term, it cannot be defined accurately. It has been carried over from early days when "soil" was conceived only as the ploughed soil and that under it as the "subsoil".

SUBSOILING. Breaking of compact subsoils, without inverting them, with a special knife-like instrument which is pulled through the soil at depths usually of 12 to 24 inches and at spacings of from 2 to 5 feet.

SUBSTRATUM. Any layer lying beneath the solum or true soil. It is applied to both parent materials and to other layers unlike the parent material, below the B horizon or the subsoil.

SUBSURFACE TILLAGE. Tillage with a sweeplike plough or blade that does not turn over the surface cover or incorporate it into the lower part of the surface soil.

SUCTION (OF SOIL WATER). The equivalent negative pressure in soil water. It is the pressure reduction required to extract water from soil. Suction, measured in pressure units, indicates the tenacity with which water is held by surface force action in soil. Experimentally, the suction of water in soil is the pressure difference required across a permeable membrane to produce hydraulic equilibrium between water in soil that is subject to surface force action and free water in bulk on the other side of the membrane. Also, Soil Suction; Soil Moisture Suction.

SURFACE SEALING. The orientation and packing of dispersed soil particles in the immediate surface layer of soil whereby it becomes almost impermeable to water.

SURFACE SOIL. The soil ordinarily moved in tillage, or its equivalent in uncultivated soil, about 5 to 8 inches in thickness.

SWAMP. Any area, such as a marsh or bog, where the ground is saturated with water throughout much of the year, but during most of the year, the surface of the soil is not deeply submerged.

SYMBIOSIS. The living together of two different organisms with a resulting mutual benefit. A common example includes the association of rhizobia with legumes; the resulting nitrogen fixation is sometimes called symbiotic nitrogen fixation. Adjective: Symbiotic.

TABIDUM. Horizon of fermentation, including duff and humic layer.

TALUDS. Short, steep escarpments formed gradually at the down-slope margins of fields by deposition against hedges or stone walls.

TALUS. Fragments of rocks and other soil material accumulated by force of gravity at the foot of cliffs or steep slopes.

TENSION, SOIL MOISTURE. The equivalent negative pressure of suction of water in soil.

TERRACE. An embankment or ridge constructed across sloping soils on the contour or at a slight angle to the contour. The terrace intercepts surplus runoff in order to retard it for infiltration into the soil and so that any excess may flow slowly to a prepared outlet without harm.

TERRACE (GEOLOGICAL). A nearly flat or undulating plain, commonly rather narrow and usually with a steep front, bordering a river, a lake, or the sea. Although many old terraces have become more or less hilly through dissection by streams, they are still regarded as terraces.

TEXTURAL CLASS. Kinds of soil material according to the proportions of sand, silt, and clay. The principal textural classes in soil, in increasing order of the amount of silt and clay, are as follows: Sand, loamy sand, sandy loam, loam, silt loam, silt, sandy clay loam, clay loam, silty clay loam, sandy clay, silty clay, and clay. These class names are modified to indicate the size of the sand fraction or the presence of gravel, cobbles, and stones. For example, terms such as loamy fine sand, very fine sandy loam, gravelly loam, stony clay, and cobbly loam, are used on detailed soil maps. These terms apply only to individual soil horizons or to the surface layer of a soil type, as in the name "Miami silt loam". Commonly the various horizons of any one kind of soil belong in different soil textural classes. (See Soil Texture.)

TEXTURE. See Soil Texture.

THERMOGENIC SOIL. Soils in which the dominant soil formation factor has been the high temperature; developed in sub-tropical and equatorial regions.

THERMOSEQUENCE. A sequence of soils whose properties are functionally related to temperatures as a soil formation factor.

TIDAL FLATS. Areas of nearly flat, barren mud, periodically covered by tidal waters. Normally these materials have an excess of soluble salt; a Miscellaneous Land Type.

TIGHT SOIL. Compact, impervious and tenacious, usually plastic soil.

TILE DRAIN. Concrete or pottery pipe placed at suitable spacings and depths in the soil or subsoil to provide water outlets from the soil.

TILL. Unstratified, glacial deposits. See Glacial Drift.

TILLAGE. The operation of implements through the soil to prepare seedbeds and rootbeds.

TILTH, SOIL. The physical condition of a soil in respect to its fitness for the growth of a specified plant or sequence of plants. Ideal soil tilth is not the same for each kind of crop nor is it uniform for the same kind of crop growing on contrasting kinds of soil.

TOPOGRAPHY. The shape of the ground surface, such as hills, mountains, or plains. Steep topography indicates steep slopes or hilly land; flat topography indicates flat land with minor undulations and gentle slopes.

TOPOSEQUENCE. A sequence of soils whose properties are functionally related to topography as a soil formation factor.

TOPSOIL. A general term used in at least four different senses: (1) A presumed fertile soil or soil material, usually rich in organic matter, used to topdress roadbanks, lawns and gardens; (2) the surface plough layer of a soil and thus a synonym for surface soil; (3) the original or present dark-coloured upper soil, which ranges from a mere fraction of an inch to 2 or 3 feet on different kinds of soil; and (4) the original or present A horizon, varying widely among different kinds of soil. Applied to soils in the field, the term has no precise meaning unless defined as to depth or productivity in relation to a specific kind of soil.

TRAFFIC PANS. Subsurface layers in soil that have been so compacted by the application of weight (e.g. by machines, tractors, etc.) that the penetration of water and roots is interfered with. Because the traffic of machines is not the only cause of these pans, some persons call them pressure pans.

TRUNCATED. Having lost all or part of the upper soil horizon or horizons.

TUFF.   Deposited volcanic ash usually more or less stratified and consolidated.

TUNDRA SOILS.   A zonal group of soils having dark-brown highly
organic surface horizons over greyish or brownish horizons which rest on
cold or ever-frozen substrata; developed under shrubs and mosses in cold,
semi-arid to humid climates, e.g. in arctic regions.

TYPE, SOIL.   A subdivision of soil series based on the texture of the
surface soil. A soil type is a group of soils having horizons similar in
differentiating characteristics and arrangement in the soil profile and
developed from a particular type of parent material. The name of a soil
type consists of the name of the soil series plus the textural class name of
the upper part of the soil equivalent to the surface soil. Thus Evesham
clay is the name of a soil type within the Evesham series.

ULTIMATE PARTICLES.   Soil particles after a standard dispersing
treatment.

UNDIFFERENTIATED SOIL GROUPS.   Soil mapping units in which
two or more similar taxonomic soil units occur, but not in a regular geographic association. For example, the steep phases of two or more similar
soils might be shown as a unit on a map because topography so domin-
ates the properties. See Soil Association and Soil Complex.

UNHUMIFIED.   Organic matter prior to its decomposition into humus.

URBAN LAND.   Areas so altered or obstructed by urban works or structures that identification of soils is not feasible. A Miscellaneous Land Type.

VARNISH (DESERT).   A glossy coating on stones, in deserts.

VARVES.   Distinctly marked annual deposits of sediment regardless of
their origin.

VERY COARSE SAND.   See Soil Separates and Soil Texture.

VERY FINE SAND.   See Soil Separates and Soil Texture.

VIRGIN SOIL.   A soil that has not been significantly disturbed by man's
activities.

VOLCANIC-ASHLAND.   Areas of nearly unmodified deposits of volcanic ash so recent they show little or no evidence of soil development
and have little or no vegetation. A Miscellaneous Land Type.

WASH.   A gully, e.g., the dry bed of an intermittent stream, sometimes
at the bottom of a canyon.

WASTELAND.   Land not capable of producing materials or services of value. A Miscellaneous Land Type.

WATER-HOLDING CAPACITY.   The capacity (or ability) of soil to hold water; field capacity is the amount held against gravity or 1 atmosphere tension or pF 2.7. The moisture-holding capacity of sandy soils is usually considered to be low while that of clayey soils is high. Often expressed in inches of water per foot depth of soil.

WATERLOGGED.   A condition of soil in which both large and small pore spaces are filled with water. (The soil may be intermittently waterlogged because of a fluctuating water table or waterlogged for short periods after rain.)

WATER RATIO.   The fraction of the total bulk volume of soil that is filled with water.

WATER REQUIREMENT (OF PLANTS).   Generally, the amount of water required by plants for satisfactory growth during the season. More strictly, the number of units of water required by a plant during the growing season in relation to the number of units of dry matter produced. The water requirement varies with climatic conditions, soil moisture, and soil characteristics. Factors unfavourable to plant growth, such as low fertility, disease, and drought, increase the water requirement.

WATER RETENTION.   The physical property of soil that is based on surface force action and that makes it necessary to do work in order to remove water from soil pores and from soil surface.

WATERSHED.   The total area above a given point on a stream that contributes water to the flow at that point. Synonyms are "drainage basin" or "catchment basin". In some countries, the term is used for the topographic boundary separating one drainage basin from another.

WATER-STABLE AGGREGATE.   A soil aggregate not readily broken down by agitation in water.

WATER TABLE.   The upper limit of the part of the soil or underlying rock material that is wholly saturated with water. In some places an upper, or perched, water table may be separated from a lower one by a dry zone.

WATER TABLE PERCHED.   The upper surface of a body of free ground water in a zone of saturation separated, by unsaturated material, from an underlying body of ground water in a different zone of saturation.

WEATHERING. All physical and chemical changes produced in rocks, at or near the earth's surface, by atmospheric agents, and which result in more or less complete disintegration and decomposition.

WILD FLOODING. See Irrigation Methods.

WILTING POINT (OR PERMANENT WILTING POINT). The moisture content of soil, on an oven-dry basis, at which plants (specifically sunflower plants) wilt and fail to recover their turgidity when placed in a dark humid atmosphere. The percentage of water at the wilting point approximates the minimum moisture content in soils under plants in the field at depths below the effects of surface evaporation.

WIND EROSION. The detachment, transportation, and deposition of soil by the action of wind. The removal and redeposition may be in more or less uniform layers or as localized blowouts and dunes.

ABC OF PLANT
SOIL REQUIREMENTS

ACACIA (most species). Will grow on dry soil.

AILANTHUS (*Ailanthus altissima*). Will grow on very sandy soil.

ALDERS (several species). Will grow on wet soil.

ALFALFA (*Medicago sativa*). Grows in slightly alkaline soils of average depth to deep, sandy loam to well-drained clay. It tolerates slight salinity, but it will not tolerate wet, poorly drained soil. Moist conditions are needed for seedling establishment. Alfalfa tolerates periods of drought if moisture is available to the roots. It is benefited by applications of mineral nutrients when needed. Its requirements of available minerals are high. Widely adapted to different climates if proper varieties are used.

ALMOND (*Prunus amygdalus*). Well-drained, light-textured soils (pH 5 to 8) are ideal. The almond will tolerate well-drained clays but not water-logged soil. The tree is drought tolerant and often is planted where the moisture supply is limited, but it needs ample moisture for good production. It has some tolerance to salt and alkali.

ALYCECLOVER (*Alysicarpus vaginalis*). Grows in highly acid to neutral soils. It is not tolerant of salinity. The soils may be of shallow to average depth and fine sand to silt loams. It requires moist or heavy-moisture conditions. Applications of mineral nutrients when needed are beneficial. It is a summer annual and requires high temperatures and a long growing season.

APPLE. A deep-rooted, long-lived deciduous tree of the temperate zone. Apples grow satisfactorily on many different soils, ranging from heavy clays to light sandy loams.

APRICOT. See Peach.

ARTICHOKE, GLOBE (*Cynara scolymus*). A deep-rooted perennial, does well on almost any deep, well-drained soil except one that is very sandy, droughty, or highly calcareous. A high content of organic matter in the soil and relatively cool temperatures are favourable. The plant is well adapted to a cool, moist climate, but the top is injured by freezing.

ARTICHOKE, JERUSALEM (*Helianthus tuberosus*). Has an optimum pH of 6.5 to 7.5. Only well-drained soils of medium texture (sandy loams and loams) are recommended for this plant. Yields are low on sandy soils, plants blow over badly on sandy and muck soils, and tubers are unreasonably difficult to harvest thoroughly from fine-textured soils that tend to become hard.

ASH, GREEN (*Fraxinus pennsylvanica lanceolata*). Will grow on dry soil.

ASH, VELVET (*Fraxinus velutina*). Will grow on dry, alkaline soil.

ASPARAGUS (*Asparagus officinalis*). A perennial, cool-weather plant that tolerates high salt and boron content of soil. Asparagus requires an annual rest period preferably imposed by cold. Deep (3 to 4 feet or more), friable soil is necessary for extensive root penetration. Sandy loam, muck, or silty muck soils are best. Loams and silt loams are productive and widely used but tend to warm up later than sandy loams. Heavy clay loams and clays are unsatisfactory because they are cold in the spring, are hard to manage, and are conducive to the production of crooked spears. Sandy soils and subsoils tend to be droughty and sandy surface soils are subject to blowing, thereby damaging the young spears. The optimum pH is 6.0 to 8.0.

AVOCADO (*Persea americana*). A tropical fruit, is subject to injury when temperatures go below 28°F. It is unusually sensitive to poorly drained soil. It grows successfully on marl soils of warm, humid regions. Rather open, well-drained soils (pH 5 to 7.5) are ideal. It will not tolerate salt in soil or irrigation water.

AZALEA (*Rhododendron* species). Acid soil.

BALDCYPRESS (*Taxodium distichum*). Will grow on wet soil.

BARLEY (*Hordeum vulgare*). Requires a well-drained sandy loam to clay, which has a reaction of pH 6 to 8.5 and is 2.5 to 8 feet deep. Very tolerant to salinity. More tolerant to sandy soil texture but less tolerant to acidity than are wheat and oats.

BAYBERRY (*Myrica* species). Acid soil.

BEACHGRASSES (*Ammophila* species). Perennials. They grow in moderately acid to neutral soils and tolerate high salinity. They need shallow to deep, fine sand to loamy sands and moist to very moist conditions, and are benefited by applications of nitrogen. They are adapted to cool conditions and are winter hardy. They are used to control dunes and blowing soil.
   American beachgrass (*A. breviligulata*). See Beachgrasses.
   European beachgrass (*A. arenaria*). See Beachgrasses.

BEANS, FRENCH KIDNEY OR DWARF (*Phaseolus vulgaris*). The optimum pH is about 5.8 to 7.5. Both garden and field types of common beans are very sensitive to high salt and boron content of the soil. The bean plant is a relatively shallow-rooted, warm-weather annual. The soil need not be more than 1 to 2 feet deep if an adequate water and nutrient supply can be assured. Crops of high value, such as snap beans for early market, are profitably grown on light sandy loams and even on sandy soils when they are well fertilized. Rich loams, silt loams, and clay loams are best for main-crop beans for market or processing and for field beans to be harvested dry. Friability, good tilth, and freedom from baking and crusting are important in obtaining good stands in the field. Inoculation with nitrogen-fixing bacteria is rarely profitable. Applications of nitrogen should be moderate.

BEECH (*Fagus*). Will grow on alkaline soil.

BEETS, GARDEN OR TABLE (*Beta vulgaris*). The optimum pH is 6.0 to 8.5. The beet, a cool-weather plant, is the most tolerant of garden vegetables to high salt and boron content of the soil. It has a high boron requirement; often it needs added boron to prevent internal black spot of the edible roots. It is highly intolerant of high soil acidity. The soil should be very deep (4 feet or more) and well drained. Sandy loams, friable loams, and mucks are preferred Soils that become crusted or hard interfere with seedling emergence and often cause the edible roots to become misshapen.

BERMUDA-GRASS (*Cynodon dactylon*). Grows in shallow to deep, highly acid to neutral soils and is tolerant of high salinity. It likes gravelly loam to well-drained clay. It tolerates drought periods but prefers heavy moisture. Applications of nitrogen are beneficial. Coastal and Suwannee are better adapted to deep sands. Midland is hardier. Greenfield grows better at low nutrient levels.

BIRCH, DAHURIAN (*Betula davurica*). Will grow on gravelly soil.

BLACKBERRY (*Rubus*). Blackberries thrive best on medium-textured, sandy loams to clay loams (pH 5 to 7.5). They do poorly on coarse sands or poorly drained clays. The plants are easily killed by waterlogged conditions but need ample moisture for good production.

BLUEBERRY (*Vaccinium*). These cannot be grown satisfactorily in soils above pH 6 in reaction. They thrive best in moist but well-drained, acid soils from sandy loams to well-drained clays. They do best under permanent mulches, particularly sawdust. The plants seem unable to obtain necessary iron under neutral or alkaline soil conditions. The best pH range is 4.5 to 5.5.

BLUEGRASSES *(Poa)*. Comprise many perennial species, which are adapted to a wide range of soil and climatic conditions.

Big bluegrass (P. ampla) grows in slightly acid to slightly alkaline soils. It is not tolerant of salinity. Soils should be of average depth or deep, gravelly loam to well-drained clay. It prefers moist conditions, although it tolerates drought. Applications of nitrogen are beneficial.

Bulbous bluegrass (P. bulbosa) grows in moderately acid to slightly alkaline soils. It is not tolerant of salinity. Deep or moderately deep silt loam to poorly drained clay are suitable. It needs moist to very moist conditions. Applications of nitrogen are helpful. It is adapted to cool-summer temperatures. It is a perennial.

Canada bluegrass (P. compressa) grows in highly acid to neutral, shallow or moderately deep, loamy sand or poorly drained clay. It tolerates moist to very moist conditions but is not tolerant of salinity. Applications of nitrogen benefit it. This perennial grows at relatively low nutrient levels.

Kentucky bluegrass (P. pratensis), a perennial, grows in slightly acid to slightly alkaline soils of average depth, deep silt loam, and well-drained clay. It needs moist to very moist conditions. Available phosphorus and calcium stimulate growth. It is adversely affected by higher summer temperatures.

The Rough bluegrass (P. trivialis) is a perennial that grows in moderately acid to neutral soils of shallow to average depth. Sandy loams to poorly drained clays are preferred. It is somewhat tolerant of shade.

BLUESTEM GRASSES. Many species which differ widely in adaptation to soil conditions. They grow in slightly acid to moderately alkaline soils. They are benefited slightly by application of nitrogen. They are adapted to a wide range of climatic conditions. The following are the more important perennial bluestems.

Angleton grass (Andropogon nodosus) grows in moderately acid to neutral soils of average depth to deep, fine sand, and poorly drained clays. It is tolerant of high salinity. It requires moist to heavy-moisture conditions, but may survive periods of drought. The application of nitrogen is helpful.

Australian bluestem (A. intermedius) grows in fine sand to sandy loam of average depth or deeper. It is drought resistant. It is not hardy.

Big bluestem (A. gerardi) grows in slightly acid to slightly alkaline soils and in sandy loam to poorly drained clay of average depth. It tolerates dry to moist conditions.

Caucasian bluestem (A. caucasicus) is benefited by applications of nitrogen.

Little bluestem (A. scoparius) is more winter hardy and is better adapted to clay and sandy soils with good moisture.

Sand bluestem (A. hallii) grows in deep, fine sand to silt loams.

Yellow bluestem (A. ischaemum) is tolerant of moderate salinity, is drought resistant, and is particularly adapted for use on eroded soils.

BOXELDER *(Acer negundo)*. Will grow on dry soil.

BOX SANDMYRTLE (*Leiophyllum buxifolium*). Acid soil.

BROCCOLI, SPROUTING (*Brassica oleracea* var. *botrytis*). (See Cabbage.) Sprouting broccoli is somewhat more sensitive to heat than is cabbage.

BROMEGRASSES (*Bromus*). Many species of perennials and annuals, which grow under widely different conditions and are benefited by the application of nitrogen.

    Field bromegrass (*B. arvensis*) grows in moderately acid to neutral soils and is not tolerant of salinity. Shallow to deep, sandy loam to poorly drained clay and moist to heavy-moisture conditions are preferred.

    Harlan bromegrass (*B. stamineus*) is a winter annual. (See Mountain bromegrass.)

    Meadow bromegrass (*B. erectus*), a perennial. (See Mountain bromegrass).

    Mountain bromegrass (*B. carinatus*) grows in slightly acid to slightly alkaline soil and is not tolerant of salinity. It grows in shallow to deep, fine sand to clay and requires moist conditions.

    Rescue grass (*B. catharticus*) is a winter annual or a short-lived perennial.

    Smooth bromegrass (*B. inermis*) grows in moderately acid to moderately alkaline soils and is not tolerant of salinity. It does best on deep sandy loam and well-drained clays that are moist. A perennial.

BROOM (*Cytisus* species). Acid soil.

BROOMCORN (*Sorghum vulgare*). See Grain sorghum.

BRUSSELS SPROUTS (*Brassica oleracea* var. *gemmifera*). See Cabbage. This vegetable is very sensitive to high temperature. The most and firmest 'heads' develop in a cool climate. It is generally grown for autumn harvest.

BUCKWHEAT (*Fagopyrum esculentum*). Needs a sandy loam to clay or drained marshland (pH 4.5 to 7.5) 2 to 4 feet deep. It is suited to infertile soils, especially those low in available phosphorus, and is very tolerant of acidity.

BUFFALOGRASS (*Buchloë dactyloides*). Grows in slightly acid to moderately alkaline soils. It tolerates slight salinity, and needs shallow to moderately deep loam or well-drained clays and dry to moist conditions. It is drought resistant and is benefited slightly by applications of nitrogen. A warm-season perennial.

BULBOUS BARLEY (*Hordeum bulbosum*). Grows in neutral to moderately alkaline soil and is tolerant of slight salinity. It grows in sandy loam to clay loam of shallow or average depth, and needs moist to very moist conditions but will tolerate drought periods. Moderately benefited by applications of nitrogen. It grows in winter and is useful for eroded soils.

CABBAGE (*Brassica oleracea* var. *capitata*).   The optimum pH is 6.0 to 7.5. High pH helps control club root, a serious soilborne disease in many districts. Cabbage is moderately tolerant to high salt content and tolerant to high boron content of the soil. This cool-weather plant grows well in almost any well-drained soil of moderate (2 feet) depth or more, provided ample water is available. Sandy soils require heavy applications of organic matter and fertilizer. Timely transplanting and cultivating may be difficult on heavy silt loam, clay loam, or the clay soils. Once established and properly fertilized, however, cabbage grows well on such soils. Sandy loams are best for early crops; loams and heavier soils are satisfactory for midseason and late crops of cabbage. Muck soils of high lime content are very satisfactory.

CAJEPUT TREE (*Melaleuca leucadendron*).   Will grow on wet soil.

CANARYGRASSES.   Include many perennial and annual species of *Phalaris*. They grow under a wide range of soil and climatic conditions.
Hardinggrass (*P. tuberosa* var. *stenoptera*) grows in slightly acid to highly alkaline soils and tolerates moderate salinity. It thrives in moist or very moist silt loam or poorly drained clay of average or greater depth. The application of nitrogen is helpful. It grows in winter and spring; in summer it remains dormant in the tuber stage.
Reed canarygrass (*P. arundinacea*), a perennial, grows in slightly acid to neutral, shallow to deep, silt loam to muck in moist or swampy conditions. It is not tolerant of salinity. It will stand flooding for short periods. Nitrogen is beneficial.

CANTALOUPS.   See Muskmelons.

CAROB (*Ceratona siliqua*).   Will grow on dry soil.

CARPETGRASS (*Axonopus affinis*).   Grows in highly acid to slightly acid soils of shallow to average depth and of fine sand to clay loam. It requires a great deal of moisture and tolerates swampy conditions. Benefited slightly by application of nitrogen. It is a perennial, warm-season grass, particularly adapted to low-lying sands. Does not tolerate salinity.
Centipedegrass (*Eremochloa ophiuroides*) grows in highly acid to neutral soils and it not tolerant of salinity. It needs shallow to deep, gravelly loam to loam and moist to very moist conditions. Used mainly as a lawn grass. It grows at low nutrient levels and is shade tolerant.
Desert saltgrass (*Distichlis stricta*) grows in slightly acid to highly alkaline soils and will tolerate high salinity. It grows in loam or poorly drained clay of shallow to average depth and moist to swampy conditions. Will tolerate drought. A perennial.

CARROTS (*Daucus carota*).   The optimum pH is 5.5 to 7.0. Carrots have little tolerance to high salt content, but are moderately tolerant to high boron in the soil. They require a very deep, well-drained soil, preferably

CARROTS (*Continued*).

a sandy loam or muck. Carrots are grown extensively on loams and silt loams, but it is usually difficult to establish good stands of plants on such fine-textured soils, which tend to form a crust, unless crust formation can be avoided. Careful control of soil moisture by furrow irrigation permits use of heavier soils than is feasible in districts of heavy rainfall. Clay soils and rocky soils impair root shape and harvest from clay soils is difficult. Coarse, undecomposed organic matter in the surface soil also tends to impair root shape.

CASTORBEAN (*Ricinus communis*). Grows in sandy loam to loam, 3 to 5 feet deep and pH 5 to 8 in reaction. It is not tolerant of drought during flowering.

CEDAR, EASTERN RED (*Juniperus virginiana*). Will grow on dry soil.

CELERIAC (*Apium graveolens* var. *rapaceum*). Optimum requirements for this 'root crop' are similar to those of celery but are less exacting. It can be grown with fair success in any good garden soil.

CELERY (*Apium graveolens*). The optimum pH is 5.8 to 7.0. Celery is intolerant of high salt content of the soil. So-called high lime mucks (pH 6.0 to 7.0) are ideal for this cool-weather crop. Very acid mucks (below pH 5.5) and alkaline mucks (above pH 7.0) are not desirable unless pH can be economically corrected.

Celery is shallow rooted and may thrive on soils only 1.5 to 2 feet deep above the water table or above hardpan. The plant has a heavy demand for water and nutrients and tolerates neither drought nor poor drainage of the surface 1.5 to 2 feet. Although mucks are ideal, celery is grown extensively on loamy sands, sandy loams and loams, and to some extent even on silt loams and clay loams provided the latter are friable and well supplied with moisture. Establishment of transplants is more difficult in coarse and fine-textured soils than in muck and medium-textured soils. Fine-textured soils are to be avoided unless soil moisture can be effectively controlled by irrigation.

CHAYOTE (*Sechium edule*). See Cucurbits. This long-season, hot-weather vine crop produces single-seeded, pear-shaped or round fruits that weigh one-half pound or more. Fruit quality is similar to that of squash.

CHERRY, SOUR (*Prunus cerasus*). See Cherry, Sweet.

CHERRY, SWEET (*Prunus avium*). This tree must be kept reasonably vegetative if it is to produce well. As it is rather lacking in winter hardiness, and cultural conditions that favour growth may delay hardening of the tissues for winter, some special problems of soil management arise.

The cherry is sensitive to poor aeration of the subsoil, and grows best on deep soils of light texture. On soils of moderate fertility, supplementary spring applications of nitrogen fertilizer are made annually.

CHINABERRY (*Melia azedarach*). Will grow on dry soil.

CHINESE CABBAGE (*Brassica pekinensis* and *B. Chinensis*). (See Cabbage.) Chinese cabbage is more sensitive to high temperature than is cabbage. It forms poor heads and tends to bolt in hot weather. It is best grown for autumn harvest or for winter harvest in winter-vegetable districts.

CHINESE CHESTNUT (*Castanea mollissima*). It is suited to the areas where peaches can be grown. It is subject to winter injury in areas where temperatures may drop to −20°F. It does not tolerate poorly drained soil but succeeds on well-drained, fine sands and loams (pH 5 to 7). It is not tolerant to salt or alkali.

CHINQUAPIN, GIANT EVERGREEN (*Castanopsis chrysophylla*). Will grow on dry soil.

CHRISTMAS-BERRY TREE (*Schinus terebinthifolius*). Will grow on dry soil.

CLOVERS (TRUE) (*Trifolium* species). Grow under a wide range of soil and climatic conditions. One species tolerates moderate salinity. It requires available mineral nutrients of phosphorus, calcium, and potassium, which must be applied if the soil lacks them. The many species of true clovers thrive in cool, humid climates and under irrigation. They are perennials and winter annuals. They have restricted use as summer annuals.

Alsike clover (Trifolium hybridum) grows in moderately acid to neutral soil. It is not tolerant of salinity. Needs shallow to deep, silt loam, or muck soils and moist to heavy-moisture conditions. Tolerates swampy conditions for short periods. A perennial, it behaves as a biennial in some regions, and may also be grown as a winter annual. It is particularly valuable for poorly drained soils.

Ball clover (Trifolium nigrescens) grows in moderately acid to neutral soils of shallow to average depth, and of fine sand to clay. Not tolerant of salinity. It makes growth at a relatively low nutrient level. A winter annual.

Berseem clover (Trifolium alexandrinum) grows in slightly acid to slightly alkaline soil. Tolerates slight salinity in soils of average depth to deep, silt loams to poorly drained clays. It needs moist conditions. A winter annual, it is the least winter hardy of all clovers.

Cluster clover (Trifolium glomeratum) grows in moderately acid to neutral soils. It is not tolerant of salinity. Soils should be shallow or of average depth and fine sand to silt loam. Needs moist to heavy-moisture conditions. A winter annual.

Crimson clover (Trifolium incarnatum) thrives in soils that are moderately acid to neutral and shallow to deep, fine sand to well-drained clay. It needs moist to heavy-moisture conditions, but does not thrive

CLOVERS (*Continued*).

in waterlogged soils. Not tolerant of salinity. Widely adapted as a winter or summer annual.

Lappa clover (Trofolium lappaceum) grows in neutral to slightly alkaline soils and loam to poorly drained clays of shallow or average depth. Ample moisture is needed. Does not tolerate salinity. A winter annual, specifically adapted to wet, heavy soils.

Large hop clover (Trifolium campestre) grows in moderately acid to neutral soils. It is not tolerant of salinity. Soils should be shallow to deep, ranging from gravelly loam to clay. Moist to very moist conditions are required, but nutrient levels can be relatively low. A winter annual.

Small hop clover (Trifolium dubium) is more tolerant of unfavourable climate and low nutrient levels than large hop clover, but otherwise requires similar conditions.

Persian clover (Trifolium resupinatum) grows in slightly acid to slightly alkaline soils of average depth, deep silt loam, or poorly drained clay that are moist to very moist. A winter annual especially adapted to low, heavy, wet soils. It is not tolerant of salinity.

Red clover (Trifolium pratense) will grow in moderately acid to neutral soils, deep, sandy loam, and well-drained clay soils. Does not stand salinity. A perennial, but behaves mostly as a biennial or a winter annual. Needs plenty of moisture.

Rose clover (Trifolium hirtum) grows in slightly acid soils to slightly alkaline soils of shallow to average depth, silt loams, and well-drained clay. It needs moist to heavy-moisture conditions. A winter annual, it is adapted to hill sites.

Strawberry clover (Trifolium fragiferum) grows in neutral to slightly alkaline soil. Tolerates moderate salinity. Grows in shallow to deep, sandy loam to poorly drained clay. Needs moist to heavy-moisture conditions. Tolerates flooding. A perennial adapted to poorly drained, salty soils.

Striata clover (Trifolium striatum) grows in slightly acid to slightly alkaline soils of average depth to deep, loam to poorly drained clay. Not tolerant of salinity. Requires moist to heavy-moisture conditions. A winter annual adapted to heavy, limy soils.

Sub clover (Trifolium subterraneum) grows in moderate acid to neutral soils. Not tolerant of salinity or waterlogged soils. Prefers shallow or deep, gravelly loam or well-drained clay. A winter annual. Varieties appear to differ in adaptation to different soil conditions.

White clover (Trifolium repens) grows in moderately acid to slightly alkaline soils. Not tolerant of salinity. Needs shallow to deep, fine sand or poorly drained clays and moist to heavy-moisture conditions. A perennial, it behaves also as a winter annual and as a biennial. Varieties differ in nutrient requirements for high production. Ladino has a higher requirement of nutrients.

COLLARDS (*Brassica oleracea* var. *viridis*). (See Cabbage.) The optimum pH is 6.0 to 7.5. Collards are hardy. Generally they are grown for autumn harvest or, in the milder parts, for winter and early spring harvest.

O

CORN OR MAIZE (*Zea mays*). Grows in well-drained, sandy to clay loam of a pH of 5.5 to 8 and 2 to 8 feet deep. Good fertility is essential for high yields, especially when corn is grown in thick stands. Corn responds well to abundant nitrogen. Calcareous soils are likely to be deficient in available potash and phosphorus.

CORN, SWEET (*Zea mays*). See Corn.

COTTON (*Gossypium hirsutum* and *G. barbadense*). Grows in soils that are sand to heavy clay, deep and well drained, reasonably high in organic matter, and pH 5.2 to 8 in reaction. Its indeterminate fruiting habit permits it to mature the number of bolls that can be supported by the extent of vegetative growth. Limited nitrogen reduces both total growth and yield. Deficiencies of potash cause extreme earliness and premature defoliation. Phosphorus is necessary for adequate maturity.

COTTONWOOD, FREMONT (*Populus fremonti*). Will grow on dry, alkaline soil.

COWPEA (*Vigna sinensis*). Grows in highly acid to neutral soil. Is not tolerant of salinity. Needs soils of shallow to average depth, fine sand to well-drained clay, and moist to heavy-moisture conditions. Benefited by the application of mineral nutrients when needed, but it will grow at relatively low levels of nutrients. A summer annual with many varieties.

CRANBERRY (*Vaccinium macrocarpon*). Exacting in soil requirements. It requires porous, acid soil (pH 4 to 5).
  Peat bogs are largely used for cranberries. They are levelled. The surface soil usually is removed. Then the bogs are coated with about 2 inches of sand before planting. They are dyked so they can be flooded during the winter to protect the vines. During the growing season, the water table is maintained about 2 feet below the surface; in dry weather, it is raised periodically to wet the soil. Culture of cranberries in mineral soil generally is not satisfactory.

CROWN VETCH (*Coronilla varia*). Grows in highly acid to neutral soils. Not tolerant of salinity and requires shallow to deep, gravelly loam to well-drained clay soils and moist to heavy-moisture conditions. Applications of mineral nutrients, when needed, are beneficial. It is a perennial and is unpalatable to livestock.

CUCUMBERS (*Cucumis sativus*). See Cucurbits.

CUCURBITS (Cucumbers, muskmelons, watermelons, squash, pumpkins, gourds, and chayote). Soil requirements of all are similar, but those of muskmelons and watermelons are somewhat more exacting than those of the others. (See Muskmelon and Watermelon.)

CYPRESS, SMOOTH ARIZONA (*Cupressus arizonica bonita*). Will grow on very sandy dry soils.

DAHOON (*Ilex cassine*). Will grow on wet soil.

DROPSEEDS. Include many species of *Sporobolus*, which grow in a wide range of soil and climatic conditions. They are benefited slightly by the application of nitrogen.
 Alkali sacaton (*S. airoides*) grows in neutral to highly alkaline soil and is tolerant of high salinity. It grows in fine sand to clay loam and is a perennial. Stands dry conditions.
 Sacatongrass (*S. wrightii*) is less tolerant of alkaline and saline conditions and requires more moisture than alkali sacaton.
 Sand dropseed (*S. cryptandrus*), a perennial, grows in neutral to moderately alkaline soil. It is tolerant of slight salinity and dry conditions.

EGGPLANT (*Solanum melongena*). The optimum pH is 5.5 to 6.5. Eggplant needs a deep soil (4 feet or more) to accommodate its extensive and deeply penetrating roots. Most commonly grown on fine sands, loamy sands, and sandy loams, eggplant will thrive on deep loams, silt loams, and clay loams. Muck soils are not recommended.

ENDIVE, ESCAROLLE (*Cichorium endiva*). See Lettuce.

EUCALYPTUS (most species). Will grow on dry soil.

FALSE CYPRESS, WHITE CEDAR (*Chamaecyparis thyoides*). Will grow on wet soil.

FENNEL, FLORENCE (*Foeniculum vulgare*). The optimum pH range is 5.0 to 6.0. Other soil requirements are similar to those of celery but are less exacting.

FESCUE (*Festuca species*). Adapted to a wide range of soil and climatic conditions.
 Arizona fescue (*F. arizonica*) grows in slightly acid to neutral soil of shallow to average depth – silt loam to clay loam and dry to moist conditions. Benefited slightly by applications of nitrogen. Grows in open pineland and is adapted to high altitudes.
 Hard fescue (*F. ovina* var. *duriuscula*) will tolerate drier sites and lower nutrient levels than sheep fescue.
 Idaho fescue (*F. idahoensis*) grows in slightly acid to slightly alkaline soil of average depth – loamy sand to well-drained clay and dry to moist conditions. Slightly benefited by applications of nitrogen. Adapted to cool to cold temperatures. Does not tolerate salinity.
 Meadow fescue (*F. elatior*) grows in highly acid to neutral soil of shallow to average depth – silt loam to poorly drained clay and moist conditions. Adapted to humid regions. It is not fully hardy.

FESCUE (*Continued*).

Red fescue (*F. rubra*) grows in moderately acid to neutral soils. Does not tolerate salinity. Grows in deep, sandy loam to well-drained clay. It needs moist to very moist conditions and is benefited by applications of nitrogen. Tolerates shade and is used widely in lawns.

Sheep fescue (*F. ovina*) grows in highly acid to neutral soils and is not tolerant of salinity. It prefers gravelly loam and well-drained clay. Used mainly as a lawn grass and is adapted to shady sites.

Tall fescue (*F. arundinacea*) grows in highly acid to moderately alkaline soils. It needs shallow to deep, gravelly loam to poorly drained clay and moist to very moist conditions. Will tolerate short periods of drought.

FIELDPEA (*Pisum sativum*).   One species, of several types, which grow in moderately acid to neutral soils of average depth or in deep, fine sand or clay loam. Prefers moist to heavy-moisture conditions. Benefited by the application of mineral nutrients, when needed. Requires cool temperatures. A summer or winter annual. The Austrian winter fieldpea is more winter hardy than the other types.

FIG (*Ficus carica*).   Figs are not exacting as to soils. They thrive in well-drained soils from fine sands to clays (pH 5 to 8). They are sensitive to nematodes. The soil should be fumigated before planting if many nematodes are present. Fig trees are moderately tolerant to salt.

FILBERT (*Corylus avellana*).   The trees are rather shallow rooted and are not tolerant to a high water table or poorly drained soil. They thrive best on sandy loams to clay loams (pH 5 to 7.5), but will grow on well-drained clays. They are rather intolerant to salt and alkali.

FIR, NORDMANN (*Abies nordmanniana*).   Will grow on gravelly soil.

FLAX (*Linum usitatissimum*).   Grows in well-drained loam to clay loam – pH 5 to 8 for seedflax and pH 5 to 7 for fibre flax. Alkaline soils are assumed to be unfavourable for the production of good linen fibres.

FOXTAIL MILLET (*Setaria italica*).   Grows in moderately acid to slightly alkaline soils. It is not tolerant of salinity. Deep, sandy loam to well-drained clay, moist to very moist are preferred. Applications of nitrogen are beneficial. It is a summer annual and will tolerate short periods of drought.

FRANKLINIA (*Franklinia alatamaha*).   Will grow on alkaline soil.

GARLIC (*Allium sativum*).   The optimum pH range is 5.5 to 8.0. Other soil requirements are similar to those of onions, except that fine-textured soils that become hard are even less desirable for garlic than for onions.

GRAIN SORGHUM (*Sorghum vulgare*). Requires well-drained sandy to clay soils 3 to 8 feet deep and having a pH of 5 to 8.5. It tolerates salinity. In semi-arid regions it succeeds best on silt loam or clay loam soils in the wetter years and on sandy soils in dry years. Lighter soils provide better water infiltration and reduced vegetative growth, which lessens injury from drought.

GRAMAGRASSES. Include many species of *Bouteloua*. The most important are perennials. They grow in neutral to moderately alkaline soil and are not tolerant of salinity. They require soil of average depth – silt loam to well-drained clay – and dry to moist conditions. They are drought resistant and are benefited slightly by the application of nitrogen.

Black grama (*B. eriopoda*) tolerates slight salinity and is more drought resistant than other gramagrasses.

Blue grama (*B. gracilis*) is widely adapted from relatively moist to dry conditions and to sandy and hard lands.

Hairy grama (*B. hirsuta*) is particularly adapted to sandy, rocky, caliche soils.

Side-oats grama (*B. curtipendula*) requires more moisture than blue grama.

GRAPEFRUIT (*Citrus paradisii*). They are adapted to a wide range of soils, but different root-stocks are used on fine-textured soils (pH 5 to 8). A medium-textured soil is ideal, but the trees can be grown on moderately well-drained clays or clay loams. They are rather tolerant to salt and alkalinity.

GRAPES (*Vitis* species). Grapes thrive best on well-aerated soils – medium sands to loams (pH 5 to 8) are ideal, but they will tolerate well-drained clays. The plants root deeply and are more drought resistant than most fruits. They are medium in salt tolerance.

GREVILLEA, SILK-OAK (*Grevillea robusta*). Will grow on very sandy soil.

GUAR (*Cyamopsis tetragonoloba*). Grows in moderately acid to moderately alkaline soils. Tolerant of moderate salinity. Soils of average depth to deep, fine sand to well-drained clay loam are satisfactory. Guar requires moist soil for stand establishment; thereafter it will tolerate dry conditions. It is benefited by an application of mineral nutrients when needed. A summer annual, it is adapted to a hot climate and long, dry growing season.

HEATH (*Erica* species). Acid soil.

HEATHER (*Calluna* species). Acid soil.

HEMP *(Cannabis sativa)*. Requires well-drained loam, silt loam, or clay loam; pH 5 to 7; 3 to 6 feet deep.

HICKORY, PIGNUT *(Carya glabra)*. Will grow on dry soil.

HOBBLEBUSH *(Viburnum alnifolium)*. Acid soil.

HOLLIES *(Ilex* species). Acid soil.

HONEYLOCUST, COMMON *(Gleditsia triacanthos)*. Will grow on gravelly soil.

HOPS *(Humulus lupulus)*. Grow on deep, sandy, well-drained loam to loam soil, 6 to 8 in pH. Soil moisture must be adequate. Soils of high salinity are unsuitable.

HORNBEAM, AMERICAN *(Carpinus caroliniana)*. Will grow on dry soil.

HORNBEAM, HOP *(Ostrya virginiana)*. Will grow on dry soil.

HORSERADISH *(Armoracia rusticana)*. The optimum pH is 6.0 to 7.0. Horseradish is grown commercially as an annual, but in home gardens is often grown as a perennial. For commercial production, deep (3 to 4 feet or more), sandy loams and friable loams are needed. If side roots and surplus shoots are to be removed from planted root cuttings as in commercial practice, a loose, friable soil is essential. For home use, any good garden soil will suffice.

INDIANGRASS, YELLOW *(Sorghastrum nutans)*. Requires fairly deep soils and reasonable moisture.

INDIGO *(Indigofera)*. Two species that grow in highly acid to neutral soils. They are not tolerant of salinity. Soils may be of shallow to average depth and fine sand to clay loam. Moist to high-moisture conditions are needed. They are subtropical and tropical plants – summer annuals and perennials that require high temperatures and a long growing season. Some species are toxic to livestock.
Creeping indigo (I. endecaphylla) a perennial, is toxic to livestock.
Hairy indigo (I. hirsuta) is an annual. It has limited adaptation to sandy soils.

JAPANESE LAWNGRASS *(Zoysia japonica)*. Grows in acid to neutral soils. It is not tolerant of salinity. Shallow to deep, gravelly loam to poorly drained clay and moist to very moist conditions are preferred. Tolerant of short droughts. Benefited by applications of nitrogen, although it grows at relatively low nutrient level. A summer-growing perennial used for lawns. It is adapted to the humid regions that have high summer temperatures.

JAPANESE MILLET (*Echinochloa crusgalli* var. *frumentacea*). Grows in moderately acid to neutral soils and is not tolerant of salinity. Soils should be of shallow to average depth and sandy loam to well-drained clay. It needs heavy moisture and is benefited by applications of nitrogen. A summer annual.

JERUSALEM-THORN (*Parkinsonia aculeata*). Will grow on very sandy, dry soils.

JOHNSONGRASS (*Sorghum halepense*). Grows in slightly acid to slightly alkaline soils. It is not tolerant of salinity. Soils should be of average to deep silt loam to poorly drained clay, moist to very moist. Applications of nitrogen are beneficial. A perennial, it grows well in fertile soils.

JUJUBE (*Zizyphus jujube*). Will grow on dry, alkaline soil.

JUNIPER, COMMON (*Juniperus communis* and varieties). Acid soil.

JUNIPER, CREEPING (*Juniperus horizontalis*). Will grow on very sandy soil.

JUNIPER, PFITZER (*Juniperus chinensis pfitzeriana*). Will grow on very sandy soil.

JUNIPER, SAVIN (*Juniperus sabina*). Will grow on very sandy soil.

JUNIPER, SHORE (*Juniperus compacta*). Will grow on very sandy soil.

KALE (*Brassica oleracea* var. *viridis*). Kale is highly tolerant to high salt content of the soil. Other soil requirements are similar to those of cabbage.

KOHLRABI (*Brassica oleracea* var. *gongylodes*). See Cabbage. Kohlrabi is usually sown in place instead of being transplanted, as are plants of cabbage. Fine-textured soils that bake or crust tend to interfere with seedling emergence and cultivation. Once plants are well established, they grow well in fertile, fine-textured soils and in sandy loams and loams.

KUDZU (*Pueraria lobata*). Grows in highly acid to neutral soils. It is not tolerant of salinity. Shallow to deep, gravelly loam and well-drained clay and moist to heavy-moist conditions are suitable. Benefited by the application of mineral nutrients when they are needed, although the plants can utilize nutrients from relatively unavailable sources. A perennial with a viny type of growth. Not hardy.

LARCH, EASTERN (*Larix laricina*). Will grow on wet soil.

LAUREL (*Kalmia* species). Acid soil.

LEEKS (*Allium porrum*). The optimum pH is 6.0 to 8.0. Other soil requirements are like those of onions.

LEMON (*Citrus limon*). Is sensitive to unfavourable soil conditions and to salt and alkalinity. It thrives best on medium to light-textured, well-drained soil (pH 5 to 7.5) but it can be grown on well-drained clay loam.

LESPEDEZA (*Lespedeza* species). Several annual and perennial species that grow in highly acid to slightly acid soils but do not tolerate salinity. Shallow soils and soils of average depth and gravelly loam to clay loam soils are suitable. Moist to heavy-moisture conditions are needed. Mineral nutrients may be needed. It is tolerant of high summer temperatures and relatively low nutrient levels and requires a relatively long growing season.

> *Bicolor lespedeza* (*L. bicolor*) is a perennial, woody species, used mostly for erosion control and bird feed. It is adapted best to loam and clay soils.
>
> *Korean lespedeza* (*L. stipulacea*) is an annual.
>
> *Sericea lespedeza* (*L. cuneata*) is a perennial that is less palatable than the annual species.
>
> *Striate lespedeza* (*L. striata*) is an annual that requires a longer growing season than Korean lespedeza.

LETTUCE (*Lactuca sativa*). The optimum pH is 5.8 to 7.5. This cool-weather annual plant is moderately tolerant to high salt content and to boron content in the soil. Without irrigation, the soil depth should be 2 to 3 feet or more. Lettuce is grown commercially on soils ranging from loamy sands through sandy loams, loams, and clay loams to clays. Loams and mucks (high lime) are best. Sands and clays can be used effectively only where soil moisture is under good control. Skill in irrigation and cultural operations is especially important in obtaining good stands of lettuce on the very heavy soils. Sandy soils generally are not recommended.

LEUCOTHOE (*Leucothoe* species). Acid soil.

LOVEGRASS (*Eragrostis*). Many annual and perennial species, few of which have agricultural value. Some species are adapted to sands to clay loams and dry or moist conditions.

> *Boer lovegrass* (*E. chloromelas*). A perennial, grows in slightly acid to moderately alkaline soils and is not tolerant of salinity. It likes gravelly loam to clay soils. Drought resistant but not cold tolerant.
>
> *Lehmann lovegrass* (*E. lehmanniana*). See Boer lovegrass.
>
> *Sand lovegrass* (*E. trichodes*) is particularly adapted to sandy soils.
>
> *Weeping lovegrass* (*E. curvula*) is most widely adapted, especially on dry, sandy soils and is used in dry regions.

LUPINS. Many annual and perennial species, which grow in highly acid to neutral soils and are not tolerant of salinity. Soils are shallow to deep, gravelly loam to loam. Moist to heavy-moisture conditions are needed. Applications of mineral nutrients may be beneficial, but the lupins grow at low nutrient levels. Species of agricultural value are grown as winter annuals. Some species are toxic to livestock.

Blue lupin (Lupinus angustifolius) is of two types – bitter blue, which is toxic, and sweet blue, which is palatable.

Yellow lupin (L. luteus) is the least hardy of the listed species.

White lupin (L. albus) is grown as a winter annual in some regions. It is hardier than blue lupin and yellow lupin.

MADRONE, PACIFIC *(Arbutus menziese)*. Will grow on dry soil.

MAGNOLIA, SWEETBAY *(Magnolia virginiana)*. Will grow on wet soil.

MANILA LAWNGRASS *(Zoysia matrella)*. See Japanese lawngrass.

MAPLE, RED *(Acer rubrum)*. Will grow on wet soil.

MEADOW FOXTAIL *(Alopecurus pratensis)*. Grows in moderately acid to neutral soils. Will tolerate slight salinity. It needs soil of average depth to deep, silt loam and clay loam and moist to very moist conditions. Tolerates flooding and is benefited by applications of nitrogen. A perennial, cool-season grass.

MEDICKS OR BURCLOVERS. Several species of *Medicago*. Grow in slightly acid to moderately alkaline soils and will tolerate salinity. They like shallow to deep, sandy loam to well-drained clay and moist conditions. Benefited by applications of mineral nutrients when needed. Require available calcium for best growth.

Most species behave as winter annuals. They are adapted to limestone and neutral soils.

Black medick (M. lupulina) is the most winter hardy of the listed species. A winter or summer annual. Less exacting in its calcium requirements than the other species.

Buttonclover (M. orbicularis), California burclover (M. hispida), Spotted medick (M. arabica) – see Medicks.

MESQUITEGRASSES *(Hilaria)*. Several species that grow in neutral to moderately alkaline soils and are tolerant of moderate salinity. They grow in shallow to deep sandy loam to clay loam in very dry or dry conditions. They are perennials and are adapted to dry conditions.

Curly-mesquite (H. belangeri) is more abundant in low desert-like sites.

Galleta (H. jamesii) will tolerate drier sites.

Tobosa (H. mutica). See Galleta.

MIMOSA *(Albizzia julibrissin)*. Will grow on dry, gravelly and very sandy soils.

O*

MINT (*Mentha piperita* and *M. spicata*). Grows in sandy loam, loam, or muck of pH 6 to 7.5. It needs a constant supply of soil moisture.

MUNG BEAN (*Phaseolus aureus*). Will tolerate droughty conditions. A summer annual. (See Cowpea.)

MUSKMELONS, including cantaloups (*Cucumis melo*). The optimum pH is 6.0 to 7.5. Muskmelons are not tolerant to high salt or boron content of the soil. A soil depth of 2 feet or more should be available. Early muskmelons are grown on sandy and sandy loam soils. Loams, silt loams, and even silty clay loams are used successfully for later crops. Sandy loams and loams are best. Muck soils and clays are not suitable.

MUSTARD (*Brassica juncea* and others). (See Cabbage.) Seed of mustard is very small and produces relatively weak seedlings. Good stands of plants are difficult to obtain on sandy soils and on the fine-textured soils, which tend to pack or crust, unless soil moisture is under control.

NEEDLEGRASS (*Stipa*). Many species that are adapted to a wide range of soil and climatic conditions.
> *Green needlegrass* (*S. viridula*) is a perennial. It is benefited by applications of nitrogen.
> *Needle-and-thread grass* (*S. comata*) grows in neutral to moderately alkaline soils and is not tolerant of salinity. Soils should be shallow to moderately deep, sandy loam to well-drained clay. They stand dry to moist conditions and are benefited slightly by applications of nitrogen.
> *Purple needlegrass* (*S. pulchra*) is adapted to coastal ranges.

OAK, CHESTNUT (*Quercus montana*). Will grow on dry soil.

OAK, OREGON WHITE (*Quercus garryana*). Will grow on dry, gravelly soils.

OAK, PIN (*Quercus palustris*). Will grow on wet, acid soils.

OATS (*Avena sativa* and *A. byzantina*). Grow in well-drained, fine sandy loam to clay, which has a pH of 5 to 8.5 and is 2.5 to 8 feet deep. Excessive soil nitrates favour lodging, and sometimes enough are absorbed by the plants to make oats hay poisonous to livestock. Manganese deficiency sometimes is evident in oats grown on peat soils.

OKRA (*Hibiscus esculentus*). The optimum pH is 6.0 to 7.5. The extensive root system of this large, warm-weather plant requires a soil 3 to 4 feet deep. It grows well on any rich garden or nursery soil.

OLIVE (*Olea europaea*). Has been widely planted in areas of limited water supply, but it requires good soil moisture for maximum production. Trees do not tolerate waterlogged soil. Open, well-drained sandy loams to clay loams (pH 5 to 8) are ideal. It is moderately tolerant to salt and alkaline soil.

OLIVE, RUSSIAN (*Elaeagnus augustifolia*). Will grow on dry soil.

ONIONS (*Allium cepa*). The optimum pH is 5.8 to 7.5. Onions are moderately tolerant to a high salt content and tolerant to a high boron content of the soil. Relatively shallow rooted, they require a soil depth of 1.5 to 2 feet. Watering should therefore be frequent, or the water-holding capacity of the soil must be high, as in mucks, loams, and silt loams, all of which are good soils for onions. Sandy loams are good if the water supply is ample. Sands, clay loams, and clays are undesirable.

ORANGE (*Citrus sinensis*). Can be grown on a wide range of soils, but it thrives best on medium- to open-textured, well-drained soils (pH 5 to 8). On soils of finer texture, special stocks must be used. For maximum production, ample moisture must be available throughout the year, although the tree will tolerate temporary conditions of water shortage. Roots die in water-logged soil rather quickly. It is moderately tolerant of salt.

ORCHARDGRASS (*Dactylis glomerata*). Grows in moderately acid to neutral soils. It is not tolerant of salinity and likes shallow to deep gravelly loam to poorly drained clay and moist to very moist conditions. Benefited by applications of nitrogen. A perennial.

OYSTER PLANT. See Salsify.

PALOVERDE, BLUE (*Cercidium floridum*). Will grow on dry soil.

PANGOLAGRASS (*Digitaria decumbens*). Grows in highly acid to neutral soils and is not tolerant of salinity. It needs moist to very moist conditions but will tolerate periods of drought. Adapted to sandy soils but requires added fertility. A perennial. Not winter hardy.

PANICUM GRASSES (*Panicum*). Many annual and perennial species, which are adapted to a wide range of soil and climatic conditions. They are widely distributed, mainly in the warmer climates.
   Blue panicgrass (*P. antidotale*) grows in moderately acid to slightly alkaline soils. It is not tolerant of salinity. Sandy loam to well-drained, fertile clay of average depth or deep are preferred. It is drought resistant but not winter hardy.
   Guineagrass (*P. maximum*) grows in highly acid to slightly acid soils and is not tolerant of salinity. A perennial, it is adapted to subtropical and tropical conditions and requires applications of nitrogen.
   Paragrass (*P. purpurascens*) grows in highly acid to neutral soils and is not tolerant of salinity. It requires moist to very moist conditions and tolerates some flooding. Benefited by applications of nitrogen. Subtropical to tropical in adaptation. A perennial which is propagated vegetatively.

PANICUM GRASSES (*Continued*).

Proso millet (*P. miliaceum*) grows in moderately acid or neutral and shallow or deep, sandy loam in dry to moist conditions. It is benefited by an application of nitrogen. A summer annual.

Switchgrass (*P. virgatum*). A perennial. It prefers sandy loams that are reasonably well supplied with moisture.

Vine mesquitegrass (*P. obtusum*) grows in neutral to moderately alkaline soils. It tolerates slight salinity. Soils should be of shallow to average depth and sandy loam to well-drained clay. Prefers dry conditions. A perennial, it is drought resistant.

PAPER-MULBERRY, COMMON (*Broussonetia papyrifera*). Will grow on gravelly soil.

PARSLEY (*Petrolselinum crispum*). The optimum pH is 5.0 to 7.0. This cool-season plant will grow well on any good garden soil, once the plants are established. The seedlings, like those of carrots, start slowly, are weak, and cannot push through compact or crusted soil. Mucks, sandy loams, and friable loams are best, but sands, silts, and clay loams can be used if the water is under control.

PARSLEY, TURNIP ROOTED (*Petrolselinum crispum*). The optimum pH is 5.0 to 7.0. Other soil requirements are the same as for carrots.

PARSNIPS (*Pastinaca sativa*). See Carrots.

PASPALUM GRASSES (*Paspalum*). Many perennial species, which grow in highly acid to neutral soils – shallow to deep, gravelly loam to poorly drained clay and moist to swampy conditions. They are not hardy. Some species grow when nutrient levels are relatively low.

Bahiagrass (*P. notatum*) is adapted to drier sites and low nutrient levels.

Dallisgrass (*P. dilatatum*) requires higher nutrient levels than other species and is less adapted to fine sand and loam sand.

PEACH. Peach trees grow well in many types of soil, which should be able to provide plenty of moisture, and maintain good fertility. Peach trees have shallower roots than most other fruit trees, and do not tolerate competition with grass and other vegetables so well as apples and pears. Peach orchards, for this reason, are often cultivated instead of being covered by grass.

Peaches need plenty of nitrogen, and nitrogenous fertilizer is applied in early spring.

PEAR. Like the apple, a long-lived deciduous tree of the temperate zone. Pears will grow in many types of soil. They are more tolerant of poorly-aerated soil than other orchard trees, and are often planted on heavy soils.

PEAS, GARDEN (*Pisum sativum*). The optimum pH is 6.0 to 7.5. This cool-season plant has a low to medium tolerance to high salt content, medium tolerance to high boron content, and low tolerance to high acidity of the soil. The calcium need is high.

Good soil drainage is especially important, because root rots are destructive in wet soils. A soil depth of at least 1.5 to 2 feet is desirable. Peas are well adapted to sandy loams for early-season production but are more extensively grown on loams, silt loams, and silty clay loams. Clay loams are suitable where water supply is under control, but are likely to be troublesome in regions of heavy rainfall. Sand and clays are not desirable.

Peas respond well to inoculation with nitrogen-fixing bacteria if the calcium supply is adequate. Despite the nitrogen-fixing relationship, peas respond to a moderately high ratio of nitrogen, especially during early growth.

PEAS, SOUTHERN OR EDIBLE COWPEA (*Vigna sinensis*). The optimum pH is 5.0 to 7.0. These peas tolerate acid soils. The cowpea, a hot-weather plant, is adapted to a wide range of soils. Most agricultural soils, except sands, are satisfactory, although loams and silt loams are best. Inoculation with nitrogen-fixing bacteria is advantageous. A high nitrogen supply tends to produce excessive vegetation in proportion to pods.

PEAVINE. Several species of *Lathyrus*, which grow in slightly acid to slightly alkaline soils but are not tolerant to salinity. Soils are shallow to deep, silt loam to poorly drained clays. It needs heavy moisture. Applications of mineral nutrients may be helpful. They are best adapted to heavy, wet soils.

Roughpea (*L. hirsutus*) is a winter annual which grows well in heavy soils.

Tangier pea (*L. tingitanus*) a winter annual, has a wide range of soil adaptation.

PENNISETUM GRASSES (*Pennisetum*). Many annual and perennial species, which grow in a wide range of soil and moisture conditions.

Buffelgrass (*P. ciliare*) a perennial, grows in slightly acid to slightly alkaline soils and is tolerant of slight salinity. Soils should be of average depth – fine sand to well-drained clay. It stands dry to moist conditions and is moderately drought resistant. Particularly adapted to sandy soils. Requires applications of nitrogen. It is not hardy. Blue buffel is better on heavy soils.

Kikuyugrass (*P. clandestinum*) is a perennial that grows in neutral to moderately alkaline soils. It is tolerant of moderate salinity. Shallow to deep, fine sand to well-drained clay are preferred. Adapted to subtropical and tropical conditions.

Napiergrass (*P. purpureum*) grows in highly acid to neutral soils. It does not tolerate salinity. Its preferred soils are of average depth or deep, fine sand or clay loam. This perennial requires moist or very moist con-

PENNISETUM GRASSES (*Continued*).
ditions. Benefited by an application of nitrogen. Adapted to subtropical or tropical conditions.
Pearl millet (*P. glaucum*) grows in highly acid to neutral soils and is not tolerant of salinity. Deep, fine sand or loam are best. It requires a great deal of moisture and is benefited by nitrogen. A summer annual.

PEPPERS (*Capsicum frutescens*). The optimum pH is 5.5 to 7.0. The garden pepper, a warm-weather plant, is moderately tolerant to a high salt content and only slightly tolerant to high boron in the soil. It is grown successfully on many kinds of soil, ranging from fine sands through sandy loams, loams, silt loams, and clay loams. The coarser textured soils are preferred for early crops. The finer textured soils are preferred for later crops. Peppers can be grown on muck, but other crops are usually more profitable.

PEPPERTREE, BRAZIL (*Schinus terebinthifolius*). Will grow on dry soil.

PEPPERTREE, CALIFORNIA (*Schinus molle*). Will grow on dry soil.

PERENNIAL VELDTGRASS (*Ehrharta calycina*). Grows in neutral to moderately alkaline soil. It is tolerant of slight salinity and likes shallow to deep loam and well-drained clay and dry to moist conditions. Benefited slightly by an application of nitrogen. A drought-resistant perennial.

PIMENTOS. See Peppers.

PINE, MUGHO (*Pinus mugo*). Will grow on gravelly soil.

PINE, PITCH (*Pinus rigida*). Will grow on very sandy, dry soils.

PINE, PONDEROSA (*Pinus ponderosa*). Will grow on dry soil.

PINE, SCOTCH (*Pinus sylvestris*). Will grow on very sandy soil.

PINE, SCRUB (*Pinus virginiana*). Will grow on dry soil.

PINE, SWISS MOUNTAIN (*Pinus mugo*). Will grow on gravelly soil.

PINE, TORREY (*Pinus torreyana*). Will grow on dry soil.

PINE, VIRGINIA (*Pinus virginiana*). Will grow on dry soil.

PLUM. See Peach.

POPLARS (*Populus*). Most species will grow on wet soil.

POPLAR, WHITE (*Populus alba*). Will grow on dry soil.

POTATOES (*Solanum tuberosum*). The potato grows well over a pH range from 4.5 to 7.0, but the soilborne disease called scab often becomes serious above pH 5.5. From the standpoints of both high yield and scab control, the optimum pH for potatoes is 5.0 to 5.5, but large acreages of potatoes are grown at pH about 7.0.

The potato, a cool-weather crop, is moderately tolerant to a high salt content and a high boron content of the soil. It is grown successfully on muck soils and on mineral soils 2 to 3 feet deep or more – fine sands, gravelly soils, sandy loams, loams, silt loams, and clay loams. Sandy loams are best for early crops. Loams, silt loams, and mucks are best for late crops.

Good drainage and a sustained, moderately high soil moisture are important. Clay loams and clays make harvesting difficult and leave the harvested potatoes unattractively dirty.

PUMPKINS (*Cucurbita pepo* and *C. moschata*). (See Cucurbits).

RADISHES (*Raphanus sativus*). The optimum pH is 5.0 to 7.0. Radish is highly intolerant to a high salt content of the soil and is moderately tolerant to a high boron content. A cool-weather crop, the radish should be grown rapidly.

The root system of the small, globe-shaped type is shallow and requires good soil only about 1 foot deep. The small, long forms of radish, however, require soil 2 to 3 feet deep.

Radishes grow well on any fertile soil, except the fine-textured soils that become very hard; in them, the edible roots may become misshapen. Sandy loams, friable loams, and mucks are best for commercial production.

RAMIE (*Boehmeria nivea*). Grows in loam or muck, pH 5 to 7 in reaction, and 2 to 4 feet deep. Abundant fertility is necessary for successive heavy crops through the season.

RASPBERRY (*Rubus*). Require ample moisture, but they are sensitive to waterlogged soil. They thrive best on sandy loams to clay loams (pH 5 to 7.5) but will grow in well-drained clay. They are relatively shallow rooted and grow best, especially in the warmer locations, if they are kept mulched with organic material.

RATTLEBOX. Many species of *Crotalaria* which grow in highly acid to neutral soil. They are not tolerant of salinity and require moist to heavy-moisture conditions. The plants will grow at relatively low nutrient levels, but fertilizers may be beneficial. Summer annuals.

Some species, toxic to livestock, are used mostly for green manure.
Lance crotalaria (*C. lanceolata*) see Rattlebox.
Showy crotalaria (*C. spectabilis*) is poisonous.
Slenderleaf crotalaria (*C. intermedia*), *Striped crotalaria* (*C. mucronata* (*striata*)). See Rattlebox.

REDCEDAR, EASTERN (*Juniperus virginiana*). Will grow on alkaline soil.

REDTOP AND BENTGRASSES (*Agrostis*). Many species that grow in highly acid to neutral soils and are not tolerant of salinity. Shallow, moist, gravelly loam to muck are preferred. Tolerate swampy conditions and benefit from the application of nitrogen. They grow when nutrient levels are relatively low. Cool-season grasses suited to humid regions.

Colonial bentgrass (*A. tenuis*), creeping bentgrass (*A. palustris*), and redtop (*A. alba*) are important perennials.

RHODESGRASS (*Chloris gayana*). Grows in moderately acid to highly alkaline soils. It tolerates moderate salinity and dry conditions. Soils of average depth to deep, loam and well-drained clay are preferred. Applications of nitrogen are beneficial. It is a perennial but is not hardy.

RHODODENDRON (*Rhododendron* species). Acid soil.

RHUBARB (*Rheum rhaponticum*). The optimum pH is 5.5 to 6.5. This cool-weather, hardy perennial thrives best in regions where the soil freezes at least a few inches deep each winter. For good production it needs a very deep (6 to 8 feet), rich, well-drained soil. The sandy loams, which warm up early, are best for early harvest. Heavier production, however, may be expected on rich loams and silt loams. Rhubarb is grown on clay loams and on mucks, but they are not preferred. The plant is a gross feeder and is benefited by heavy applications of manure and fertilizer. The excessive use of nitrate of soda may develop undesirably high content of nitrates in the edible petioles.

RICE (*Oryza sativa*). Grows in loam to heavy clay (adobe) that has a retentive subsoil and a reaction of pH 4.5 to 7.5 and is 2 to 3 feet deep. The soil must be wet or flooded. It is sensitive to salinity in excess of 500 grains per gallon of water. The potash requirement is low, but abundant ammonium nitrogen is essential to high yields.

RICEGRASSES (*Oryzopsis*). Many species, which grow in slightly acid to moderately alkaline soils and are tolerant of slight salinity. They thrive in sandy loam to clay loam that is of average depth or deeper. Stand very dry to dry conditions and are tolerant of wide ranges of temperature. Benefited slightly by application of nitrogen.

Indian ricegrass (*O. hymenoides*) is drought resistant. It is a perennial. Smilo (*O. miliacea*) tolerates dry or moist conditions. It is grown in places that have wet winters and dry summers.

RUTABAGA (*Brassica napus* var. *napobrassica*). The optimum pH is 5.5 to 7.5. Rutabaga has a relatively high need for boron. This medium long-season, cool-weather plant produces a surprisingly large and deep root system. For best plant development, the soil should be at least 4 to 5 feet deep. Loams and silt loams are preferred. Sandy loams are generally misshapen and to make harvest difficult.

a little less productive. Clays tend to cause the marketable roots to be

RYE (*Secale cereale*). Is more tolerant of sandy soils than is wheat, oats, and barley. Rye grows in sand to clay soil of pH 4.5 to 8.5 and 3 to 8 feet deep.

RYEGRASSES. Annual and short-lived perennial species of *Lolium*. They grow in highly acid to neutral soils and are not tolerant of salinity. Shallow to deep, fine sand to poorly drained clay are suitable, as are moist to very moist conditions. They are benefited by the application of nitrogen.
   Italian ryegrass (*L. multiflorum*) is an annual.
   Perennial ryegrass (*L. perenne*) is a short-lived perennial.

SAFFLOWER (*Carthamus tinctorius*). Grows in well-drained sandy loam to clay of pH 5 to 8 and a depth of 3 to 5 feet. It tolerates salinity.

SALSIFY (*Tragopogon porrifolius*). The optimum pH is 6.0 to 7.5. Other soil requiremenst are the same as for carrots. It is less difficult to get good stands of salsify than of carrots.

SASSAFRAS (*Sassafras albidum officinale*). Will grow on dry and gravelly soils.

SERVICEBERRY (*Amelanchier* species). Acid soil.

SESAME (*Sesamum indicum*). Needs well-drained sandy loam to clay loam, 3 to 5 feet in depth and pH 6 to 8.5 in reaction. It stands medium drought.

SESBANIA (*Sesbania exaltata*). Grows in highly acid to neutral soils. It is tolerant of slight salinity. The soils can be of shallow to average depth and gravelly loam or well-drained clays. Moist conditions are required for seedling establishment; thereafter plants tolerate periods of drought. Applications of needed mineral nutrients are beneficial, although plants grow at a relatively low nutrient level. It is a summer annual.

SHALLOTS (*Allium ascalonicum*). The optimum pH is 5.5 to 7.0. The plant is relatively shallow rooted and is grown best on loam soils, although sandy loams and silt loams are also good. Sandy soils and clays are undesirable.

SORGO (SWEET SORGHUM) (*Sorghum vulgare*). Grows in well-drained sand to clay loam – pH 5 to 8.5, and depth 3 to 8 feet. Excessive nitrogen results in sorgo syrup of low quality.

SORREL (*Rumex acetosa*). It tolerates a pH of 4.0 to 7.0. This plant is a perennial kin to dock (a common perennial weed) and is sometimes called "sour grass". It will grow in soils too acid for other vegetables, ranging from sandy soil to clay and muck. Like most plants, it grows better in rich soils than in poor ones.

SOYBEANS (*Glycine max*). Grow in highly acid to slightly alkaline soils – shallow to deep, fine sand to muck. They need moist to heavy-moisture conditions and do not tolerate salinity. Benefited by the application of mineral nutrients when needed. Soybeans do not do well in dry land regions and localities where cool daily temperatures prevail.

SPINACH (*Spinacia oleracea*). The optimum pH is 6.0 to 7.0. It is tolerant to high salt content and boron content in the soil and is very sensitive to high acidity. Additions of manganese may be needed to correct chlorosis on strongly alkaline soils. The root system is shallow; the soil need not be more than 1.5 to 2 feet deep, but it must be well drained and highly fertile for good yields. Sandy loams are satisfactory for early market crops, but the more fertile, deep loams, silt loams, clay loams, and mucks are preferred where earliness is not important. Clay soils can be used where moisture in the soil is under control.

SQUASH (*Cucurbita pepo, C. moschata*, and *C. maxima*). (See Cucurbits).

ST. AUGUSTINEGRASS (*Stenotaphrum secundatum*). Grows in highly acid to slightly alkaline soils. It is not tolerant of salinity. Grows in shallow to deep, gravelly loam to muck in wet or swampy conditions. Benefited by applications of nitrogen. Used mostly for shady lawns. A perennial.

STRAWBERRY (*Fragaria*). Plants root to 2 feet, and the water table should be lower than that. They thrive on loamy sands (pH 5 to 7.5). They can be grown on well-drained clays, but soils of light to medium texture are preferred. They are not tolerant of salt or alkali.

STRAWBERRY-TREE (*Arbutus unedo*). Acid soil.

SWEETCLOVER (*Melilotus*). Two species are widely grown. Slightly acid to moderately alkaline soils are needed. They will tolerate slight to moderate salinity and grow on shallow to deep, gravelly loam to poorly drained clay. Moisture is needed for stand establishment; after that they will tolerate dry conditions. Fertilization may be beneficial. The plants particularly require readily available calcium.

The two important species are widely grown wherever the soil is neutral or sufficient lime is applied to correct acidity.

Sourclover (*Melilotus indica*) is a winter annual.

White sweetclover (*Melilotus alba*) has biennial and annual forms.

Yellow sweetclover (*Melilotus officinalis*) a biennial, will grow under slightly more adverse climatic conditions than white sweetclover.

SWEET CORN (*Zea mays*). (See Corn.) Optimum pH is 5.5 to 7.0. Sweet corn is moderately tolerant to high salt and to high boron content of the soil. It grows well on any well-drained soil that produces good yields of other crops. Deep, naturally rich soils that are easy to work are preferred but are not essential. Sweet corn requires relatively heavy manuring and fertilizing of soils that are not naturally highly fertile. Fine sandy loams and sandy loams are best for crops for early market; loams, silt loams, clay loams and clays can be used for later crops.

SWEETGUM, AMERICAN (*Liquidambar styraciflua*). Will grow on wet soil.

SWEETPOTATO (*Ipomoea batatas*). The optimum pH is 5.5 to 6.5; good yields are possible in a pH range of 5.2 to 7.0. Sweetpotato is best adapted to slightly acid soils and has little tolerance to either high salt or high boron content of the soil. Loamy fine sand, loamy sand, and sandy loam surface soils are suitable for sweetpotatoes when they are well fertilized and underlaid by firm, well-drained subsoils of finer texture at approximately 1 foot depth. Sandy or gravelly subsoils tend to be infertile and droughty and to cause too deep penetration of the enlarged roots; the results are poor shape of the roots and difficulty of harvest. Friable, moderately deep loams and silt loams, such as Lintonia silt loam, are very desirable. Clay loams and clays are conducive to poor root shape and difficult harvest; they are not recommended. Muck soils cause poor root shape, although large tonnages can be produced on them. Sweetpotato requires high potash, medium phosphorus, and medium to low nitrogen supplies.

SWISS CHARD (*Beta vulgaris* var. *cicla*). The optimum pH is 6.0 to 7.5. This leafy form of beet is highly tolerant to high salt and high boron content of the soil. It can be grown successfully on any good garden soil from loamy sands and sandy loams to clay loams and muck, if the soil is not strongly acid.

SUDANGRASS (*Sorghum sudanense*). Grows in moderately acid to neutral soils of average depth or deep, loamy sand to well-drained clay. It requires moist conditions although it tolerates drought periods after it is established. Benefited by the application of nitrogen under moist conditions. A summer annual adapted to localities of high summer temperatures.

SUGAR BEET (*Beta vulgaris*). Grows in deep clay to silt loam, or sometimes fine sandy loam or muck, alkaline to slightly acid, well drained, and free from hardpan. It is very tolerant of salinity. It requires ample available phosphorus and responds to abundant nitrogen. It is sensitive to boron deficiency and to manganese deficiency on slightly alkaline soils in the Great Lakes region.

SUGARCANE (*Saccharum officinarum*). Needs loam, clay loam, or muck, including calcareous soils and soils derived from volcanic ash. Sandy loams require more moisture and fertilizers. The pH should be 5 to 8. Depth should be 1.5 to 5 feet, but the shallower soils are suitable only if moisture and fertility are abundant. Muck soils require applications of mineral fertilizers, except nitrogen, and usually such trace elements as iron, manganese, and copper.

SUMMERSWEET (*Clethra* species). Acid soil.

TALL OATGRASS (*Arrhenatherum elatius*). A short-lived perennial that grows in moderately acid to neutral soils and is moderately tolerant of salinity. Soils should be of shallow to average depth and loam to poorly drained clay. It requires moist to very moist conditions but thrives in rich, well-drained soils.

TAMARACK (*Larix laricina*). Will grow on wet soil.

TEA-TREE, AUSTRALIAN (*Leptospermum laevigatum*). Will grow on very sandy soil.

TIMOTHY (*Phleum pratense*). Grows in highly acid to neutral soils. Not tolerant of salinity. Benefited by applications of nitrogen. Widely used in sandy loam or poorly drained clay.

TOMATO (*Lycopersicon esculentum*). The optimum pH is 5.5 to 7.5. The tomato has medium high tolerance to both high salt and high boron content of the soil. It is one of the most widely adaptable of vegetables. Most varieties produce a large root system that will fill the soil to a depth of 4 feet if the soil is suitable. It is grown commercially on soils ranging from fine sands to marls and clays. It is rarely grown on mucks. Manganese additions are necessary on marls. On the sands and sandy loams, heavy to very heavy fertilization is necessary. The tomato has a high requirement for phosphorus and potassium. Nitrogenous fertilizers and manures must be used judiciously because excess nitrogen often causes excessive plant growth, dropping of blossoms, and consequent low yields. Tomato is very sensitive to fluctuations in water or in nutrients, which commonly cause blossom end rot of fruit and dropping of blossoms. The best yields are obtained on deep (4 feet or more), rich loams, silt loams, and clay loams that are well supplied with moisture.

TREE OF HEAVEN (*Ailanthus altissima*). Will grow on dry, gravelly soils.

TREFOIL. Several perennial and annual species of *Lotus*. Trefoil grows in moderately acid to neutral soil. It is tolerant to salinity and grows in soils of shallow or average depth – sandy loam to poorly drained clay. Moist to very moist conditions are needed. It tolerates short dry periods.
> *Big trefoil* (*L. uliginosus*) is less winter hardy than birdsfoot but is better adapted to swampy conditions. It is a perennial.
> *Birdsfoot trefoil* (*L. corniculatus*) is more winter hardy than big trefoil. It is a perennial.
> *Narrowleaf birdsfoot trefoil* (*L. tenuis*) is a perennial and is more tolerant of high salinity.

TURNIPS (*Brassica rapa*). The optimum pH is 5.5 to 6.8. Turnips tolerate a high boron content in the soil. Roots for early market and greens for market and processing are commonly grown on sandy loams. Roots for storage and forage are better grown on the more fertile loams and silt loams. Rich clays can produce heavy yields if the soil moisture is under control.

VELVETBEAN (*Stizolobium deeringianum*). Several varieties that differ in maturity. They are grown as summer annuals. (See Cowpea.)

VELVETGRASS (*Holcus lanatus*). Grows in highly acid to slightly acid soils. It is not tolerant of salinity. Soils should be of shallow to average depth and fine sand to poorly drained clay. Requires heavy moisture. Benefited by applications of nitrogen, although it grows at a low nutrient level. Will tolerate swampy sites.

VETCHES. Many species of *Vicia*, which grow in highly acid to slightly alkaline soils. They are tolerant of slight salinity. Shallow to deep, fine sand to poorly drained clays and moist to heavy-moisture conditions are preferred. Some species are adapted to a wide range of climatic conditions.

    Common vetch (*V. sativa*) is a winter annual.
    Hairy vetch (*V. villosa*) is a winter or summer annual. It is the most winter hardy of all vetches.
    Hungarian vetch (*V. pannonica*) a winter annual.
    Purple vetch (*V. bengalensis*) is a winter annual. It is the least hardy.
    Woollypod vetch (*V. dasycarpa*) is a winter annual.

WALNUT. The walnut grows well in many different soils. Nitrogen is needed during the growing season, and 100 pounds to the acre is commonly used in walnut orchards. Boron is needed to promote maximum production in some areas.

WATERCRESS (*Radicula nasturtium-aquaticum*). The optimum pH is 6.0 to 8.0. Watercress is grown commercially in running spring water, chiefly in limestone regions where the water is high in calcium and carries adequate amounts of other nutrients, including nitrates. The plants are set in 2 to 4 inches of compost on carefully graded bottoms of flooded beds. Other than preparation of compost, no fertilization is commonly given.

WATER-ELM (*Planera aquatica*). Will grow on wet soil.

WATERMELONS (*Citrullus vulgaris*). (See Cucurbits.) The optimum pH is 5.5 to 6.5. Watermelon, a warm-weather plant, is grown chiefly on loamy sands, sandy loams, and well-drained loams. The plant is a gross feeder and responds well to heavy applications of manure and other organic matter and to fertilizer, but it is not adapted to mucks. Certain friable silt loams are satisfactory, but clay loams and clays are not recommended.

WHEAT (*Triticum* species). Prefers well-drained silt loam or clay loam but will grow in fine sandy loam to clay – pH 5 to 8.5; depth 2.5 to 8 feet. It requires balanced fertility and ample available nitrates to produce grain of high protein content.

WHEATGRASSES (*Agropyron*). Many species grow under a wide range of soil conditions but are not adapted to acid soils. Some species tolerate salinity and are adapted to the drier sites. They are benefited by applications of nitrogenous fertilizers when the shortage of moisture is not acute.

Beardless wheatgrass (*A. inerme*) is slightly more tolerant of drought than crested wheatgrass.

Bluebunch wheatgrass (*A. spicatum*) requires semihumid conditions and a higher nutrient level.

Crested wheatgrass (*A. desertorum*) grows in neutral to slightly alkaline soils. It is tolerant of moderate salinity, gravelly loam or well-drained clay of average depth, and dry to moist conditions.

Fairway wheatgrass (*A. cristatum*) is better adapted to extreme northern conditions than crested wheatgrass.

Intermediate wheatgrass (*A. intermedium*) is less drought tolerant and requires a higher nutrient level. Adapted to well-drained, sandy loam to clay loam. It is less hardy.

Pubescent wheatgrass (*A. trichophorum*) tolerates a lower nutrient level than intermediate wheatgrass.

Quackgrass (*A. repens*) grows in highly acid to neutral soils. It is not tolerant of salinity. Soils should be of average depth to deep, fine sand to clay loam. Demands moist to very moist conditions. Benefited by applications of nitrogen. Adapted to humid regions. It is weedy.

Siberian wheatgrass (*A. sibericum*) is better adapted to sandy soils having hardpans than crested wheatgrass.

Slender wheatgrass (*A. trachycaulum*) requires more moisture than crested wheatgrass.

Streambank wheatgrass (*A. riparium*) is tolerant of heavy moisture. It forms dense sod for waterways.

Tall wheatgrass (*A. elongatum*) tolerates poor drainage and high salinity.

Thickspike wheatgrass (*A. dasystachyum*) (see Crested wheatgrass).

Western wheatgrass (*A. smithii*) is better adapted to moist swales and has a wider range of climatic adaptation.

WILDRYE. Many perennial species of *Elymus*. They grow in a wide range of soil and climatic conditions. Some are benefited by the application of nitrogen.

Blue wildrye (*E. glaucus*) grows on drier sites than Siberian wildrye.

Canada wildrye (*E. canadensis*) grows in highly acid to moderately alkaline soils and tolerates moderate salinity. It requires shallow to deep, gravelly loam to clay and moist to very moist conditions. Benefited by the application of nitrogen. A widely adapted species.

Giant wildrye (*E. condensatus*) grows in neutral to moderately alkaline soils. It is tolerant to moderate salinity. A perennial, it needs shallow to deep, stony loam to well-drained clay and very dry to moist conditions. Benefited slightly by the application of nitrogen. Moderately drought resistant.

Russian wildrye (*E. junceus*) grows in neutral to moderately alkaline soils. Tolerates high salinity. Requires soil of average depth to deep,

WILDRYE (*Continued*).

sandy loam to clay loam and dry to moist conditions. Requires a high nutrient level and is benefited by applications of nitrogen.

Siberian wildrye (*E. giganteus*) grows in slightly acid to moderately alkaline soil. Not tolerant of salinity. Tolerates dry to moist conditions and is benefited slightly by applications of nitrogen. Particularly useful for the stabilization of inland sand dunes but is not adapted to coastal conditions.

WILLOW (*Salix*) (most species).   Will grow on wet soil.

WINTERGREEN (*Gaultheria procumbens*).   Acid soil.

YELLOW MUSTARD (*Brassica alba*). Requires fine sandy loam to clay. Brown mustard (*B. juncea*) grows in sandy loam. The reaction is pH 6 to 8. A soil depth of 3 to 5 feet is needed.

MANURES AND FERTILIZERS

ORGANIC MANURES AND FERTILIZERS

BONE MEAL. The mineral matter of bones consists largely of calcium phosphate and calcium carbonate. Fresh bones include also a mass of protein which permeates the mineral matter, and a quantity of fat. The fat may be removed easily by boiling the bones, leaving the protein, which amounts to about one third of the dry weight.

Boiled bones are an excellent source of phosphorus (25–30%) and nitrogen (3–5%). The phosphorus is mainly tricalcium phosphate, and this is a slow acting fertilizer. The porosity of bones provides a large surface area, and ground bones act more rapidly than phosphate rock.

Steamed Bone Meal is made by grinding bones which have been steamed under pressure to remove the protein. Steamed bones can be ground more finely than boiled bones, and make their phosphorus available more rapidly. They contain a higher percentage of phosphorus, but very little nitrogen.

Bone meals are slower in action than superphosphate, but provide a useful 'background' of phosphorus, especially in soils where iron removes superphosphate rapidly from the solution. They are available in coarse, medium and fine grades, the activity increasing as the particles become smaller. Coarse bone meals will provide a steady source of phosphorus for several years. They are commonly used on soils in which trees and shrubs are planted, at the rate of 4–6 oz. per square yard.

Finer grades of bone meal may release their phosphorus in a matter of months. They are often used as constituents of compound fertilizers.

COMPOST. See page 194.

DRIED BLOOD. This contains about 10% nitrogen in the form of organic matter, with very little phosphorus. Dried blood decays quickly, especially in warm, moist soil, and it is one of the most rapid-acting of organic fertilizers. It is slower, however, than inorganic fertilizers such as nitrates.

Dried blood is used largely as a top dressing around established plants, at the rate of about 2–3 oz. per square yard. It is forked into the surface.

FARMYARD MANURE. A mixture of the excrement of animals and
the litter that is used in stables and farm buildings. It contains nitrogen,
phosphorus and potassium in amounts which vary greatly, but an average
farm manure in a moist condition is commonly given the formula
0.6 : 0.35 : 0.5, representing the percentages of nitrogen, phosphoric oxide
and potash respectively. A ton of this manure would contain roughly
13½ pounds of nitrogen, 8 pounds of phosphoric oxide and 11 pounds of
potash.

The manure from different animals varies greatly in quality. Horse
droppings are drier than those of other farm animals, and the urine of
horses is more concentrated. Manure from a stable does not compact so
easily as that from a cow-shed or pig-sty, and air can enter it freely. It
ferments more rapidly than other farm manures, and will soon heat up
so that it steams. This readiness to ferment and generate heat makes horse
manure especially suitable for hotbeds on which early crops are grown.

Cow and pig manures are much more solid and compact, and contain
smaller amounts of nutrient elements. They do not ferment readily, and
are commonly regarded as 'cold' manures. They do not decompose so
quickly as horse manure in the soil, and are especially useful in sandy
soils.

Pig manure is relatively low in nitrogen and high in phosphorus. It
should be mixed with plenty of straw or litter and allowed to decay for
a few months before being used. If it is used in a fresh condition, it may
prove too concentrated for young plants.

The value of a manure depends upon the food that the animals have
been eating, and on the condition of the animals. Manure from grass-fed
animals, growing stock and milk-cows is not so rich as manure from
animals being fattened, or from work animals being fed liberally on
concentrates.

Growing animals and milking cows use more of the nitrogen and other
nutrient elements for building body materials and milk than do mature
stock on maintenance rations or fattening.

Composting Manure. Fresh manure is an ideal breeding place for the
micro-organisms that cause decay. It has plenty of carbohydrates in the
vegetable litter and animal waste, a supply of readily-available nitrogen
in the chemicals of the urine, and it is moist and warm. If air can enter
the heap, the micro-organisms have everything they need to flourish.

When farmyard manure is stored in a heap, it will rot as the microbes
attack it. This 'composting' of manure reduces the amount of quick-acting
nitrogen, some of which becomes incorporated in the body material of
the microbes. The effect of the composting is to create a better balance in
the content of available nitrogen, phosphorus and potash. But composting
means an inevitable loss of nitrogen as ammonia gas which escapes into
the air, and of potash and other soluble materials which escape in the
drainage liquid.

When large amounts of well-rotted manure are used on a garden, better
results are obtained if the manure is composted first. This may well be

FARMYARD MANURE (*Continued*).
due to the fact that composting has created a better balance of plant nutrients. But some authorities claim that when manure is used only in moderate amounts, it is better to use it fresh, adding extra phosphorus and potassium fertilizer chemicals to it. This counterbalances the high proportion of available nitrogen, without involving losses due to composting.

When manure is stored, it should be under cover to prevent leaching of soluble nutrients by rain. If this is not practicable, the heap should be as compact as possible, and shaped to allow rainwater to flow away down the sides. If the heap is not compacted, air will enter too freely, and fermentation will continue too rapidly. Nitrogen will be lost as ammonia gas escapes into the air.

Manure is generally deficient in phosphorus, and superphosphate is often added to give a better balance.

Using Farmyard Manure. Manure is used primarily as a source of the humus which is so essential to the creation of a good soil structure. It releases nutrient chemicals slowly and steadily over a period of years, and so provides a source of background feeding. But the use of inorganic fertilizers can often do this job more conveniently and more economically.

Manure may be mixed into the subsoil or topsoil during digging, or it may be spread on the surface as a mulch, about 3–4 inches deep. It will protect the soil from battering by heavy rains, conserve moisture by shading it from the sun and sheltering it from the wind, and keep down weeds. Then, it may be forked lightly into the topsoil to provide humus.

FISH MANURE. Waste material from fish processing. It is largely protein, and provides an excellent source of nitrogen and phosphorus as it decays in the soil.

Fish manures are often mixed with inorganic fertilizers, which add a quick-acting boost to the sustained effect of the decomposing protein. They are usually mixed into the soil in spring before planting or sowing, at the rate of 4–6 oz. per square yard.

GREEN MANURE. See page 197.

GUANO. The accumulated droppings of sea-birds on islands off the coast of Peru. It is an excellent fertilizer, and was at one time in widespread use throughout the world. It has now been largely superseded by manufactured fertilizers.

The term guano is often used for various types of animal droppings, and for waste materials such as fish and meat scraps which are used as fertilizer.

HOOF AND HORN MEAL (8–13% N). Protein, which provides a slow-acting source of nitrogen. It is available in a number of grades or grists, which differ in size of the particles. Fine grades decompose more rapidly, and are quicker in action than the coarser grades.

Hoof and horn meal is usually mixed into the topsoil before planting, at the rate of 4–6 oz. per square yard.

HOP MANURE (0.5% N; 1% P_2O_5).   Spent hops which have been used in brewing. It is essentially a coarse cellulosic material which contains small percentages of nitrogen and phosphorus but very little potash.

Hop manure is used primarily for improving the soil structure by increasing humus content. It is often mixed with inorganic fertilizers and forked into the topsoil.

LEAF MOULD.   Material formed from decayed leaves on the floors of woods and forests. It is generally acid, especially when it contains a preponderance of oak or beech leaves. It makes an excellent mulch for acid-loving plants, decomposing slowly into humus.

Leaf mould may be made by composting fallen leaves, using a nitrogenous fertilizer to supply nitrogen needed by decay micro-organisms. This is spread over layers of leaves as they are built up on the compost heap (see page 194).

PEAT.   The remains of plant materials that have accumulated under airless conditions in boggy ground. There are two main types, sphagnum and sedge, which have formed from different kinds of plant.

Sphagnum Peats (Peat Moss; Highmoor Peat) have been formed from species of sphagnum plant. They contain less than 1% nitrogen and less than 0.1% phosphorus and potassium. They are very acid, with pH values between 3.0 and 4.5, and have a good water-holding capacity equal to as much as 30 times their own weight. These peats do not decompose easily.

Sedge Peats (*Lowmoor Peat*) come from sedges, reeds, mosses and trees. They are of much more variable composition than sphagnum peats. Nitrogen content is 1.5–3.5%, and they contain less than 0.1% of phosphorus and potassium. These peats held up to 8 times their own weight of water. pH values range from 3.5 to 7.0.

Peat derived from trees is sometimes treated separately as a *forest peat* or *peat mould*. It is intermediate in composition between the sphagnum and sedge peats, and contains many particles of wood. It makes an excellent mulch.

Peats contribute little to the nutrients available in the soil, and are used mainly to improve physical structure, especially of fine soils. They increase the water-holding capacities of most soils. Heavy applications are commonly made, reaching as high as 50% of the soil volume.

Acid-loving plants will grow well in pure peat, or in soils mixed with peat. When peats are used with plants which prefer a slightly acid or neutral soil, the acidity should be reduced with limestone.

Peat decomposes very slowly, and has a much longer life in the soil than farmyard manure. It should always be soaked in water before being mixed with soil, or it will absorb much of the soil moisture in competition with the plants.

Coarse peats are preferred for sandy soils, and finer grades for loams and clays.

POULTRY MANURES. These are highly concentrated, and contain little humus-making material. They are rich in nitrogen and phosphorus but contain little potash.

Poultry manure may be used fresh, but it is usually dried either by mixing it with soil or by spreading it in a thin layer and leaving it exposed to the air and sun. It must be kept covered to avoid loss of soluble nutrients by leaching.

Dry manure may be mixed with potassium sulphate at the rate of 1 lb. of sulphate to 10 lb. of manure. It makes an excellent top dressing, and is applied at the rate of 7 oz. per square yard. It should be used sparingly on clay soils.

SAWDUST. Sawdust and fine wood waste are largely cellulose and lignin, a gummy material produced by plants. They supply only very small amounts of plant nutrients, but can be a useful source of humus. Mixed with a readily-available source of nitrogen, such as an inorganic fertilizer or poultry manure, sawdust will decompose slowly. The moistened sawdust should be heaped and sprinkled with the nitrogenous material, and left for 6 months or more. Composted sawdust is dug into the soil at the rate of 12 lb. per square yard, or used as a mulch.

SEAWEED. In coastal regions, seaweed is often available in almost unlimited quantities. Chopped up and dug into the soil, it serves as an excellent source of humus, and provides useful amounts of nitrogen and potash.

Seaweed may be dried in the open air and then ground up into a meal. This is dug into the soil at the rate of up to 1 lb. per square yard.

SEWAGE SLUDGE. Activated sludge is made by treatment of sewage in the presence of oxygen. The dried material contains about 5 to 6% of nitrogen, which is available to the plant about 4 weeks after adding to the soil. It is widely used for many crops in certain regions, where supplies are readily available.

SHODDY. Waste wool; a protein similar to hoof and horn meal. It contains 12 to 14% nitrogen, which is released slowly as the wool decomposes in the soil.

Shoddy is dug in at the rate of 1½–2 lb. per square yard. It will release nitrogen for as long as 5 years.

SLAUGHTERHOUSE WASTE. General waste material from the slaughterhouse, which varies greatly in composition. It is slower in action than dried blood, but contains other essential nutrient elements in appreciable amounts, notably phosphorus.

Various items of slaughterhouse waste are used individually as fertilizers, all of them supplying organic nitrogen. They include bones, horns, hooves, hair and waste wool, hides and leather, etc.

FERTILIZERS WHICH PROVIDE NITROGEN

The absorption of nitrogen-containing chemicals by the plant is a complex process, but in general terms *nitrates* can be regarded as the form in which the plant prefers its nitrogen supplies. Nitrates are produced in the soil by nitrification bacteria, which attack *ammonia* obtained in turn from *organic nitrogenous materials.*

Supplies of nitrogen can be made available in the soil by adding to it materials corresponding to any of the three stages involved in the decomposition of organic matter, i.e. organic matter itself, ammonia or nitrates. The speed with which nitrogen will become available to the plant increases in this same order.

1. Organic Materials

The remains of almost any plant or animal matter contain nitrogen, commonly in the form of protein. The process of decay releases the nitrogen as ammonia and then nitrates, together with other constituent elements as simple chemicals. These organic materials are used as general fertilizers, but there are some organic substances which are used specifically as nitrogenous fertilizers. They include dried blood, fish manure, guano, hoof and horn meal, poultry manure, sewage sludge, shoddy and slaughterhouse waste (see Organic Manures and Fertilizers, page 433).

2. Ammonia Fertilizers

The production of ammonia is an intermediate stage in the release of nitrogen from organic matter, and by making ammonia fertilizers synthetically we are taking a short cut in the natural nitrogen-releasing process. Ammonia and its derivatives must still be converted to nitrates before they are generally available to the plant; as fertilizers, they are slower in action than nitrates themselves.

AMMONIA (Liquid), NH_3 (82% N). A highly concentrated source of nitrogen which may be injected into the soil or into irrigation water. At ordinary temperatures, ammonia is liquid only under pressure, and the use of this fertilizer requires special types of pressurized equipment.

AMMONIA SOLUTIONS (with ammonium nitrate or urea). These are used in a manner similar to liquid ammonia, but require simpler and cheaper non-pressurized equipment.

AMMONIUM NITRATE, NH_4NO_3 (33.5% N). A concentrated source of nitrogen which is supplied partly as ammonia and partly as nitrate.

AMMONIUM PHOSPHATE, $NH_4H_2PO_4$ and $(NH_4)_2HPO_4$. Fertilizers which supply nitrogen and phosphorus.

AMMONIUM SULPHATE $(NH_4)_2SO_4$ (21% N). This chemical has long been used as a nitrogenous fertilizer. It is obtained as a by-product in coal distillation and other processes, and is produced synthetically in enormous quantities from atmospheric nitrogen.

Ammonium sulphate is slower in action than nitrates. It will take effect in less than a fortnight in warm weather, but may lie inactive for a week or two longer in cold weather.

This fertilizer develops an acid reaction, and the soil will need plenty of lime when ammonium sulphate has been used on it. The fertilizer is often ploughed in with potatoes and other crops, especially in wet districts. It is also applied as a top dressing where acidity is not detrimental, for example on grass, and is a common constituent of compound fertilizers.

CALCIUM CYANAMIDE, $CaCN_2$ (20.6% N). Ammonia is formed when cyanamide reacts with soil moisture.

SOOT. A finely-powdered carbon which contains many different chemicals mixed with it. About 1–5% of the total weight of soot consists of ammonium compounds, which serve as a source of inorganic nitrogen in the soil. Other constituents provide useful amounts of various trace elements.

Some of the chemicals in soot are objectionable and even toxic to plants, and fresh soot should never be used as a fertilizer. It is best to store the soot under cover for a month or two before use. Most of the unwanted constituents will evaporate or decompose into harmless materials, and the soot may then be safely used.

Make sure that soot is stored under cover, or the ammonium salts will be washed out by rain.

Soot may be used as top dressing, or forked into the ground after digging, at the rate of 6 oz. per square yard.

UREA, $CO(NH_2)_2$ (45% N). One of the most concentrated of nitrogenous fertilizers. Ammonia is liberated by urea in the soil.

3. Nitrate Fertilizers

Nitrate is the final stage in the release of nitrogen from organic matter. Synthetic nitrate fertilizers make nitrogen immediately available to the plant, and they are the quickest-acting fertilizers of all.

Nitrates are very soluble, and are readily carried away by drainage water. Nitrates produced during the summer are commonly lost during the winter, being washed out by rain-water. A late crop is often sown to make use of the nitrate in the soil before it is lost.

CALCIUM NITRATE, $Ca(NO_3)_2$ A useful fertilizer which provides both nitrogen and calcium.

NITRO CHALK. A mixture of ammonium nitrate and chalk, which contains 15.5% nitrogen. It is used as top dressing at the rate of about 1 oz. per square yard, acting quickly without leaving the soil acid.

POTASSIUM NITRATE (Saltpetre; Nitrate of Potash) KNO_3 (15% N; 10% K_2O). An excellent source of nitrogen and potash which acts very quickly when used as a top dressing. It is applied at the rate of 2 oz. per square yard.

SODIUM NITRATE (Nitrate of Soda; Chile Saltpetre), $NaNO_3$ (15–16% N). One of the oldest inorganic fertilizers in use. It has long been obtained from the famous natural deposit in Chile, which once supplied the bulk of the world's nitrogenous fertilizers.

Sodium nitrate is used as a quick-acting top dressing during spring and summer. If the fertilizer is watered in, the effects will be seen in a day or two. It is used at the rate of about 1 oz. per square yard, and is especially useful in acid soils. It should be used sparingly on clayey soils, as it may destroy the crumb structure.

FERTILIZERS WHICH PROVIDE PHOSPHORUS

The phosphorus content of a fertilizer is expressed in terms of phosphoric oxide, P_2O_5. This is often referred to as 'phosphoric acid'.

BASIC SLAG (15–18% P_2O_5). Phosphorus is removed from the molten metal during steel manufacture by oxidation and treatment with lime to form a slag. The slag is a by-product which provides a useful source of phosphorus for agricultural use.

The active ingredient of basic slag is mainly a calcium silico-phosphate. This is an insoluble material, which is less active than superphosphate in the soil. It acts more rapidly than mineral phosphate, however, and is especially useful on soils rich in organic matter, and on clayey soils.

BASIC SUPERPHOSPHATE. See Superphosphate.

BONE MEAL. See Organic Manures and Fertilizers, page 433.

MINERAL PHOSPHATE. Phosphate rocks are mined in many parts of the world, and are widely used as fertilizer. The main constituent is tricalcium phosphate, $Ca_3(PO_4)_2$.

Tricalcium phosphate is only very slightly soluble in water; it dissolves slowly in acid solutions such as those common in soils.

Mineral phosphate is a slow-acting fertilizer, the speed with which it makes phosphorus available depending upon the fineness with which it is ground. It is most effective in damp soils with a high humus-content.

SUPERPHOSPHATE (Superphosphate of Lime; 'Super') (18% P_2O_5). Rock phosphate is treated with sulphuric acid, the tricalcium phosphate being converted to monocalcium phosphate $CaH_4(PO_4)_2$. This is the active ingredient of superphosphate.

Monocalcium phosphate dissolves readily in water, and is immediately available to growing crops. In acid soils, it is converted quickly into insoluble iron and aluminium phosphates, and is no longer available to the plant. In alkaline soils, it reverts to tricalcium phosphate.

Superphosphate is used as a readily-available phosphorus fertilizer on almost all soils, especially those rich in lime. It is most effective in the first year, but by the second year will often have reverted almost completely. A further application will then bring excellent results, even though the crop has used only a fraction of the phosphorus supplied previously.

Basic Superphosphate, $Ca_2H_2(PO_4)_2$, is less soluble in water than the monocalcium phosphate of superphosphate, but it provides available phosphorus for the plant. It is less readily converted to insoluble iron phosphate or aluminium phosphate in acid soils, and is used for supplying phosphorus under these conditions.

FERTILIZERS WHICH PROVIDE POTASSIUM

Potassium is needed in comparatively large amounts by plants. It makes its way to the seeds, fruit and nuts as these develop. Root crops also require large amounts of potassium.

Unlike nitrogen and phosphorus, potassium does not appear to become part of complex organic structures in the plant. It is released readily when the plant dies, and manures and composts usually provide available potassium without undergoing extensive decomposition.

The potassium content of fertilizers is expressed in terms of potassium oxide (potash), K_2O. Potassic fertilizers are usually soluble salts of potassium which are obtained from natural sources in various parts of the world.

KAINIT. A mixture of crude potash salts, containing common salt, which is commonly used on root crops.

MURIATE OF POTASH (Potassium chloride; KCl) (50% K_2O). A quick-acting source of potash which must be used with care. Application rate about 2 oz. per square yard.

POTASH SALTS (20–30% K_2O). A crude mixture of potassium salts.

P

SULPHATE OF POTASH (Potassium sulphate; K_2SO_4) (48% K_2O).   The commonest potassium fertilizer, which is applied at the rate of about 2 oz. per square yard. It is dug in before planting, and is also used as a top dressing. Potassium sulphate is a common constituent of compound fertilizers.

WOOD ASHES.   Freshly made wood ashes contain potassium carbonate, K_2CO_3. This is soon washed out by rainwater unless the ashes are adequately protected.

Wood ashes are used at the rate of up to 12 oz. per square yard. They tend to neutralize acidity.

FERTILIZER MIXING CHART

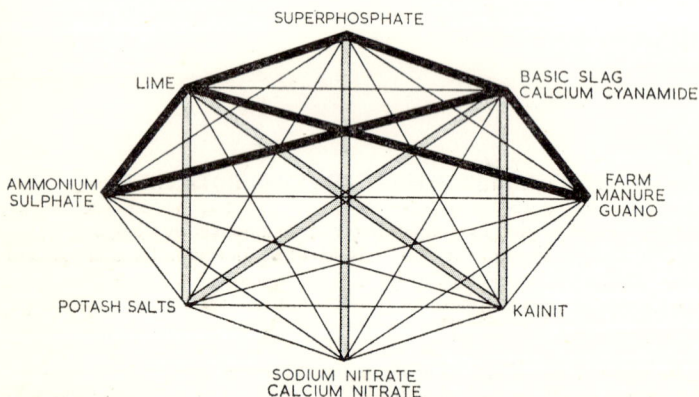

The fertilizers joined by the *thin lines* may be mixed together, and will keep indefinitely without any reaction. The fertilizers joined by the *shaded lines* may be mixed and will not react immediately. They should, however, be used at once and not stored. Fertilizers joined by the *thick lines* will react together immediately upon mixing, to the detriment of both.

JOHN INNES COMPOSTS

(Courtesy of John Innes Institution)

When plants are grown in pots or under other enclosed conditions, the quality and composition of the "soil" may be accurately controlled. Soils may be made up in such a way as to provide the plants with everything they need in adequate amounts. The well-known John Innes Composts were devised many years ago by scientists at the John Innes Horticultural Institution with this in mind, and they are now in widespread use throughout the world.

By making use of the formulae devised for the John Innes Composts, the grower can be certain of providing his plants with a growing medium of specified quality. He can ensure consistency of results, at least so far as his soil is concerned.

The term "compost" used in describing these special soil mixtures does not correspond in meaning with "compost" as it is now generally understood. But the name "John Innes Compost" has become part of everyday horticultural language, and there seems little point in suggesting that a less ambiguous term should now be used.

Similarly, one of the ingredients specified in John Innes Composts is described as "loam". This, too, is an ambiguous term. In modern terminology, "loam" refers to a specific class of soil texture, and relates only to the proportions of mineral particles in the three size ranges (see page 268). Used in connection with the John Innes Composts, however, the term carries its traditional meaning as described below.

The Ingredients of John Innes Composts

The chief ingredient of the J. I. Composts is steam-sterilized loam, to which are added (1) peat and sand to improve the physical properties of the loam, and (2) fertilizers to increase its nutrient value.

LOAM

Types. Loam is a name applied, in this instance, to good soil in good condition. By this is meant a soil well-balanced in its proportions of sand, silt and clay particles and containing usually between 2 and 7 per cent of organic matter. Medium loams contain just enough clay to be slightly greasy when smeared, without being sticky, and are usually yellow-brown to reddish brown in colour. Light loams contain more sand, and heavy loams more clay, than medium loams. Light, heavy and chalky loams should not be used for composts. Suitable loam is slightly on the acid side (pH 6.5–5.5). Loams are obtained either from arable or pasture land, the first being *arable loam* and the second *turf* or *garden loam*.

Value. Loam is the main ingredient of seed and potting composts, to which it gives "body". Its chief function is to supply the clay and actively decomposing organic matter and humus which are so essential for good plant growth in pots. The best loam for composts is turf loam, which contains more humus and nitrogen than arable loam.

Turf Loam. This is the product obtained when turves, cut from a pasture on a medium loam soil, are stacked in a heap until the grass and some of the roots have rotted. The best material comes from a good pasture and consists of the top 4–5 inches of turf and soil cut into turves about 12 by 9 inches. A good pasture is one which has been properly drained, and has had sufficient lime, manure (by grazing) or fertilizers to encourage a thick sward of fine grasses. The loam which will grow good pot plants is the one which has grown good grasses.

Inferior loams should not be used; they are cut from poor, thin, pastures, or from the second spit in fields where turf has previously been cut and the sward has not had time to grow thick and turfy again. This means they usually have a low humus content. Inferior loams often lack clay, and water drains through them too freely, carrying away valuable plant nutrients. The crumb structure is usually poor, inevitably so in too-light or too-heavy soils and probably so in any soil whose humus content is on the low side. Inferior loams are often infertile; coming from neglected and badly-drained pastures they tend to be acid, deficient in available nutrients and poorly aerated. These conditions discourage the activity of beneficial bacteria and fungi.

Inferior loams may have severe ill effects if used in J.I. Composts. Since little available nitrogen is supplied by the peat and none by the sand, lack of humus in the loam may lead to pot-bound plants showing nitrogen deficiency earlier than usual. In light loams, clay deficiency is likely to increase the washing-out of nutrients, due in part to the very free drainage obtained when a light loam is mixed with peat and sand, and in part to its lower storage and exchange capacity. Clay acts as a bank where plant nutrients can be deposited or exchanged. Poor crumb structure will affect aeration and the regulation of the water content of the compost. And biological inactivity will affect every aspect of growth.

Arable Loams. Where turf loam is not available, loamy soil from arable land may be used. The chief danger with arable loam is humus deficiency, and texture and crumb structure may be poor. The most suitable arable soils are deep fertile loams in "good heart".

Choosing a Loam. First, the grower should avoid loams which are light, silty, heavy or chalky. Used in pots, light loams dry out too frequently and the plants starve early. Silty and heavy loams pack down tightly and the roots of plants are suffocated. Heavy loams also tend to become waterlogged. Chalky loams are unsuitable for most plants, and react unfavourably when sterilized.

This narrows down the choice to good textured soils in the medium loam range. The grower should make a test on samples of loam by sowing tomato seeds in them, first sifting the loam through a quarter-inch sieve. The seed vessels should be placed in a warm house (60–65°F.) to encourage good germination and seedling growth. It is essential to have a standard for comparison, and for this, the loam the grower has been using is perhaps as suitable as any, since he will know from experience just how satisfactory it has been. In this loam also, seeds should be sown and the plants raised alongside the samples being tested.

The vigour and colour of the tomato seedlings should be noted. A good rate of growth and a medium to light green colour show that the loam is satisfactory. Early yellowing and fall of the cotyledons usually indicates grave nitrogen deficiency. A tinge of purple all over the plant suggests a deficiency of phosphate: if the purple colour is deep the loam is not satisfactory. Tests such as these are easy to make and the results can be had in from three to four weeks' time.

Turf loam from average pasture land may be of good texture, but contain less nitrogen, phosphate and potash than a fertile arable loam. On the other hand, the texture of many arable loams is unsatisfactory for pot plants, though they have a good nutrient content. If a mediocre turf loam has to be used it is therefore wise to mix with it, layer by layer, an equal quantity of fertile arable loam.

Stacking. The best time to cut turves for stacking is in the early summer when the grass is thick and green and the soil still moist from spring rains. Turves should be stacked grass side downwards with slight gaps, for aeration, between the sides and ends of the turves. A certain amount of soil breaks away from the turves while stacking the loam. This loose soil should not be thrown in the middle of the stack but spread evenly over the turves. The stack should not be built too high or too wide, otherwise aeration may be inadequate. Six feet high by six to eight feet wide are suitable dimensions.

The turves should never be stacked in dry condition. Moisture is essential for rotting down, and the best results will be obtained if the turves are cut when the soil is naturally moist. Failing this, the hose pipe should be used while stacking is in progress. If the turves are thoroughly moist the stack need not be touched again until it is rotted enough for use, i.e. in about six months' time. It will then be ready when it is needed in the new year.

If an inferior loam has to be used, it may be improved by adding a 2-inch layer of cow or horse manure every 12 inches when building the stack. This is not advisable with good loams.

Turf which is only half-rotted should never be used for composts. The best results are obtained if the stack is used shortly after the turves have rotted sufficiently. In an old stack, where the grasses and roots have rotted completely, the texture will have deteriorated, the humus content probably decreased and the loam becomes less satisfactory.

Handling before Sterilization. Loam or soil which is to be sterilized in bins should be dry. This can be achieved quite easily by proper handling of the stack. If the loam is thoroughly moist when stacked the turves will rot down fairly quickly. Then, a month or two before the loam is wanted for use, all that remains to be done is to keep rain off the stack by covering it. The stack will then dry out of its own accord. The grower will soon learn from experience precisely when the stack should be covered. When chopping down the stack, a spade should be used and thin cuts made from top to bottom across the full breadth of the stack. By so doing, the effects of variations in the quality of the turves are minimized and intimate mixing ensured.

PEAT

Peat is usually found in regions with a humid temperate climate where the land is swampy. The plants found in such localities are the moisture-loving types such as sphagnum mosses, sedges and cotton grass. As the plants, or their parts, die and fall they are covered by the surface water which largely excludes air and the bacteria responsible for the processes of decay. Because of this, and owing also to the action of organic acids present, complete decay of the plant remains is prevented and "peat" is formed. If these conditions persist they lead to the gradual accumulation of peat, and with the passage of time deposits many feet thick may be formed. The nature of the peat (its texture, chemical composition, acidity, etc.) will depend mainly on the type of vegetation from which it is formed; and this in turn will vary with the changes in the climate, drainage and soil conditions. Thus peat deposits may show different layers derived from different sorts of plants. These layers sometimes include roots of trees and shrubs and mineral soil. Peat also varies in character with the depth at which it is found. Near the surface it is brown, fibrous, light and porous; lower down it tends to be black, heavy and dense, the blacker peat being the more decomposed. Some 3½ million acres of peat deposits occur in Great Britain and Ireland, comprising moss peats and sedge peats found in moorland bogs and the gardener's "Rhododendron" peat found on heaths and commons. There are numerous brands of peat on the market, not all of which are suitable for pot plants. Therefore in purchasing peat it is wise to stipulate "for use in the J.I. composts". Peat suitable for composts is sold either in compressed bales or loose, and is variously described as moss peat, sedge peat, granulated peat, etc.

Value. The value of peat in a compost is as a soil "conditioner". Its spongy nature makes it unique: it can aerate a compost and regulate its moisture-holding qualities. It remains effective for a long time, since it decomposes slowly. Though most horticultural peats contain little or no humus, they are of value as a source of this material: they contain 70 to 97 per cent organic matter which, as it rots, is changed into humus. Peat has the merits of being (1) naturally highly sterile and free from weed seeds, pests and diseases, (2) highly uniform in texture and varying only a little in quality. This uniformity is a great asset to the grower who wishes to make up standard composts.

Texture. In choosing a peat the most important factor is texture. The peat should be of a fibrous or granulated type, relatively undecomposed and not dusty or apt to powder when handled. The particles should grade fairly evenly up to ⅜ inch in size, with a preponderance of ⅛ inch particles. Dusty, fine peats should be strictly avoided, also black, greasy, decomposed ones. "Rhododendron" peat, which contains bracken roots, together with silt and sand, should not be used.

Degree of Acidity (pH). A pH between 4.0 and 5.0 is to be preferred. However, for the J.I. composts, the precise degree of acidity is only of small consequence so long as it is not less than 3.5.

Lime requirement. Some peats require more lime than others in order to raise their pH to a given value. In the J.I. composts, however, this variation between peats is smoothed out by the action of the loam and carbonate of lime and therefore, with rare exceptions, is of no importance.

Storage. Peat, whether purchased loose or in bales, should be kept dry and clean under cover, where weeds and weed seeds cannot contaminate it.

Handling. Baled peat must first be broken up by rubbing it through a ⅜ inch sieve. Before peat is used in a compost it should be spread out thinly and well moistened (but not saturated) with a rose can. Baled peat can also be moistened by making a hole or two in the end of the bale with a crowbar and pouring in water every day until all the peat is wetted and loosened and the bale bursts. Peat should never be used dry in a compost.

Sterilizing. Good horticultural peat does not require sterilizing: it is naturally highly sterile.

LEAF-MOULD

Leaf-mould may be used in composts as an alternative to peat, though it will never serve so well. Mixed with soil, it rots away more quickly than peat and its effect as a soil conditioner is therefore not so lasting. Its quality is highly variable and depends in the main on (1) the manner and degree of decomposition, (2) the kind of leaves from which it is made. Leaves which decompose in a thin layer on the woodland floor seem to make a much better mould than those rotted in a heap in the garden. The degree of decomposition is also important; unless the material is thoroughly rotted, adverse, even toxic, effects on plant growth may result.

Oak and beech leaves are traditionally held to be superior to all others for pot plants, but other leaves are generally satisfactory.

Leaf-mould, as sold or collected, often contains soil and sand. It may also carry weed seeds, plant pests, and disease, and therefore, unlike peat, requires sterilizing.

SAND

Types. Horticultural sand is usually obtained from sand pits (i.e. where ancient rivers once flowed). Occasionally it occurs as an industrial by-product, e.g. Cornish sand washed out by rain from the china clay dumps. Sea-shore sand generally contains salt and lime (shells) and is therefore unsuitable for the J.I. composts. Yellow sands are stained with iron compounds. Unstained sands are known as "silver" sands. The colour is of no importance.

Value. The function of sand in the composts is to assist in draining-off excess water. Coarse sands do this much better than fine sands.

Grade. Very few growers use sand which is sufficiently coarse, i.e. grading up to ⅛ inch. The ideal sand contains roughly 40 per cent coarse, 30 per cent medium and 20 per cent fine particles, in sizes ranging evenly from about ⅛ inch down to "dust" i.e. coarse material preponderates.

Quality. A good sand is coarse, clean (free of clay, silt, salt and organic matter) and relatively lime-free (containing few or no particles of chalk or shell).

Storage. Wet or moist sand does not mix easily when making up a compost, and it is best to keep sand quite dry to ensure uniformity of mixing.

Sterilizing. Clean sand does not require sterilizing.

SUMMARY

The most important ingredient of the compost is the loam. If the loam is of the right quality, variations among peats and sands, though not negligible, are largely smoothed out. Further, in the J.I. potting compost, the addition of base fertilizers and carbonate of lime smooths out variations between medium loams. Thus, consistently good results in the growing of pot plants depend not only on the use of standard ingredients, but on the effect of different ingredients in balancing one another, i.e. on the make-up of the compost.

Making and Using John Innes Composts

The John Innes Seed and Potting Composts are tested composts of standard formula designed to:
1. Give the best possible growth.
2. Suit all kinds of pot plants.
3. Dispense with animal manure.
4. Economize in time, materials and labour.

Two composts in widespread use are made up as follows: —

1. *John Innes Seed Compost*
2 parts sterilized loam, 1 part peat, 1 part sand (all parts by bulk or volume). To each bushel of this mixture are added 1½ oz. of superphosphate and ¾ oz. of chalk (or ground limestone).

2. *John Innes Potting Compost*
7 parts sterilized loam, 3 parts peat, 2 parts sand (all parts by bulk or volume). To each bushel of this mixture are added 4 oz. John Innes Base, and ¾ oz. chalk or ground limestone.

This standard potting compost is called J.I.P.1. If the amounts of John Innes Base and chalk are doubled (i.e. 8 oz. and 1½ oz. per bushel respectively) the compost is called J.I.P.2; if the amounts of John Innes Base and chalk are trebled, it becomes J.I.P.3, and so on.

I. NOTES ON INGREDIENTS

1. *Loam*
Good loam (e.g. Kettering loam) is slightly greasy when smeared, without being sticky. The turves should be stacked until well rotted. The loam should be sterilized.

2. *Peat*
Good peat is of relatively coarse texture (⅛ in. to ⅜ in.), free from dust and undecomposed. Several peats on the market, sold as granulated peat, moss peat, etc. are suitable as composting materials. Sterilized leaf-mould may be used instead of peat.

3. *Sand*
The ideal sand grades evenly up to ⅛ in. Fine sands should be avoided. If a light loam is used, less sand and peat will be required.

P*

4. *J.I. Base*

The J.I. Base can be bought ready mixed. Its formula (parts by weight) is:

> 2 Hoof and horn, ⅛ in. grist (13% nitrogen)
> 2 Superphosphate of lime (16% phosphoric acid)
> 1 Sulphate of potash (48% potash)

Its analysis is: nitrogen 5.1%, phosphoric acid 6.4%, potash 9.7%.

5. *Chalk (or ground limestone)*

This is an essential ingredient of the compost. It should always be added, except when the loam used contains a fair amount of lime. Hydrated lime should not be used.

II. PREPARING THE COMPOSTS

Sift the loam through a ⅜ in. sieve. Moisten the peat with a rose-can. Add the fertilizers and chalk to some of the sand and mix thoroughly, then add the fertilized sand to the compost and again mix thoroughly. The composts may be used the next day, or stored for any period not exceeding eight weeks. After that, they may become too acid.

III. USING THE COMPOSTS

Under average conditions, the seed compost is used for seed sowing and pricking off, and the potting compost for potting into 3½ in. or larger pots. The vigour of the plant and the prevailing climatic conditions, however, may necessitate modification. Examples are given below:

(1) *Seeds and Seedlings*

Materials and conditions	Sowing	Pricking-off
I. Fine seeds (e.g. begonia)		
II. Slow growing plants (e.g. auricula)	Seed compost	Seed compost
III. Delicate plants (e.g. salpiglossis)		
Medium seed (e.g. nemesia)		
(a) Oct.-Jan., or bad light conditions	Seed compost	Seed compost
(b) Feb.-Sept., or good light conditions	Seed compost	J.I.P.1.
I. Large seeds (e.g. sweet pea)		
II. Strong plants (e.g. tomato)	J.I.P.1.	J.I.P.1.
III. Bedding plants in boxes		

(2) *Plants in Pots*

Materials and conditions	Pot Size	Compost
Plants grown mainly through the summer, e.g.:		
arum lily		
asparagus fern		
begonia		
carnation	3½ in.	J.I.P.1
chrysanthemum		
cyclamen	↓	↓
Cytisus canariensis	4½ in.	J.I.P.2
erica		
pelargonium	↓	↓
Primula malacoides		
P. obconica	8–12 in.	J.I.P.3
schizanthus		
tomato		
Plants grown through the winter:		
(a) moderately vigorous, e.g.:	4½– 6 in.	(a) J.I.P.2
beans		
hydrangea		
Solanum capsicastrum		
(b) Vigorous, e.g.:		(b) J.I.P.3
calceolaria		
cineraria		
strawberry		
Plants planted out:		
(a) moderately vigorous, e.g.:	3½ in.	(a) J.I.P.1
bedding plants		
cauliflower		
tomato		
(b) vigorous, e.g.:		(b) J.I.P.2
cucumber		
marrow		
Miscellaneous:		J.I.P.1
Stove plants		
Rooted carnation cuttings		
Rooted chrysanthemum cuttings		

Growth in J.I.P.2 or 3 is not necessarily improved or accelerated as compared with J.I.P.1, but it is prolonged; feeding need not start so early, and the compost "holds" well. If J.I.P.1 has already been mixed it can be converted into J.I.P.2 or 3 in a few moments by adding an extra one or two doses of John Innes Base and chalk and mixing thoroughly.

The J.I. Base may also be used for digging into outside borders, etc., at the rate of ¼ to ½ lb. per square yard. It is not suitable as a quick-acting feed.

(3) *Carnations in Beds*

The suggested proportions for moderately heavy soils are 8 parts by bulk of loam, and up to 2½ parts peat and 1½ parts coarse sand. For light soils, little or no sand will be required. The peat, however, should not be less than 10 per cent of the whole. The J.I. Base is thoroughly mixed with the loam, peat and sand at the rate of 15 lb. of base and 3 lb. of ground chalk, limestone, or hydrated lime per cubic yard. Planting may begin a day or two after the beds have been made up. The equivalent rates of application for a bed six inches deep are 2½ lb. J.I. Base plus ½ lb. chalk per square yard.

IV. PROPAGATING COMPOSTS

A useful compost for striking cuttings is:

Parts		1	...	...	...	...	...	Loam
by		2	...	...	...	...	...	Peat
bulk		3	...	...	...	...	...	Sand

No fertilizers are added.

The J.I. Seed Compost may be used for striking cuttings of the stronger growing plants, e.g. geraniums, calceolarias, fuchsias and chrysanthemums.

V. JOHN INNES FEEDS

These standard feeds are balanced mixtures suitable for all kinds of pot-bound plants except carnations and tomatoes.

	"L" for liquid feeding	"D" for dry feeding
Formula, parts by weight	15.00 ammonium sulphate 2.75 potassium nitrate 2.25 mono-ammonium phosphate	The same as "L", but mixed with a carrier
Rate of application	½ to 1 oz. per gallon of (preferably soft) water. Use fresh.	½ to 1 teaspoonful per 5 in. pot.
Analyses:		
Nitrogen	18.65	6.80
Soluble phos- phoric acid	6.20	1.94
Potash	6.20	1.94

STERILIZATION

All manner of insects, earthworms, fungi, bacteria and other organisms play a part in the cycle of life and death in the soil. In a healthy soil, a balance is achieved and maintained, and the soil supports a cover of vegetation from year to year. But under certain circumstances, the natural balance of life in the soil may be disturbed. Some insects, fungi or other organisms may begin to flourish at the expense of the crop growing in the soil. They become pests, and cause diseases.

This will often happen when crops are being grown intensively, for example in glasshouses. And it becomes necessary to destroy the harmful organisms in the soil by sterilization, using either heat or chemicals.

Heat Sterilization

All the living organisms in the soil are killed by being heated to 260°F. But below this temperature, different organisms vary in their ability to withstand heating.

Earthworms, eelworms, many fungi and viruses and bacteria (including nitrification bacteria) are destroyed at about 130°F. The bacteria which convert organic matter into ammonia, on the other hand, produce spores which resist temperatures of up to 212°F. for several hours.

When soil is sterilized, it is commonly steamed to raise its temperature to 180–200°F. This is sufficient to destroy most of the harmful organisms, leaving others—including ammonia-producing organisms—unharmed. It is really a partial sterilization, rather than a complete sterilization (which would destroy all living organisms).

When soil is steam-sterilized, the production of ammonia from organic matter continues. But the nitrification organisms, which convert ammonia to nitrates, have been destroyed. Ammonia accumulates, and will escape from the sterilized soil.

The steam sterilization of soil containing organic matter will often result in considerable loss of nitrogen in this way. The effect is intensified if the soil has been limed.

A concentration of ammonia may be detrimental to seedlings and young plants, and in sterilizing seed or potting composts it is imperative to sterilize the loam separately (see John Innes Composts, page 443). Organic matter (e.g. leaf mould) should also be sterilized separately, or horticultural peat (which is naturally sterile) should be used.

Phosphate should be added to sterilized soil to restore the balance following release of excess ammonia.

APPARATUS AND METHODS

In general, soil is sterilized by heating to 180–200°F. and maintaining this temperature for about 10 minutes. If the sterilization is to be effective, every part of the soil must be heated adequately, and a number of techniques have been devised for doing this. They are described in detail in 'Soil Sterilization', Bulletin No. 22 of Ministry of Agriculture, Fisheries and Food, published by H.M.S.O.

Small amounts of soil may be sterilized as follows:·

(1) about ½ inch of water is put into a saucepan which is then filled with soil, brought to the boil and simmered for 15 minutes.

(2) Soil is suspended in coarse sacking over several inches of boiling water in a domestic boiler. It is heated for 30–40 minutes.

Note

    (a) These may be sterilized together: Loam, Sand.

    (b) No two of these may be sterilized together: Loam, Leaf Mould, Peat, Manure, Fertilizers, Lime.

    (c) These need not be sterilized: Clean sand, Moss peat, Sedge peat, Fertilizers, Lime.

In preparing soil for John Innes Composts, the loam is sterilized first and then mixed with the other compost ingredients and the fertilizers. If full benefit is to be had from the sterilized soil, the pots, pans, boxes, etc., should be sterilized also, and the strictest hygiene practised in all operations.

Chemical Sterilization

Chemicals may be used to destroy living organisms in the soil. Two materials commonly used are (a) commercial formalin (30–40 per cent formaldehyde) and (b) tar acids, e.g. cresylic acid.

Formaldehyde is effective in destroying fungi, but is of limited use against animal organisms. It kills protozoa, but is not very effective against insects and eelworms.

Tar acids, including cresylic acid, will destroy insects and other animal pests such as wood lice and millipedes. They will kill root knot eelworms, but are ineffective against other eelworms. They have little effect on fungi.

Detailed information on the use of chemicals in soil sterilization is given in the H.M.S.O. publication 'Soil Sterilization' (see above). The following methods may be used for sterilizing small quantities of soil: —

(1) *Formaldehyde* Soil is forked over and watered with a solution made by mixing 1 gallon of commercial formalin (37.5–40.5 per cent formaldehyde) with 49 gallons of water. The diluted solution is applied at the rate of 100 gallons to 20 square yards of soil. The soil is covered with wet sacks for two or three days. The sacks are removed and the formaldehyde vapours are allowed to disperse before planting is carried out. This may take 4–5 weeks in late spring and summer, and 6–8 weeks in winter or early spring.

(2) *Tar Acids* A dilute solution is made by adding 1 gallon of 97–99 per cent cresylic acid to 40 gallons of water. This is applied to the soil at the rate of 40 gallons to 10 square yards. The soil should be left for at least 6 weeks before planting is carried out.

INDEX

INDEX